Published by The International Chinese Snuff Bottle Society
2601 North Charles Street, Baltimore, Maryland 21218

Visit online at www.snuffbottle.org

Copyright © 2009 by The International Chinese Snuff Bottle Society

Photographs by Denis Mortell, Dublin, Ireland

All images © The Trustees of the Chester Beatty Library, Dublin
Produced by Pressroom Printer & Designer, Hong Kong

ISBN: 962-7287-57-1

FRONT COVER:
No. 140 (without later stopper)
Limestone breccia, of pebble shape, the natural markings suggestive of bamboo stems, branches and roots
1750-1880
Height: 6.1 cm

TO MY EVER-LOVING WIFE, LISA,
AND OUR TWO CHILDREN, IAIN AND LIVIA

IN MEMORY OF MY MOTHER, FATHER AND BROTHER

CONTENTS

FOREWORD   7

PREFACE AND ACKNOWLEDGEMENTS   9

INTRODUCTION   10

SNUFF BOTTLES
    Jade   14
    Quartz   80
    Other Stones   166
    Organic   192
    Glass   226
    Inside-Painted   254
    Porcelain   268
    Metal & Enamel   334

BIBLIOGRAPHY   366

INDEX   369

FOREWORD

It is a great pleasure for me to introduce the catalogue of the snuff bottles of the Chester Beatty Library by Michael Hughes which is published to coincide with the meeting of the International Chinese Snuff Bottle Society in Dublin in October 2009.

Chester Beatty as a boy was already a collector. We know that under the influence of a favourite uncle, he developed a strong interest in rocks and minerals (a presage of his later career as a mining engineer) and he soon expanded this to the collection of objects made out of rocks and minerals. This led him very naturally to snuff bottles, many of which are carved from hard, semi-precious stone. Indeed clever carving by Chinese craftsmen enabled them to use the veins of colour in the stones to represent animals, fish and plants and other motifs vividly and to intensify the difference between background and foreground. The virtuosity of the carving of some of the bottles is simply stunning. Beatty did not of course confine himself to examples made of stone and in building up his collection of almost two thousand examples, he included the full range of materials used to manufacture snuff bottles. Throughout his life, Beatty had the habit of making presents of groups of snuff bottles to friends and so it was that his private collection was whittled down to something just under a thousand which today form part of the great collection which he bequeathed to the public. Visitors to the old Chester Beatty displays recall with affection that almost all the snuff bottles were on permanent exhibition there in our Founder's Chinese Library. The visit of the International Chinese Snuff Bottle Society to the Chester Beatty Library, in itself a cause for celebration, brings with it not just Michael Hughes's splendid book with photographs by Denis Mortell, but also the very welcome opportunity to feature these masterpieces in miniature prominently in our exhibitions.

In thanking the Society, the author and the photographer, I would like to add our particular thanks to Dr Shane McCausland, Ms Laura Muldowney, Ms Jessica Baldwin, Ms Kristine Rose and Ms Sinéad Ward who have done so much to make the publication possible.

Michael Ryan
Director

PREFACE AND ACKNOWLEDGEMENTS

A chance meeting in late October 2004 in London with Dr. Shane McCausland, the curator of the East Asian Collections at the Chester Beatty Library; a short conversation about the merits of publishing the Chinese snuff bottle collection in his care; and a subsequent week-long visit to Dublin in February 2005 to review the complete collection of 942 bottles; led to this publication. After that initial visit, it was agreed that a more manageable number of approximately 300 bottles should be published. We achieved a final count of 275 after careful but judicious culling based on duplication, damages, and quality. In April 2006, I approached the Board of the International Chinese Snuff Bottle Society (ICSBS) with a proposal to finance the publication through its Education Fund. The Board reconvened in October of the same year to vote on the proposal, and they came back with a resounding yes. Three more visits to Dublin in May and August 2007 and a final visit in May 2009 resulted in this publication.

Initially we had planned to digitally add stoppers to photographs for those bottles missing them. However as 121 bottles fell in to this category it seemed disingenuous to do so. We have therefore allowed the photographs to remain honest to the collection, even if an added stopper here or there would have improved the 'finished product'. The sizing of images when different bottles share a page are to scale, though not always actual size.

In this publication all height measurements for bottles do not include the stopper unless otherwise indicated. Mouth and neck measurements are all diameters. Each entry is followed by accession number in parentheses, which begins with the initials CBL (being the Library's acronym), followed by a C for the Chinese Collection. Coincidentally the accession numbers for my previous publication, *The Blair Bequest: Chinese Snuff Bottles from the Princeton University Art Museum*, also begin with the initials CB for Col. Blair.

Wherever possible the *pinyin* system of transliteration has been used except for the titles of publications using an alternative system. The catalogue entries and footnotes are entirely my responsibility and do not necessarily express the opinions of the Chester Beatty Library.

I am exceedingly grateful to the staff at the Chester Beatty Library who made all my visits so pleasurable. In particular I am most grateful to Dr. Shane McCausland, for his invaluable help; Dr. Michael Ryan, Director of the Chester Beatty Library, for his support of the project; Laura Muldowney, assistant to the East Asian Curator for her invaluable help with the collection and the enormous time spent in preparing the exhibition that accompanies this publication; Sinéad Ward, Rights and Reproductions Officer, for overseeing the colossal photography project with such meticulous care; Denis Mortell, for an outstanding job of photography which speaks for itself; and the Trustees of the Chester Beatty Library, for financing this portion of the project. I would also like to especially thank Charles Horton, Curator of the Western Collections and archivist at the museum, and Celine Ward, Reference Librarian, for their kind help; and also the Head of Conservation, Jessica Baldwin, Kristine Rose, Book Conservator, Rachel Smith, Paper Conservator, Hyder Abbas, Library Assistant, and Mme. Anne Juin, for their help along the way.

I should also like to acknowledge the support of the Board of the ICSBS in particular President Dr. Vince Fausone. I am extremely grateful to John Newton, my incomparable editor, and to Mr. C.M. Ma for his translations of texts. During my research it became clear to me how indebted all snuff bottle connoisseurs have to be to Hugh M. Moss for his prodigious work in this field and to Therese Tse Bartholomew for her impressive writing on subject meanings. My thanks also to Sue Donnelly, Archivist at the London School of Economics and Political Science. I also would like to thank the following for their help: Michael Bass, John Finlay, Ben Hall, Robert and Lindsey Hall, Elizabeth Hammer, Sam Hines, Kumiko Hirakawa, Humphrey Hui, Gayle Grey Laverlochere, Martin Lorber, Errol Manners, Jamie Nitze, David and Kathy Odell, Susan Page, Roderick Ropner, Jonathan Rendell, Rodney Richardson, Romie Scott, Jonathan Snellenburg, Laurence Souksi, Simon Teakle, Peter Tunstall-Behrens, John Vollmer, and Sarah-Ann Wong.

I should also like to thank Désirée Bucks at Pressroom Printer in Hong Kong for her fine work on this project. I should not forget the support of my siblings, Peter, Kathy, Sheila and Mark.

I must save my most heartfelt thanks to my wife, Lisa, and our two children, Iain and Livia, for allowing me to be absent from parental duties for a large chunk of the past year (or so).

I should like to end by praising the City of Dublin for its many charms and the depth of its cultural heritage. The Chester Beatty Library is a gem set at the heart of an important European crown. I encourage you to visit.

Michael C. Hughes
August 2009

INTRODUCTION

Sir Alfred Chester Beatty (1875-1968)

At the end of a letter he wrote in 1915 to M. Gordon Smith, a fellow collector, Alfred Chester Beatty included a postscript, 'I would be very glad if the book [of the Beatty collection] is published to give you some of the copies. Of course, I would not expect to publish this book for a year or so.' This catalogue fulfills Beatty's wish, albeit more than 90 years behind schedule, and provides readers around the world a comprehensive look at this remarkable collection.

The long and fruitful life of Alfred Chester Beatty (1875-1968), or simply Chester Beatty as he preferred to be known, has been comprehensively explored and chronicled particularly in relation to his book collecting by Charles Horton the Curator of the Western Collections and archivist at the Chester Beatty Library, in his compelling *Alfred Chester Beatty: From Miner to Bibliophile* published in 2003 and also by A.J. Wilson in *The Life and Times of Sir Alfred Chester Beatty* published eighteen years earlier and which included large sections of a lengthy unpublished biography by the Dublin journalist, John Murdoch. [1]

I will take the liberty of listing some of the information from these publications documenting Beatty's life and add a few snippets of additional information that have come to light more recently. Beatty today is acknowledged as one of the great collectors of his era in the field of printed books, stamps, European and Persian manuscripts, Old Master prints, and a wide range of East Asian arts from China and Japan, including the decorative arts with an emphasis on rhinoceros horn and snuff bottles, and extremely fine paintings, manuscripts, and printed material. He was able to fund his insatiable and cultured collecting habits due to his incredibly hard work and phenomenal success, first as a mining engineer, and then as an entrepreneur with copper mines in the United States, Yugoslavia, Siberia, Rhodesia, the Congo, and Sierra Leone.

The son of banker John Cuming Beatty and his wife Hetty Bull Beatty, Alfred Chester Beatty was born on 7 February 1875 of Ulster-Scots, English, and Irish ancestry. At an early age Beatty's interest in minerals had already manifested itself, as a charming story relayed by Horton attests ibid, p. 8, when, at the youthful age of ten, Beatty attended an auction in New York City and purchased a piece of pink calcite for his burgeoning mineral collection, outbidding everyone else at the 'adult' gathering. He would pursue these interests first at Princeton and then Columbia University School of Mines where he graduated top of his class with a mining engineering degree in 1898. According to Jan Chapman he had begun to purchase snuff bottles as a student in New York.[2] In all likelihood, given that he was buying mineral samples at age 10, he may well have started his snuff bottle collection at a similar age.

After graduation, Beatty headed to Denver, which was still the real 'Wild West' and where lawlessness within his chosen field was notorious. According to Murdoch, ibid, at least one attempt was made on his life when a 'tampered' cage he was in, traveling down a mine shaft, inexplicably fell hundreds of feet and Beatty was lucky to survive (pp. 68-69). When on horseback, Beatty always carried a gun in his boot and a Winchester strapped to his saddle (p. 8 and pp. 28-30). On one occasion, a split second ahead of a rugged mine manager's grab for his Winchester, he pulled out his six-shooter from his long boot and saved his own life by facing up to the tyrant who had 'salted' samples of ore [3] in an attempt to dupe the 'innocent looking greenhorn'. Such occurrences were commonplace.

Murdoch notes that, 'He tasted life in the rip-roaring days of the early gold diggers in places like Cripple Creek and the Klondike and the stampede men who abandoned house, home, and belongings in the rush for gold' (p. 7). Saloons had no closing hours and drinking and gambling were malignant problems. The bottles on Beatty's mind, however, were not the whisky bottles that prevailed out West.

Despite these dangers Beatty survived and made his fortune in just a few years. He was a millionaire by the age of thirty.

Beatty was married twice. His first marriage in 1900 to Grace Madeline Rickard, with whom he would have a daughter Ninette, born in 1902, and a son Alfred Chester Jr., born in 1907, ended tragically with her early death from typhoid fever in 1911. The anguish of her untimely death, his own ill health, and his desire to become a mining financier, prompted his move to London, then the centre of international trade. Beatty remarried in 1913 to Edith Dunne Stone of New York who died in 1952.

At the time of his departure for London, Beatty was a member of over 20 clubs, which included the Metropolitan Club, Sons of the Revolution, American Institute of Mining Engineers, Sewanakha-Corinthian Yacht Club, Shawinigan Club (fishing), University Club, and the Sleepy Hollow Country Club (golf). He was also a member of the Metropolitan Museum of Art and the Museum of Natural History.

He and his new wife travelled to Egypt almost every year as Beatty found the climate relieved his health problems. Between 1915 and 1917, according to Horton, ibid, p. 13, snuff bottles were added to the collection almost on a monthly basis. In 1917, Beatty travelled to the Far East for the first time. He took an extended six-month trip with his family to China and Japan and purchased Chinese and Japanese items directly from the best dealers in Kyoto, Yokohama, and Osaka.

Sadly we do not know a great deal about Beatty's purchasing other than a number of invoices in the archives (dated between 1911 and 1918) and a list of dealers' names on a single sheet (believed to refer to his far East trip in 1917) above which it is typed 'The great bulk of the purchases were made from the following dealers'. The listing in order reads:

a. S. H. Kuhn, Regenis Building, Peking; b) Hui Ku Chai, Liu Li Chang, Peking; c) Tiff Amy, Hata Men Wai, Peking; d) a number of articles were bought from small dealers and brokers who called at my Hotel in Peking; e) Y. C. Tsu, 280 Shanteng Road, Shanghai; [the list then continues with Japanese dealers:] f) K. Yokayama, Kyoto; g) S. Nomura, Kyoto; h) T. Tameguchi, Kyoto; i) Y. Kawashima, Kyoto; j) A. Fukuda, Kyoto; k) T Wakabayashi, Kyoto; l) K. Inouye, Kyoto; m) T. Murakami, Kasana-machi, Osaka; n) N. Kida, Nara, Japan; o) Japanese broker; [this is then followed by a handwritten addition:] p) S.M. Franke, 20 Commonile Street, London, EC England

The purchases from these dealers covered a wide range of objects including snuff bottles.

Other invoices and dated letters from dealers, shippers, and collectors between the years 1911 and 1918 give us further insights into the mind of Beatty and also about his buying habits and oversight of his collection. It also adds a few more provenances to identifiable bottles in the collection today:

3 January 1911: Invoice from Thomas B. Clarke, prominent New York dealer. Listing 13 bottles of various media including amethyst, silver, ivory and rose soufflé but mostly comprising blue and white porcelains of which one is listed as 'landscape decoration with people walking in a garden – with Yongzheng seal'.
   - *The blue and white bottle described may be No. 208 in this publication.*

20 January 1911: Letter to G. Heliot, a prominent dealer in Paris, from Beatty in New York, in which he writes 'I beg to acknowledge receipt of your letter of December 28th, with reference to a collection of snuff bottles you have recently brought from China. I would appreciate it very much if you will write me a full description of the finest bottles, as I may want you to send me some to America on approval. I would be willing to pay a moderate amount for the expense of the shipment providing you can have a few of the best bottles photographed and these photographs sent me first.'
   - *This letter does say quite a lot about the mind of the dealer who is prepared to save his best bottles for his best client and about the best client who can fairly demand the best service.*

25 March 1911: Letter to J. M. Mitchell of F. P. Vandergrift & Company, shippers from Beatty's New York Office regarding the shipment of 107 snuff bottles from London on the S/S *Celtic*, 2 September 1910, mentioning that 'Mrs. Beatty has been very low with typhoid pneumonia and Mr. Beatty has not been able to attend to any business for some time. This accounts for the delay in Mr. Beatty giving the matter attention. Regretting you have been inconvenienced to this extent, and hoping to have the matter cleaned up soon for you.'
   - *Three days later his wife died from typhoid fever.*

A notarized shipping invoice attached does not list the bottles individually but does list the dealers he acquired them from which include: 'Lawrent Heliot, rue Berlin, Paris; Madame Langweil, Place Saint Georges, Paris; Bluett & Sons, Oxford Street, London; John Sparks, London; Larkin & Son, Bond Street, London; and from about ten to fifteen small dealers in antiques scattered through London and Paris during my trip abroad in June and July 1910.'

July, August, September 1911: hand-written invoice from G. F. Marshall, 1 Thomas Street, Oxford Street, London includes 'A collection of 139 antique Chinese snuff bottles in agate, crystal, porcelain [?], metal and jade[?] – 486 Pounds 10 shillings.'

September 1911: Accounts list – Snuff Bottles – $2,147.
   - *A rather large sum by all standards.*

12 October 1911: Invoice from F.W. Kaldenberg's Sons, Pipe maker and dealer in ivories and oriental curios at Fifth Ave. and 17th Street included 27 snuff bottles (non identifiable) – $388.50.

12 October 1911: Invoice from He Chong, Yum & Co. of 20 West 30th Street for three bottles; one green jade – $12; one white jade – $15; and one 5-colour porcelain bottle – $20.

19 October 1911: Letter from F.W. Kaldenberg's Sons regarding invoice above, 'Your favor with remittance was duly received for which please find receipt and also our check for $8.00 which pays you for the return of one of the bottles less the cost of the stopper.'

7 November 1912: Letter from J. M. Mitchell of F. P. Vandergrift & Company, shippers, 'We have papers for a shipment of 209 old snuff bottles for your account on the S/S *Minnetonka*….'

5 May 1913: Letter from Roland N. Moore, dealer 'We have recently received some snuff bottles which we think you would be interested to see. One is quite unique, of dark green jadeite in parts deep black and with markings of white. I have never seen one like it. We are in town for only this week. If you care to see this bottle but cannot find time to call before Saturday I should be pleased to leave it over night at your home. I think it is a perfect beauty ($100 net to you). Our price is $150.'
   - *This may be No. 60 in this publication; a jadeite bottle of chloromelanite type.*

20 June 1913: Letter from Beatty's brother William Gedney Beatty to colleague – 'Old things are much harder to find than they were last year, but Chester has gotten about 40 snuff bottles….'

June and August 1913: Account listing of purchases include 'July: Snuff Bottles – 135 Pounds, 9 shillings and sixpence' and 'August: More snuff bottles – 90 pounds'.

8 October 1913: Letter from Carl Deutsch, Japanese Fan Company to Chester Beatty 'We have just received a new lot of snuff bottles–some thirty-three pieces–which we would like you to see before we show them to anyone else.'

18 November 1913: Letter from Wah Tai Company of 6 West 29th Street (with branches in Hong Kong, Shanghai, Canton, Yokohama, and Kobe) regarding a previous invoice for four snuff bottles (two returned).

29 October 1914: Letter from Beatty in London to E. L. Gruver, a colleague in New York, 'I note that Takenaka has brought back some snuff bottles and that you have given him the balance to be repaired. I think it would be a good idea to call him up and follow up this matter as he is very slow, but does very fine work.'
   - *Mr. Takenaka, it seems, was entrusted with the repair and restoration of damaged bottles and it is quite telling that Beatty would be quite so involved in the minutiae of his collection from such a distance.*

23 February 1915: Letter to Thomas B. Clarke, a prominent New York dealer, 'I am going to drop in to see you in the course of a few days to thank you for your kindness in regard to the snuff bottles. The bottles you so kindly let me have are a great addition to my collection; in fact, I feel that it is through your help that I have been able to make the collection what it is.'

3 March 1915: Letter from Chester Beatty in New York to M. Gordon Smith in Kobe, Japan, in which he invites him to see his snuff bottle collection if he is ever in New York and continues 'I was very much interested in what you say in regard to a book on the subject of snuff bottles. I have thought of some time getting out a book on snuff bottles, one of the principal features of which would be illustrations in the three color process, and when you have finished your manuscript, I would be very glad if you would give me a chance to purchase it first rather than the museums, [Smith had mentioned in his previous letter to Beatty that he was thinking of giving a manuscript he was working on of his own collection to the Victoria and Albert Museum for them to publish on their account] because I will probably use same in connection with the book I expect to publish some time.' He continues later, 'The collecting of snuff bottles is indeed fascinating,' and in response to certain questions received in previous correspondence with Smith, 'I have one white coral bottle, but I have never seen an ambergris bottle. I have amber bottles and also a copal gum bottle which looks very much like amber. I wonder if you have ever seen a black amber bottle. One expert on amber spoke to me about them and he said that the black was natural amber. Personally, I think they are coloured. In regard to the red coral bottles, I believe nearly all of them are modern. I think you have an old one in your collection. One of the most curious bottles I have is that cut out of a single garnet. It is very unusual to find one of that material. One thing I would like to ask you and get your opinion about is the question of so-called snuff bottles which they find in the tombs of Egypt. I assume these bottles are around the Ming time and, of course, they were probably shipped to Egypt and, no

doubt, contained perfume and ointment; they are very crude bottles and are described in the books on Egyptian subjects. There are also a good many of these bottles in Egypt. I would very much like to know if you have one of these bottles. I may run across one, and if you do not have such a bottle. I would be very glad to send you one with my compliments. In giving a description of these bottles in one of the Egyptian books, in one case it is claimed one was found in an open tomb. I spent last winter in Egypt and I doubt this statement very much. In the various books I have read they state they were found in the tombs opened many years ago. The bottles are not so very rare or fine, but the finding of them in Egypt makes them interesting.' Beatty adds the following postscript 'P.S., I would be very glad if the book is published to give you some of the copies. Of course, I would not expect to publish this book for a year or so.'

> - *Beatty's busy work and travel schedule never allowed for his long-dreamed for publication of the collection. It is therefore personally very gratifying, albeit almost a century late, to have the honour of fulfilling his wish.*
> - *The white coral bottle that Beatty mentions is no longer in the collection. Whilst the collection does have amber, 12 of which are published here (Nos. 152-163), his copal gum bottle remains something of a mystery. Copal gum is used as a shellac or varnish for japanning purposes, and the dark type he mentions was perhaps more commonplace in his day. The single garnet noted may be the very rare ruby or sapphire bottle (Nos. 135-136). As to the Egyptian bottle reference, which today seems far-fetched, this was certainly not the case in the first half of the twentieth century when so little had been written on the subject. In fact as late as 1938, the Brooklyn Museum scholar Elisabeth Riefstahl published a 10-page article with illustrations regarding the noteworthy recovery in Egypt of Chinese snuff bottles (still in Brooklyn Museum) from a cemetery outside Cairo.[4] Their remarkably 'crude' quality (an identical adjective attributed to them by Beatty) at first convinced the Egyptologists that they were 'ancient'.[4] Later the theory was debunked.*

26 April 1915: Letter to his accountants in New York acknowledging receipt of invoice for $53.20 covering balance of duty on 110 Chinese Snuff Bottles which arrived on S/S *Philadelphia*, September 3, 1913.

3 November 1917: Letter from Y. Okita, Nara, mentioning his return from a lengthy visit to mainland China where he purchased various objects on Beatty's behalf and which included 25 snuff bottles listed as 'the snuff bottles are [a] mixture, such as top pieces, rare pieces, and a few cheap ones, but strange pieces, etc.' The price: 'about $800 for 25 snuff bottles.'

5 February 1918: Letter from Y. Okita, Nara, in which amongst other items he lists, 'I bought a rare snuff bottle. It is black metal and inlaid with silver and quite [an] old piece. We see same work among the Chinese vase, but I never saw such a snuff bottle.'

> - *This may well refer to the bottle No. 260 in this publication, though without a full description we cannot be sure.*

3 May 1918: letter from the shippers Day & Meyer, Inc. sending invoice for the 'snuff bottles packed at your above address (265 Central Park West, New York City) for shipment to Europe.'

Among the archives of the Chester Beatty Collection is a handlist dated 2 March 1914, where the incredible number of over 1600 bottles is already listed in his collection. Almost half of these are mineral examples. Beatty was acquiring on average an incredible number of almost 90 bottles a year if indeed he did start collecting c. 1868 when a student. Unfortunately the handlist describes material only and it is impossible to identify with certainty more then a few bottles in the collection today. It is now known that Beatty disposed of a third of his collection through a London dealer prior to his move to Dublin in 1950. He was also known to have given generous gifts of bottles to family members and friends. The present collection numbers 942 bottles and the breakdown of categories is fully listed by Chapman, ibid, p.57.

Beatty became a naturalized British subject in 1933 but became disillusioned when the British public unceremoniously kicked out Winston Churchill and the Conservative government at the end of the Second World War in 1945 and returned a Labour government in its place. In 1950 he moved his entire collection to Dublin.

In 1954, Beatty was knighted by Queen Elizabeth II, for his wartime services to Britain. In 1957 he became the first honorary citizen of Ireland.

Sir Alfred Chester Beatty died on 19 January 1968 in Monaco and was the first private citizen to be accorded a state funeral by the Irish Government.

Footnotes:

[1] John Murdoch, *Chester Beatty Biography*, unpublished manuscript, located in the The Selection Trust Archive, London School of Economics and Political Science Library, London.

[2] Jan Chapman, 'The Chester Beatty Collection of Snuff Bottles', *Arts of Asia*, March-April 1988, p. 57.

[3] Salting – A confidence trick in which the fraudulent addition of a more valuable substance to a core sample of lesser value takes place.

[4] Elisabeth Riefstahl, 'A Tempest in a Snuff Bottle', *Brooklyn Museum Quarterly*, vol. 25, no. 1 (January 1938): pp. 36-48.

Bibliography:

Chapman, Jan, 'The Chester Beatty Collection of Snuff Bottles', *Arts of Asia*, March-April1988.

Durnett, Raymond E. (ed.), *Mining Tycoons in the Age of Empire, 1870-1945: Entrepreneurship, High Finance, Politics and Territorial Expansion*. A selection of essays on mining tycoons including: 'Chapter 9 – Alfred Chester Beatty: Mining Engineer, Financier, and Entrepreneur, 1898-1950' by John Phillips, Farnham, Surrey: Ashgate Publishing, 2008.

Horton, Charles, *Alfred Chester Beatty: From Miner to Bibliophile*, Dublin: TownHouse, 2003.

Jeremy, David J. (ed.), *Dictionary of Business Biography*, London: Butterworths, 1984-86 (5 volumes) 1984. Includes an essay by Cyril A. Kidd and Simon Katzenellenbogen, 'Sir Alfred Chester Beatty', (pp. 230-233).

Murdoch, John, *Chester Beatty*, unpublished 346-page biography, located in the Selection Trust Archive, London School of Economics and Political Science Library, London.

Riefstahl, Elisabeth, 'A Tempest in a Snuff Bottle', *Brooklyn Museum Quarterly*, vol. 25, no. 1 (January 1938): pp. 36-48.

Wilson, A.J., *The Life and Times of Sir Alfred Chester Beatty*, London: Cadogan Publications, 1985.

SNUFF BOTTLES

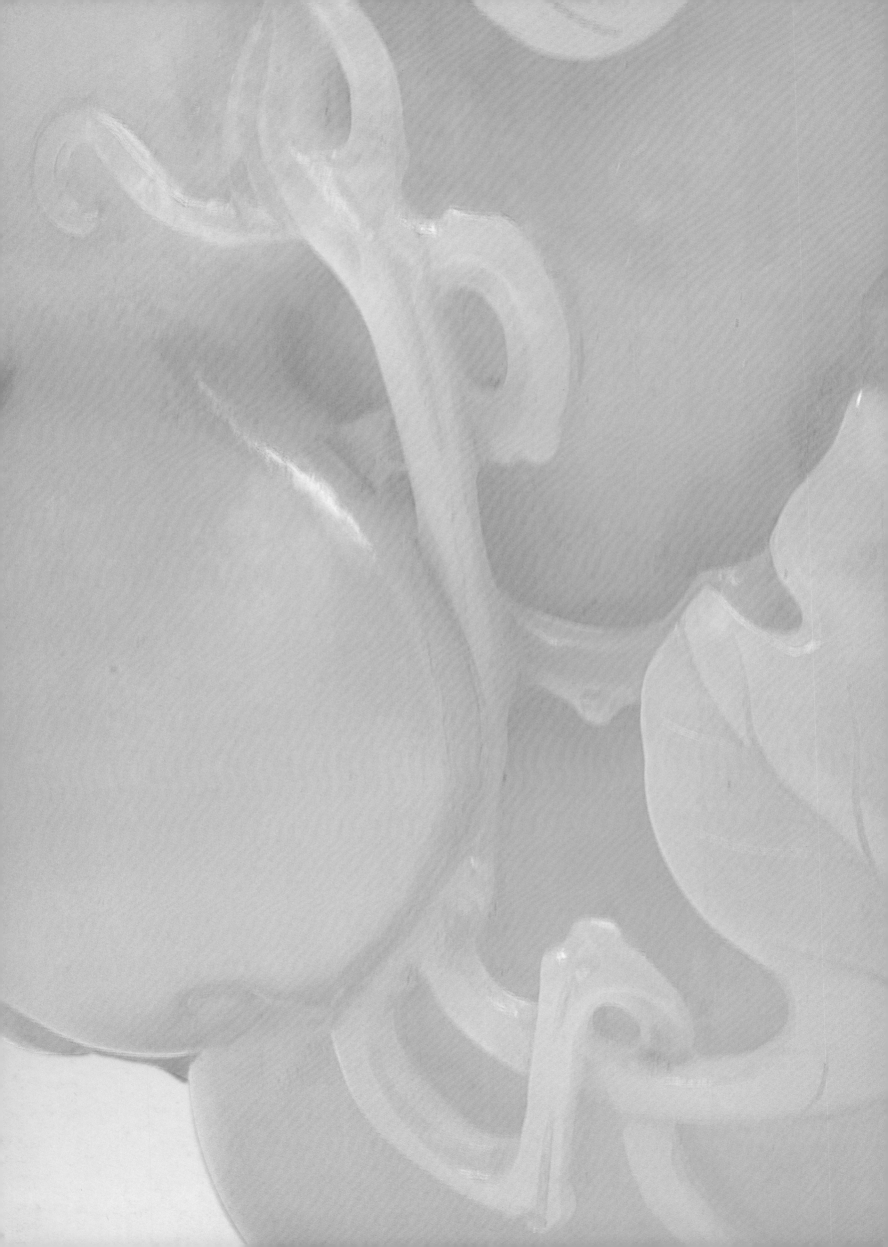

JADE

1

Nephrite, one main face of black material, the other main face of a pale olive green, a vertical division of stone colour at the narrow sides, the neck of oval section, the mouth circular and a very well hollowed interior, the base flat

1760-1860

Stopper: Jadeite, silver collar and spoon

Height: 7.0 cm
Mouth: 0.85 cm
Neck: 1.5-1.7 cm (oval)

Most plain nephrite bottles are curved at both the shoulders and feet. This bottle is unusually rectilinear in form and was perhaps an expedient choice by the lapidary to reduce the workload. It is certainly an odd feature. The craftsman has very simply resolved the issue of tapering from a square flat surface to the circular mouth by adapting the neck to an oval shape with slightly flattened edges. The rectangular body of the bottle very gently spreads towards the foot.

The lapidary carefully selected this most unusually coloured stone of two tones and rendered an exquisite bottle, both simple in its appearance, yet remarkably sophisticated in its representation of Daoist dualism. The demarcation of strata down the length of the stone, presents the viewer with one side that is polished, dark, and reflective, whilst the other is lightly textured of a sponge-like turnip-grain pale-olive stone that, unlike the other side, draws in the viewer. Yet at the narrow sides there is a gentle resolution of these contrasting sides, evocative of the dualistic yinyang symbol. The magical choice of material evokes both the darkness of the night sky and the swirling constellations.

The use of a pure black stone (on one side only in this example) is unusual though not without precedent. For further discussion of this see Moss, Graham, and Tsang, A Treasury of Chinese Snuff Bottles: The Mary and George Bloch Collection, Vol.1, Part 2, pp. 414-415, no. 160 and also Moss, Graham, and Tsang, The Art of the Chinese Snuff Bottle, p. 120, no. 58.

Another bottle of simple spreading rectangular shape using a two-colour black-and-white jade, in horizontal rather than vertical bands, and probably slightly later in date (1800-1900) than ours was illustrated by Hughes, The Blair Bequest: Chinese Snuff Bottles from the Princeton University Art Museum, p. 45, no. 12 and signed Yitang. With undecorated bottles of this type there are few clues to accurate dating and though this bottle might date to the mid-eighteenth century a wide date range is more prudent.

(CBL C 705)

2

Nephrite, each main face displays a vertical half of black material and a vertical half of grey-white material, the black stone turning to grey tones at the narrow sides and the grey-white stone with a vertical inclusion of a clearer white visible on both sides, the neck of circular section, fairly well hollowed

1780-1850

Stopper: Nephrite, probably cut from the same stone

Height: 5.2 cm
Mouth: 0.55 cm
Neck: 1.5 cm

In contrast with the previous bottle the lapidary in this case has chosen to use two colours of stone in a more obvious and perhaps less successful fashion. Here the demarcation is clearly visible when viewed from the normal perspective. Even the slightly wavering edge line where the colours meet has been left, probably a happy coincidence, as it is somewhat evocative of the curving lines of the yinyang symbol. The stopper on this bottle is almost certainly the original one, as the bands of colour appear to continue very successfully from neck to stopper. The natural markings of the stone should be read just as if viewing a Dali marble stone (or 'dreamstone' in the West). Dali was a small town in Yunnan province that was the source of marble for inlaid furniture and 'stone pictures' which were mounted as screens or as hanging panels. The delightful figuring could be teased out of the stone by the deft hand and judicious tool of a carver but often needed little assistance to produce a finished 'landscape picture'. The stones were much beloved by the literati. The Western term 'dreamstone' is a perfectly acceptable alternative name, evoking as it does a landscape caught between reality and dream. The markings on our bottle which run vertically, rather than the more usual horizontal banding, might be read as a cascading waterfall, perhaps a cliff face, or even as sheets of approaching rain. For an example of a 'dreamstone' used as an inlay on a painting table at which sits the noble figure of the Kangxi Emperor with calligraphic brush in hand, see Kangxi, Empereur de Chine, p. 59, cat. 48.

For another bottle using a similar stone, arguably more subtly, see Moss, Graham, and Tsang, The Art of the Chinese Snuff Bottle: The J & J Collection, pp. 114-115, no. 54, where the authors argue that the bottle they discuss may have been created by a jade workshop in Suzhou. They base their opinion on the colour and type of stone that bears comparison, as does ours, with a large group of carved nephrite bottles that are attributed to the Suzhou school. They also argue that the lack of handles to the narrow sides is another typical feature of this group and whilst the school is renowned for its exquisite carved decoration, there seems to be no good reason to suggest that they would not also have turned their hand to the more simple production of plain bottles. It must be remembered, however that the Suzhou workshops did not have a monopoly on this particular type of black and white nephrite, and the possibility that a totally different centre produced the plain bottles cannot be ruled out.

It is also interesting to compare our stone with that used on the Yitang-signed Princeton bottle cited in the previous entry in this publication, see Hughes, The Blair Bequest: Chinese Snuff Bottles from the Princeton University Art Museum, p. 45, no. 12. Whilst it is more rectilinear in shape, the type of nephrite used evokes a powerful natural scene not unlike ours, which requires no further embellishment. In this regard it is also perhaps worth considering other black-and-white jade bottles bearing the Yitang seal. The group as a whole uses similar nephrite, often with no surface decoration other than the inscriptions and might be linked to this type of un-marked bottle. For an example see, Moss, Graham, and Tsang, A Treasury of Chinese Snuff Bottles: The Mary and George Bloch Collection, Vol.1, pp. 382-383, no. 147. See also ibid, pp. 318-335, nos. 126-131, for a group of carved Suzhou black and white nephrite bottles.

(CBL C 707)

Unless otherwise stated all height measurements are without stoppers and all mouth and neck measurements are diameters throughout this publication.

1 (three views)

2 (two views)

3

Nephrite, one main face very lightly engraved with a lengthy poem carefully placed on a simply outlined rock, cleverly using a brownish-black area of the otherwise grey-cream stone, further darker flaw lines integrated in to the engraved design with bamboo, beneath the large rocky outcrop sits a lone fisherman in his craft, the scene continuing on the other more monochrome face with further rocks and a single figure in a pavilion under a tree canopy amidst further rocks, with another fisherman in his boat approaching a bridge, the sky with five birds in flight, the neck circular with a fairly small mouth but remarkably well hollowed interior

The bottle 1760-1850, the engraving possibly later

Height: 8 cm
Mouth: 0.8 cm
Neck: 2.5 cm

The poem, in four seven-character stanzas, reads:
Shou ai xu xin nai shui han
Jie lu jin xi jin lang gan
Qing xian he huan chao ju zi
Du ba nan hua xin diao gan

This can be translated as:
I always like the hollow inside (bamboo) which can stay cold
I am happy to create the pavilion near Langgan (bamboo)
Once I am relaxed and peaceful I can recall old times (1000 years ago)
Finish reading (Sutra) then go fishing with my rod

The talented engraver has very carefully placed his 28-character poem within the confines of a simply delineated rock face which has itself been cleverly outlined using the edge of a brownish-black area of the otherwise grey-white stone to magical effect. Further darker flaw lines in the stone have similarly been incorporated into a design of bamboo to one edge. A landscape scene, evoking the poem itself, and depicting a small figure of a man fishing from a boat under a tree near a rocky promontory with a bridge, continues around the bottle with a second fisherman in another boat below a group of flying birds. The scene is similar to many portrayals by scholar/artisans of high-minded philosophers lost in a world of introspection and mental speculation away from the never-ending woes of the 'real' world. The vast backdrop and simple solitary figures embody the metaphor perfectly.

Interestingly a stone of similar shades of colour signed Yitang and illustrated by Moss, Graham, and Tsang, *A Treasury of Chinese Snuff Bottles: The Mary and George Bloch Collection*, Vol.1, pp. 380-381, no. 146, though un-engraved and of smaller rectangular shape, may well be connected in some way to our bottle. It seems that most of the bottles bearing the Yitang seal appear to be carved from jade of two colours, though this might be coincidental.

In our example the inscription and the engraving may well have been added at a later date than the production of the bottle itself. This was a common practice and in no way detracts from the work's artistic merits.

Stylistically the engraving might be favorably compared to the carved output of the so-called 'Rustic Crystal Master'. See for example Moss, Graham, and Tsang, *A Treasury of Chinese Snuff Bottles: The Mary and George Bloch Collection*, Vol. 2, Part Quartz, pp. 194-195, no. 254. The term the Rustic Crystal Master was coined by Moss et al. to group a rather wide ranging, sometimes inconsistent school of hard-stone carvers, whose basic distinguishing features are rustic scenes (as with our example), winter landscapes, and themes following in the tradition of the literati painters.

The very small mouth and fairly well hollowed interior are further indications of quality.

A nephrite stopper (not illustrated) in the form of an official hat was stored with this bottle but is almost certainly an addition, cut from a stone of more celadon tone.

(CBL C 712)

4

Nephrite, carved in an archaistic style with low-relief seal-script calligraphic square panels with wide borders on each main face, one with four characters, the other with two of almost pictographic nature, the narrow rounded sides with low-relief handles formed by bi- or trifurcated-tailed *chilong* rising and emitting spray from their mouths, a short cylindrical neck and a well hollowed interior, an oval flat foot ring, the base engraved in deep channels with a maker's mark, the stone pitted, mottled and polished

1740-1820

Height: 6.5 cm
Mouth: 0.8 cm
Neck: 2.5 cm

A panel on one side is carved in relief with four characters that read:
Qian jin yu hu

This translates as:
One thousand ounces gold jade bottle

The panel on the other side has two characters that read:
Bing xin

This translates as:
Pure heart

The base has a four-character engraved mark:
Zhi qing shi zhou

This translates as:
Made by the Zhiqing family

Presently we have no records of the Zhiqing family.

We can however assume from the product before us that the artisans of the workshop were talented. The lapidary's choice of an extremely attractive pitted variegated stone was a brilliant one, presumably dictated by the stones 'archaistic' qualities. The overall effect of the stone and the archaistic seal script characters is powerful, reminiscent of ancient jade carvings. The combination of the seal script characters and the *chilong* handles formed as bi- and trifurcated-tailed dragons spewing spray are masterful.

The stone has darker areas of olive-green and brown in the upper half fading to a creamy-white with black mottling in the lower half, which also has significant uneven pitting to the surface. The entire bottle has also undergone a fine polishing which renders a superb semi-gloss appearance.

The *chilong* handles carved on the narrow side are somewhat reminiscent of those found on the 'Master of the Rocks School' bottles. For a number of examples see Kleiner, *Chinese Snuff Bottles: The White Wings Collection*, pp. 40-41, no. 20, which also has seal characters on one side, and also Moss, Graham, and Tsang, *A Treasury of Chinese Snuff Bottles: The Mary and George Bloch Collection*, Vol.1, pp. 370-371, no. 142. This may be merely coincidental, however, as the stone is most unusual for the School, which generally, if the literature is correct, preferred brown skins with a pale yellowish-green core. However the shape would certainly be acceptable.

For another nephrite bottle of more orange-brown colour but carved in relief with an archaic seal script from the Gerry P. Mack Collection, see Kleiner, *Precious Playthings: Important Chinese Snuff Bottles*, p. 27, no. 15

(CBL C 713)

4 (mark)

3 (two views)

4 (three views)

5

Nephrite, the stone of dark-grey tones with a fine misty black matrix, a thin white band encircles the entire body and other smaller pale inclusions are scattered through the stone, a short cylindrical neck with a small mouth and a well hollowed interior, a flat oval foot ring and shallow cut flat base

Possibly Suzhou, 1750-1850

Stopper: Amethyst, metal collar

Height: 6 cm
Mouth: 0.7 cm
Neck : 2.3 cm

For a similarly striated black-and-white jade bottle see Moss, Graham, and Tsang, *The Art of the Chinese Snuff Bottle, The J & J Collection*, Vol. 1, pp. 114-115, No. 54, where the authors discuss not only the associations to be drawn with 'dreamstones' (see entry No. 2 in this publication) but also with a variety of 'ink-stones', used by the scholar for grinding his inks. In particular there is a certain type of Duan stone, *Duanshi*, that is treasured for a single band of colour running through them. These inkstones are from the Zhaoqing region of Guangdong (formerly called Duanzhou and hence the name Duanshi) and are specifically named for the mines from which they came. The material was highly valued for its distinctive colour and markings, which included 'eyes' and striations. The 'eyes' are natural inclusions in the stone that appear as circles and dots on the surface of the stone and are often incorporated in to the design. For examples of inkstones with 'eyes' and bands of colour see *Mei Ken Ten (An Exhibition of Noted Inkstones)*, 9-15 October 1987, nos. 6, 11-16 and 25-28. Moss et al note that one variety of purple colour with bands of green running through it was particularly treasured and inkstones with a single band of colour were refered to as 'jade belt around the middle' stones because they suggested a purple robe encircled with a jade belt. By extension any stone that is ringed by a band of colour in this way might convey the same association.

The marking on this bottle can also be interpreted as a 'dreamstone' might be. The horizontal banding allows for interpretation as either a misty horizon, or perhaps waves lapping at a shorline, or even a river running through a landscape. Whatever the reading, the quality of this jade bottle would have been much treasured.

The type of stone used in this bottle was one favored by the jade carvers of the Suzhou workshops, and generally accepted on points of style and inscription to date from the middle of the eighteenth century into the early nineteenth century. The material with distinctive colour contrasts was often of large proportions. The flat surface with gently curved sides was considered an advantageous canvas for displaying the stone's inherent qualities.

For another similar bottle see, Brody, *Old Wine Into Old Bottles: A Collector's Commonplace Book*, pp. 64-65 and also illustrated in *Snuff Bottles: Little Gems of Delight*, p. 69, no. M 219 from the Joseph Grimberg Collection. See also Hughes, ICSBS, *Journal*, Spring 2007, for a discussion of two jade bottles of similar colour but differing date and a qualification on the dating, in an article entitled, 'Eighteenth or Nineteenth Century: Guesswork or Fact?'

(CBL C 708)

5 (two views)

6

Spinach nephrite, the short spreading neck with a vertically beveled edge and a small circular mouth, a fairly well hollowed interior, a simple flat oval foot ring and a deep flat base, the semi-opaque stone with areas of black and paler green mottling running diagonally across the stone

1760-1800

Stopper: Spinach nephrite, original in form of official hat

Height: 7.1 cm (excluding stopper)
Mouth: 0.6 cm
Neck: 1.75 cm

Various features of this delightful, smooth, silky, undecorated stone suggest a possible Palace workshop provenance. The stopper, which is original to the bottle, is shaped almost like an official hat and the bottle, like many attributed to the workshops, has the addition of a straight-sided collar. The mouth diameter is extremely small but the interior is very well hollowed, another Imperial feature. For another spinach nephrite bottle (of *meiping* shape) displaying many of these features see Moss, Graham, and Tsang, *A Treasury of Chinese Snuff Bottles: The Mary and George Bloch Collection*, Vol. 1, Jade, pp. 202-203, no. 82. Whilst it is of a much darker type of spinach nephrite, it also has the typical Palace stopper with an integral finial and straight-sided collar. The authors note that the unusual dark stone is very much in keeping with known Qianlong-marked larger vessels made for the Court. Whilst our stone is quite different, the other features certainly suggest a link of some kind. See also Moss et al, ibid, nos. 152-153, for a discussion of our distinctive type of paler spinach nephrite that appears to have become readily available after the conquest of Chinese Turkistan in 1759. The material is of a bright dark-green type with black flecks diffused throughout. The type of stone had been available prior to this date as attested to by other vessels of an earlier date in the Palace collections today, however it was only after 1759 that the material became easily and readily available. The authors illustrate two slightly smaller examples and suggest a dating of 1800-1854 as both bear *Xingyouheng Tang* (Hall Of Constancy) marks. The form of the first Bloch bottle, no. 152, is more in keeping with traditional nineteenth century shapes, whilst the second, if it were not for the hall mark might have been given an eighteenth century dating. The compressed ovoid shape of our bottle is far more consistent with an eighteenth century attribution.

For a Qianlong-marked spinach nephrite or jadeite bottle (listed as jasper) from the Qing Court Collection, with a similar 'more rounded' official hat stopper with straight-sided collar, see *Gugong Complete Snuff Bottles*, p. 138, no. 202.

(CBL C 722)

7

Spinach nephrite, each main face carved in low relief with a *shou* character with C-scrolls, dots, and dragon-head surrounds which might represent an archaic *bi* disc with *kui* dragons, a tall spreading neck and small mouth, a very well hollowed interior, the semi-transparent stone with areas of black and paler green mottling and inclusions, a flat oval foot-ring and deeply cut base

1760-1800

Height: 7.5 cm
Mouth: 0.7 cm
Neck: 1.8 cm

For a discussion of the distinctive stone used for this bottle see the remarks for the previous entry in this publication.

With the exception of minor differences in shape; our bottle has a slightly taller and less flaring neck and the ovoid shape reads slightly more as a pear shape, which is less compressed; only the decoration on this bottle differentiates it from the previous example. The mixture of c-scrolls, dots, and dragon-head decoration is perfectly placed within the confines of the bottle's shape and carefully flanked on the narrow sides by further dots (bosses) and scrolls. It may represent a stylized archaic *bi* disc with clambering dragons. The attention to details, such as the raised line borders that surround the *shou* character; the perfect placement of the design on a slightly awkward shape; the material itself and the high degree of hollowing; all suggest an Imperial workshop may well have been involved in its creation. Unusually, the dragon-heads themselves are not connected to dragon bodies but appear almost miraculously from the archaistic scroll and dot design. This rather formalized approach is typical of confronted dragons on archaistic eighteenth-century production and is reminiscent of decoration found on a series of glass bottles from the Qianlong period attributed to the Imperial glassworks, see *A Treasury of Chinese Snuff Bottles: The Mary and George Bloch Collection*, Vol. 5, Part 2, Glass, pp. 334-343, nos. 822-827. In particular, no. 822 bears a close resemblance in form to ours as well as depicting confronting *kui* dragons which are discussed at length in the entry including their significance as a longevity symbol when depicted in an unending design.

(CBL C 726)

6

7

8

Spinach nephrite, one main face lightly engraved with a large chrysanthemum spray with buds, the other main face engraved with a 33-character Imperial poem written in clerical script, *lishu*, the narrow edges delicately rounded, the spreading neck with a vertically beveled edge, the interior of the mouth unusually funneled to a regularly hollowed interior, the foot simply cut as a concave oval

Probably Imperial, 1760-1800

Height: 6.8 cm
Mouth: 0.6 cm
Neck: 1.9-2.1 cm (oval)

The poem, in four seven-character stanzas, reads:
Yu ti wan shou ju

Ye jie lu chong wei zheng bi
Hua zhung fu po shi zhen huang
Tun feng ba yue cheng shang ju
Chang bao xian zhuang zan lu long

This translates as:
Imperial inscribed – longevity and chrysanthemum

The leaf of chrysanthemum is very green just like jade
The flower is really yellow like amber
In the eighth month compose a poem at banquet
Always hold immortal and drinking (home)

The designation *Yu ti* written before a poem indicates the Emperor wrote it. It does not necessarily bestow Imperial patronage on the bottle itself. However, all the other qualities of this bottle, such as the strength and neatness of the calligraphy, the fine material, and the delicate depiction of the flowers suggest that it may have been a court production. It also quite obviously relates to the following bottle, No. 9 in this publication, which bears the more important *Yu zhi* (Imperial command) designation, which does indeed link it to the Court. The only jarring feature that does not relate to the Imperial group is the neck interior, that rather than being cylindrical and opening up at the shoulder interior as one would expect, is actually funneled from the mouth edge to the interior. Whilst this may be due to an unforeseen flaw in the stone it is an uncommon feature.

For a discussion of the series of primarily nephrite snuff bottles incised with floral decoration accompanied on the reverse side by poems by the Qianlong Emperor, see Moss, Graham, and Tsang, *A Treasury of Chinese Snuff Bottles: The Mary and George Bloch Collection*, Vol. 1, Jade, pp. 260-263, no. 107. Whilst the nephrite group has always been associated with a large group of identically shaped porcelain bottles (compressed slender spade and broad flared cylindrical neck) that bear Qianlong and Jiaqing marks and are similarly painted with floral scenes to one side and Imperial poems to the reverse, their exact relationship to each other has not been clear. For various examples see No. 226 in this publication and also *Gugong Complete Snuff Bottles*, p. 198, no. 308 and p. 204, no. 314; and Hughes, *The Blair Bequest, Chinese Snuff Bottles from the Princeton University Art Museum*, pp. 164-165, no. 203.

However, Moss et al, ibid, now strongly believe that the porcelain bottles are based on the group of nephrite bottles, of which ours can be numbered. Among the reasons for not making this assumption sooner was the fact that many of the nephrite bottles were inscribed with rather undistinguished calligraphy. This is certainly not the case with our bottle. The authors suggest that this failing in standard could be blamed on a 'qualitative hierarchy of inscriptions'. Those pieces individually selected by the Emperor for a poetic encomium are of the finest quality, whilst those of less immediate interest employed less exacting calligraphers.

(CBL C 718)

9

Spinach nephrite, one main face lightly and exquisitely engraved with bamboo and rocks, the other main face engraved with a 25-character Imperial poem in standard script, *kaishu*, the narrow edges beveled flat, the spreading neck with a vertically beveled edge, a small circular mouth opening and a well hollowed interior, a simply cut concave oval foot

Imperial, 1760-1800

Height: 5.1 cm
Mouth: 0.4 cm
Neck: 1.55 cm

The poem, in four five-character stanzas, reads:
Yu zhi shi zu shi

Zhou a jun chu qun
Feng die ren fen fen
Ba yu mi wu wei
Zhong yin jin chi jun

This translates as:
Imperial command – Poem of rock and bamboo

Bamboo grows tall above everything
Bees and butterflies fly around
Person himself not fighting for (power/promotion)
Because he is close to bamboo and rocks

As mentioned in the previous entry, in the hierarchy of Imperial marks the *Yu zhi* designation is considered the most important, as it indicates direct Imperial involvement. This being the case, it also cements the theory that the nephrite group as a whole may well be connected to the Imperial workshops of the Qianlong period. Although the stone itself is perhaps a shade less refined than the richest type sometimes seen in this group, the same cannot be said of the engraving which is as exquisite as any. The handling of the rocks is particularly striking and resembles the calligraphic lines of an ink painting. The variety of thickness of line to create a bold and arresting image is masterful. The subject of this bottle is obviously the same as that in the poem on the reverse side, however according to Bartholomew, *Hidden Meanings in Chinese Art*, p. 189, the bamboo, *zhu*, is a pun for 'congratulate', *zhu*, and the rock, *shoushi*, symbolizes longevity. Together they can be read as 'congratulation on your birthday' suggesting that this may have been a commission to be given as a birthday gift.

The compressed spade shape with high shoulders and the exquisite nature of the decoration and calligraphy can be favorably compared to a number of other Qianlong Imperial bottles, see Moss, Graham, and Tsang, *A Treasury of Chinese Snuff Bottles: The Mary and George Bloch Collection*, Vol. 1, Jade, pp. 260-265, nos. 107-108; Moss et al, *The Art of the Chinese Snuff Bottle: The J & J Collection*, Vol. 1, pp. 94-95, no. 38; No. 133 in this publication, for a lapis lazuli example; and Moss, *Chinese Snuff Bottles 3*, pp. 27-28, figs. 15-16 and 17-18.

(CBL C 719)

8 (two views)

9 (two views)

10

Spinach nephrite, comprising two conjoined bottles with slightly spreading necks with small circular mouths, and well hollowed interiors, both with flat oval foot rings and very slightly concave bases, the green stone with paler grey-white inclusions and black flecking

1760-1840

Stoppers: Coral (or glass imitating coral), engraved brass collars

Height: 5 cm
Mouths: 0.7 cm
Necks: 1.9 cm

Conjoined spinach nephrite bottles are quite rare. The marriage here is well rendered, as both appear to emerge from the side of the other without awkward corners or channels and with clear unifying strata within the stone running diagonally through them.

The question of 'why a double bottle?' has been thoughtfully answered by Moss, Graham, and Tsang, *A Treasury of Chinese Snuff Bottles: The Mary and George Bloch Collection*, Vol. 1, Jade, pp. 412-413, no. 159, where the authors illustrate a less conventional double form where the bottles are joined at their main faces rather than, as in our case, along the narrow sides. The most obvious reason for a double-bottle design would be to hold two different kinds of snuff. Quoting Richard John Lynn's translation of Zhao Zhiqian's *Yonglu xianjie*, which Moss cites in his lengthy and illuminating footnote:

> Ah, my honoured friend, you pay me great respect in complimenting the negligible qualities of my 1874 flying duck's green snuff, but deign to sample the 1776, which is in the other half of my poverty-stricken bottle….

Other reasons for a double-bottle design are purely metaphorical. Double elements were familiar symbols of conjugal bliss, such as paired mandarin ducks, paired phoenix, and double happiness characters (*xi xi*). Interestingly many double-form bottles appear to take the form of twin fish, yet another symbol for a happy marriage. It might also represent a form of Daoist dualism, or even as suggested by Moss, op cit, be nothing more than simply 'his and hers' containers.

The spinach nephrite used for this bottle bears resemblance to other bottles whose likely date of production post-dates the conquest of Chinese Turkistan in 1759. The shape of our bottle can certainly be found in late Qianlong and early Jiaqing porcelain bottles, see No. 229 in this publication, and hence the quite wide date margin given for this bottle.

(CBL C 724)

11

Spinach nephrite, of ewer shape, the handle on one narrow side formed as an archaistic scroll with phoenix-head finial, on the other narrow side a twisting *chilong* clambers up the neck forming a pseudo spout, the flat circular mouth fairly wide and the interior well hollowed, standing on a tall spreading foot with a flat oval foot ring, and deeply cut base, the pale green stone with black and brown swirling inclusions that run diagonally across the stone

1760-1790

Height: 6.5 cm
Mouth: 0.5 cm
Neck: 0.9 cm

This bottle can also be favorably compared to a white nephrite jade bottle attributed to the palace workshops illustrated by Moss, Graham, and Tsang, *The Art of the Chinese Snuff Bottle: The J & J Collection*, Vol. 1, pp. 96-97, no. 39, with handles carved in the archaic taste around an imitation vase form, not normally associated with the normal snuff bottle output.

The Chinese always revered the past. In particular they looked back to the great Bronze Age of China which has come down to us mainly in the ritual bronze vessels that symbolized the power and prestige of China's first three dynasties: the Xia, the Shang, and the Zhou. This reverence for tradition helped guide the pursuit of everyday life and also found expression in many art forms from the pre-dynastic period to the end of the Qing Dynasty. What began as precise faithful copies of earlier forms and decorations, like those of the Han paying homage to their ancestors, later became, by the time of the Ming and Qing Dynasties, wise interpretations or diluted versions, within the ongoing art forms.

In our example the strictly linear handle is finely counter-balanced by the sinuous form of the bifurcated-tailed *chilong* climbing at the neck, a form which whilst archaic in its references would never have appeared in this combination on vessels of that era.

For further discussion of the Qianlong emperor's involvement with archaic design on jade production in the eighteenth century and illustrations of archaistic jade vessels alongside their Bronze Age counterparts, see *The Refined Taste of the Emperor: Special Exhibition of Archaic and Pictorial Jades of the Ch'ing Court*, pp. 47-104, National Palace Museum, Taipei, 1997. Qianlong wrote a poem in 1779 in which he admonished what he called the 'new style' in jade carving. Exactly what the Emperor meant by 'new style' is uncertain. What is clear is that it simply did not meet his exacting aesthetic standards. In his view it was a coarse design, which lacked a feeling of natural delicacy and often had gaudy embellishments. He was possibly referring to layers of openwork, ostentatious filigree, and uncorrected flaws. Not content to limit himself to strongly worded criticism, he actively promoted traditional designs. He proposed to 'restore ancient ways' and suggested that the lapidaries turn to antiquity for models.

(CBL C 731)

12

Spinach nephrite, of fish form, the body gently curving in a slender S-shape, the large side fins sweeping upward, the low dorsal fin running the length of its back, the tail fin of quite small proportion in comparison, whiskers neatly delineated around the mouth and scales marked on the body, a well hollowed interior, the green stone with brown and paler green inclusions on the sides and small black flecks throughout

1760-1840

Length: 7.3 cm
Mouth: 0.5 cm

The fish is an extremely popular subject in Chinese art. This example almost certainly depicts a carp (*liyu*), though it might possibly represent a catfish (*nianyu*), as indicated by the lightly carved whiskers around the mouth. Catfish however have a small dorsal fin. Less likely, it depicts a goldfish, which is in fact a smaller domesticated version of the East Asian carp, though generally not depicted with whiskers.

The Chinese characters for 'carp' (*liyu*) and 'profit' share the same sound, as do the characters for 'fish' (*yu*) and 'affluence' or 'abundance'. If the bottle were given as a gift, its recipient would most certainly understand this hidden double meaning. The carp is symbolically associated with passing the civil service examinations. The story goes, according to tradition, that carp swimming up the Yellow River against the current must leap the rapids of Dragon's Gate; the first to succeed transforms itself into a dragon. This story is a metaphor for a poor scholar who, by passing the civil service exams, raises himself to the status of a high official.

The lips of the fish have been very carefully delineated and form the mouth of the bottle itself. Clearly the carving was intended as a snuff bottle from its inception and was not, as is true of some other fish bottles, a conversion from a fondling piece, where the mouth is simply drilled through an existing surface. The tail of our example may have been slightly reduced at its upper edges where some chips and uneven surface are visible.

For other fish bottles see Low, *More Treasures from The Sanctum of Enlightened Respect*, p. 53, no. 47, and also Hui, Polak, and Sin, *Hidden Treasures of the Dragon*, pp. 44-45, nos. 78-80.

(CBL C 730)

10

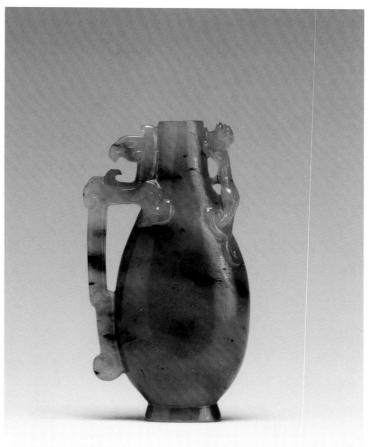

11

12

13

Spinach nephrite, of gourd shape, deeply carved and reticulated, the exterior carved continuously with dense trailing leafy gourds with a beetle, a butterfly, and two six-legged insects, one possibly a cicada, the neck formed as a short cylinder with a flat lip and cylindrical mouth, very well hollowed to the interior which mimics the external gourd shape, the pale green stone with some darker inclusions and black flecks, the flattened base with a simple dimple at the centre, the bottle partially supported by the fruit extending to the foot

1760-1790

Height: 6.6 cm
Mouth: 0.5 cm
Neck: 1.9 cm

Published: Chapman, 'The Chester Beatty Collection of Snuff Bottles', *Arts of Asia*, March-April, 1988, p. 61, fig 6.

This gem of a bottle can be favorably compared with an example illustrated by Low, *Chinese Snuff Bottles from the Sanctum of Enlightened Respect III*, p. 73, no. 54. The author discusses the symbolism of this double-gourd form, *hulu*, which is said to embody heaven and earth, and to contain spiritual energy that wards off evil spirits. One of the Daoist treasures, the gourd is also the vessel of magic elixirs, a symbol of mystery and necromancy, and the attribute of the immortal Li Tieguai. Our example however seems rather more naturalistic in concept, displaying as it does a plethora of hemipteran insects amidst the foliage.

Superbly carved, it is patently a candidate for a palace workshop provenance during the second half of the Qianlong emperor's reign. The quality of even the smallest of details such as the twisting gnarly branches juxtaposed with the deliciously smooth skins of the fecund gourds, the variety of industrious insects, and the superb polish make for an outstanding masterpiece. It is suggested by Moss, Graham, and Tsang, *A Treasury of Chinese Snuff Bottles: The Mary and George Bloch Collection*, Vol. 1, Jade, pp. 154-155, no. 62, that the entire group of fruit, flower, and vegetable form bottles could easily be grouped together under one generic heading of 'naturalistic' bottles. The popularity at court of these 'naturalistic' bottles cannot be in doubt as they form a large proportion of the published nephrite bottles from the Imperial collection. However, the use of a spinach-green nephrite within this group is exceedingly rare. The majority is carved from a white or greenish-white nephrite, some with areas of brown skin. A group of well known aubergine-form bottles do have spinach-green calyx collars, see No. 43 in this publication for an example and some bamboo shoot bottles are also embellished with additional spinach-green branches and leaves, see No. 45 in this publication, however individual 'naturalistic' bottles made entirely of spinach-green material are few. Amongst these can be listed this example; the Low example, op cit, p. 73, no. 54; and aubergine in the Bloch collection, Moss, Graham and Tsang, op cit, pp.180-181, no. 72. A few others are also recorded.

An ill-fitting jadeite and brass stopper stored with this bottle was deemed unsuitable for publication.

(CBL C 733)

14

Nephrite, of archaic *cong* shape, primarily a cylinder within a square form, five slightly concave horizontal bands forming a trigram-like design around the body, three alternate bands wrap entirely around the body whilst two partially wrap around the body, the pale green stone with large areas of russet colouring with cream inclusions and an extremely attractive soft polish overall to a lightly pitted surface, the circular neck rising from the rounded shoulders with a very small mouth, the interior quite well hollowed, a flat circular foot ring with a deep concave base

1740-1840

Height: 7.6 cm
Mouth: 0.45 cm
Neck: 1.5 cm

Refer to the entry for No. 11 in this publication for a discussion of the use of archaic forms.

The *cong* was an archaic jade burial object that, because of its unusual form (a circle within a square), came to represent heaven and earth. However the function and meaning of these enigmatic Neolithic period ritual jades is still under discussion. The decorative motifs on the early Liangzhu culture (c. 4,000-2,500 BC) *cong*, comprise face patterns, relief bars, and circles. It was typical for Liangzhu *cong* to be decorated with masks on the four corners but arranged in simple horizontal bars, which themselves are subdivided by horizontal lines and grooves. Our simplified form however still clearly exhibits its Neolithic antecedent. For further discussion on the Liangzhu forerunners see Rawson, *Chinese Jade from the Neolithic to the Qing*, pp.122-129.

The lapidary has clearly been cleverly selective in his choice of stone. It is predominately brown with cream inclusions and two areas with celadon-green patches and the surface, whilst polished, is also minutely pitted throughout. This combination is reminiscent of certain jades after many hundreds of years of burial, an effect that cannot have escaped the carver.

For an almost identical bottle, see Li, *The Medicine-Snuff Bottle Connection, Chinese Miniature Containers: a Dual Role*, p. 76, no. 315 and illustrated on the front cover.

(CBL C 738)

15

Nephrite, carved in low-relief on each main face with an archaistic design of stylized *taotie* masks dividing a wide central band comprised of six vertical wave or whorl panels, each narrow side carved in high relief with twisting *chilong* climbing to the rounded shoulder, a fairly well hollowed interior, one side of the otherwise pale creamy-white-green stone with a patchwork of russet inclusions, the stone with a 'turnip-grain' internal structure, a rounded oval foot ring and shallow cut base

1740-1800

Height: 5.6 cm
Mouth: 0.5 cm
Neck: 1.5 cm

It is tempting to ascribe this bottle to the 'Master of the Rocks' school based on the use of a two-coloured stone, a standard of the school, in combination with the extraordinarily fine rendering of the *chilong* handles. These bear close comparison with an example illustrated by Moss, Graham, and Tsang, *A Treasury of Chinese Snuff Bottles, The Mary and George Bloch Collection*, Vol. 1, Jade, pp. 370-371, no. 142. However this combination may be nothing more than coincidental and our bottle could also be consigned to another private workshop.

Again refer to the entry for No. 11 in this publication for a discussion of the use of archaic forms and decoration.

It should be noted that the shape of this bottle does not follow any prescribed archaic form though the design on each of the main faces does. The central band of vertical wave or whorls is descended from the decoration found on Eastern Zhou (770-256 BC) and Han dynasty (206 BC-AD 220) jade burial pieces such as discs and scabbards. In these the surface is carved with a series of comma-like shapes, referred to in traditional Chinese literature as the grain or sprouting grain pattern. This was itself supposedly derived from the silkworm pattern found on earlier Zhou dynasty jades. For further discussion see Rawson, *Chinese Jade from the Neolithic to the Qing*, pp. 246-253, nos. 15:2 and 17:2.

Additional to this is the design of *taotie* masks that frame the central band. These are derived from an even earlier period than the Zhou dynasty, appearing as they do on bronzes and jades of the Shang Dynasty (c.1600-1100 BC).

This bottle is definitely cut from a pebble, as many bottles are. This is clearly indicated by both the area of russet skin on one side of the rectangular-shaped bottle and also by the rounded profile of this side in contrast to the compressed surface of the other side.

(CBL C 747)

13 (two views)

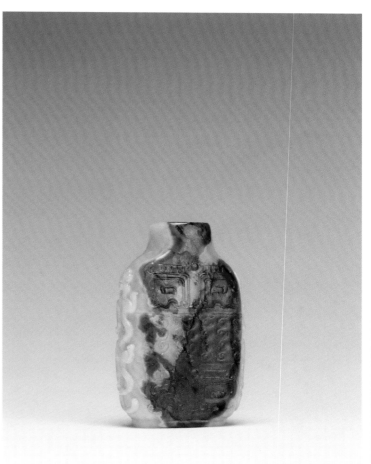

14

15

16

Nephrite, of compressed rectangular shape, carved in low relief primarily from the brown skin with a continuous landscape bordered by waves below, one main face with the sun rising from the waves with a vapor plume winding upwards, the other main face with a similar vapor plume rising from a *lingzhi* (fungus) and rocks, one narrow side carved with a pavilion amidst clouds, the other narrow side with an elderly bearded gentleman with a staff, a short cylindrical neck, a small mouth and a well hollowed interior, a rounded oval foot ring and shallow cut base

Master of the Rocks school, 1760-1850

Height: 6.6 cm
Mouth: 0.5 cm
Neck: 2.1 cm

See Moss, Graham, and Tsang, *A Treasury of Chinese Snuff Bottles: The Mary and George Bloch Collection*, Vol. 1, Jade, pp. 350-353, no. 136, for another classic example of the Master of the Rocks school, where the lapidary has similarly made great use of rather abstractly patterned material. One of the common features of this school is the use of the core colour (green in this instance) to cleverly distinguish the sky from the landscape, here carved from the brown skin in a very low relief. Rather cleverly the highest relief is to be found in the swirling plumes of vapor that cut through the entire scene on either side of the bottle and which direct the viewer's attention through the landscape. Another common feature of the school is the depiction of a rustic setting. In our example an elderly world-weary gentleman, presumably a Daoist, is staring dreamily and dwarfed by the immensity of the natural world around him. He has escaped the drudgery of normal existence in exchange for the tranquility and solitude of country life. The vapor plume found on each of the main faces and on one narrow side of the bottle is a common Daoist device to suggest the ethereal world of the alchemists and geomancers and the mysterious elixir of life said to reside on the Island of the Eastern Sea or in the Daoist paradise known as the Hills of Longevity. The rising sun may here simply be a pictorial contrivance but more likely symbolizes a rise in rank, *xuri gaosheng*, 'May you rise high like the morning sun', see Bartholomew, *Hidden Meanings in Chinese Art*, p. 128, no. 5.33.1.

Two other bottles also illustrated by Moss et al, op cit, pp. 344-345, no. 134 and pp. 354-357, no. 137, bear great similarities in their decoration to our bottle. The first has cresting waves from which rises a sun on one side, whilst the second, though pebble-shaped, has similar cliff faces and rocky outcrops with wisps of formalized clouds that match the vapour plumes of ours.

Many bottles of the school are of quite a large size and have vigourous landscape scenes with dynamic subject matter, which includes natural phenomena of turbulent water, craggy rock formations, and clouds.

For a slightly larger bottle with a similar design from the Carl F. Barron collection, see Moss, *The Barron Collection: Illustrated Handlist*, ICSBS Convention, Boston, 2008, p. 2, no. 3153.

(CBL C 736)

17

Nephrite, carved in low relief on the brown skin with two separate depictions of the *Hehe erxian,* one main face with the two figures alongside one another, one seated holding a box and cover from which a vapor plume and a pearl rises, the other boy standing and holding a lotus stem set before craggy rocks, the other main face with the two figures carved on separate areas of skin, one seated holding a vessel from which a vapor plume and pearl rises, the other boy standing holding a box and cover carved on an area of skin which curves around the narrow side of the bottle, a cylindrical neck, a small mouth and a well hollowed interior, some pale inclusions in the green core colour of the stone, a slightly rounded oval foot ring and regular cut base

Master of the Rocks school, 1760-1850

Stopper: Glass imitating a hard stone

Height: 6.25 cm
Mouth: 0.6 cm
Neck: 1.8 cm

See the previous bottle in this publication, No. 16, for a brief description of the customary features of the Master of the Rocks school. For further discussion and illustrations of various examples see Moss, Graham, and Tsang, *A Treasury of Chinese Snuff Bottles: The Mary and George Bloch Collection*, Vol. 1, Jade, pp. 340-370, nos. 133-142, where it is noted that many bottles of this type are basically of a compressed rounded rectangular or square outline, like this and the previous bottle in this publication. This shape certainly allows for easy storytelling with its unbroken continuous canvas. The authors also tentatively suggest a possible Suzhou connection with another bottle of this school, ibid, p. 340, no. 133 but do so with caveats. Still, it is an intriguing possibility.

The exact dating of the Master of the Rocks school has to be based on a qualitative judgment. There are no dated bottles or bottles signed by artists whose working dates are known to us. What can be said is that in general the carving is exemplary, sometimes miraculous; the compositions usually confident and fluent, the forms have a formal integrity, the pronounced foot rims are neat and crisp when undecorated, which is usually the case, but occasionally the decoration continues on the base in an uninterrupted flowing manner. The subtle use of skin and ground material is often as fine as any found on Suzhou school bottles; often the mouth is extremely small and the interior carving highly commendable. Whilst an eighteenth century date for many bottles of the school is a distinct possibility, a wider date range seems prudent.

The subject our bottle depicts the *Hehe erxian* , the immortals of Harmony and Unity who preside over harmonious marriages. These two gods are actually later manifestations of two Tang Dynasty (618-906) poet-monks, Hanshan and Shide. Depictions of these monks varied over time but they are nearly always shown bearing wide grins (hence the often used sobriquet, 'Laughing Twins'), and because of this mirthful countenance the Yongzheng emperor designated them as the saints of Harmony and Unity in 1733. At some point in their iconographical development the two monks became young boys.

The staple attributes of the boys is the box (*he*) and the lotus (*he*), which represent harmony and unity and hence the name *Hehe erxian*.

(CBL C 737)

16 (two views)

17 (two views)

18

Nephrite, the stone of 'yellow steamed-chestnut' type with one pale creamy-russet area to the edge of the lower left quadrant on one main face, a few smaller inclusions in the upper right quadrant and neck of the same face, the neck short and cylindrical, a wide flat oval foot ring and exceedingly shallow cut base

1750-1820

Stopper: Glass imitating coral on an ivory collar imitating turquoise

Height: 6.8 cm
Mouth: unknown (stopper not removable)
Neck: 3 cm

Unfortunately, the stopper on this bottle cannot be removed and we are unable to ascertain either the size of the mouth or the exact flatness of the lip. However from the extremely light weight relative to the very large size of the bottle, we can deduce that it is especially well hollowed.

This particular jade, whilst tinged in an underlying green colour, has become known as 'yellow' jade. However in the 1860s Zhao Zhiqian in his *Yonglu Xianjie* (translated by Richard John Lynn, ICSBS *Journal*, Autumn, 1991, p.18) under the heading of 'Jade snuff bottles' mentions a type, of which some are made with the skin colour, called 'yellow steamed-chestnut' (*huangzhengli*). Not only is this term more endearing it is actually better suited to the jade colour itself. We also know from a bottle published by Moss, Graham, and Tsang, *A Treasury of Chinese Snuff Bottles: The Mary and George Bloch Collection*, Vol. 1, Jade, pp. 276-277, no. 112, which bears a poem written by the Qianlong Emperor, on a jade bottle of similar colour to ours, that he also referred to this stone as 'yellow' jade. Whilst many bottles (and also other objects and vessels) made from this particular colour of jade are indeed assigned to Imperial production of the Qianlong period, they are done so on a combination of criteria which includes shape, decoration, mouth and foot size, degree of hollowing, and inscriptions. It would be a mistake to assign every high quality jade bottle of this kind to the group. In the case of our bottle, we can only assume that it is well hollowed and as yet do not know the shape or size of the mouth and the lip. Another difficulty in dating or assigning a school or place of production for plain bottles of this kind is the complete lack of any decoration or inscription on which to make a judgement. One day when more studies of degrees of exterior polish and interior hollowing, specific foot shapes, depths of bases, and other characteristics have been carried out, we might be able to identify the origin of the bottle more precisely. However, the formal integrity of this bottle, its quiet sophistication, the extremely short foot with a wide flat foot ring, and the use of a superb 'yellow' jade, suggest an extremely competent workshop, and possibly an Imperial one.

Interestingly and perhaps importantly the snuff bottle that comes closest in shape and colour of stone to our bottle is a nephrite example with a highly Imperial Qianlong *yuzhi* mark (the only one presently recorded), see Moss, Graham, and Tsang, *The Art of the Chinese Snuff Bottle: The J & J Collection*, Vol. 1, pp. 81-82, no. 32. Though decorated with an archaistic design and slightly more squat than our bottle, it is otherwise manifestly similar. The possibility that our bottle may be in some way linked to it cannot be totally ruled out.

(CBL C 740)

19

Nephrite, twin bottle, of large fruit shape, comprising two conjoined lobed melons, each forming a separate bottle, enveloped in a russet skin carved to form a leafy surround to the lower portion of the carving, one side incorporating two butterflies, the upper part of the bottle with thick branch tendrils and leaves which bisect the two small mouth openings, and further string-like vine tendrils trailing down the sides, the underside flattened forming an irregular flat foot with engraved veins

1740-1820

Stopper: One coral, the other glass imitating coral

Height: 9.7 cm
Mouth: Each approximately 0.6 cm across but unevenly cut
Neck: No neck

It is uncertain if this was originally carved as a bottle or was adapted from another use at a later date. There are good reasons for suggesting either and the strongest argument seems to be in favor of an adaptation. The fact that the bottle stands un-aided as illustrated, however, might suggest that it was indeed made as a bottle. Most conversions were fondling pieces, which invariably were made for turning in the hand and thus have no necessity to stand. Similarly, the format of fruit forms and insects carved from this type of jade is well established in the snuff bottle oeuvre. The arguments against such a position are the unusually large size of the bottle, rendering it particularly unwieldy; the unevenly cut mouths, which though not seemingly cutting in to the design, are oddly placed in relation to the branch tendrils that rise above them, making the removal of snuff awkward at best. Finally the interiors of both bottles are not especially well hollowed. Nevertheless, whichever position we take, it is now, unquestionably, a bottle and was presumably treasured as such by its previous owners.

For further discussion on the group of 'naturalistic' jade bottles, see No. 13 in this publication.

For an example of a gourd bottle with butterflies carved from an off-white stone see Moss, Graham, and Tsang, *The Art of the Chinese Snuff Bottle: The J & J Collection* Vol. 1, p. 46, no. 9. Interestingly in the footnote the authors discuss the merits of the jadeite stopper that may or may not be original to the bottle and suggest that bottles of this type were always intended to have contrasting stoppers (without giving reasons why, but presumably because the majority of the published Palace fruit bottles do indeed have contrasting stoppers). Without matching material and design to indicate an original stopper it is impossible to be certain. In the case of the stoppers on our bottle, one might well be original (coral twig of v-shape in illustration), whilst the other (glass imitating coral), though not identical, was made to replace a missing stopper and to correspond to a stopper that was felt to be original.

See also Moss, Graham and Tsang, *A Treasury of Chinese Snuff Bottles: The Mary and George Bloch Collection*, Vol. 1, Jade, pp. 44-45, no. 14 and pp. 138-141, no. 55, for two 'naturalistic' bottles carved from a similar stone which bear comparison.

For an enlightening discussion on the subject of gourds (*gua*) and butterflies (*die*) see Bartholomew, *Hidden Meanings in Chinese Art*, p. 62, 3.3.4. The author notes that the gourd, melon, pumpkin, and squash were interchangeable as subjects when paired with butterflies, and that the rebus *guaddie mianmian* ('may there be ceaseless generations of sons and grandsons') applies to all. She further adds that this auspicious phrase comes from the *Book of Odes*, the earliest collection of Chinese poetry and is related to a charming New Year's Eve ceremony story regarding butterflies and melons.

(CBL C 744)

18

19 (two views)

20

Nephrite, of Buddha's Hand citron shape, superbly carved with eight finger-like segments, one side has a long leaf trailing down the fruit from a thick branch carved at the neck with a further branch and leaf running vertically alongside to mask a flaw line, a well cut small mouth and a quite well hollowed interior, traces of a pale yellow skin in two places which has been enhanced with staining, stands on its fingers

1730-1820

Height: 7.3 cm
Mouth: 0.5 cm
Neck: No neck

The Buddha's Hand citron (*Citrus medica* 'Sarcodactylis') takes its common name from the shape of the finger-like segments that make up the bulk of the fruit and which resemble the idealized, lotiform fingers of the Buddha. It has a thick peel but is seedless and juiceless. It is however very fragrant and was a favorite fruit of the Empress Dowager Cixi (1835-1909), who used large containers of the fruit to perfume her palace in the Forbidden City in Beijing. It was and still is a common altar offering during the New Year celebration.

The subject of the Buddha's Hand citron, *foshou*, can also be interpreted as 'blessings' or 'riches' (*fu*) and 'longevity' (*shou*), see Bartholomew, *Hidden Meanings in Chinese Art*, pp. 30-31, no. 1.2 and 1.2.1, where she illustrates a Ming dynasty nephrite water container in the form of the fruit.

For a snuff bottle in jadeite that actually stands on a branch support with fingers stretching upwards, see Hughes, *The Blair Bequest: Chinese Snuff Bottles from the Princeton University Art Museum*, p. 48, no. 17, and another in amber in the same publication, p.92, no. 92, which can be favorably compared to another in *Snuff Bottles in the Collection of the National Palace Museum*, Taipei, no. 389. A third example in nephrite, of similar size, is illustrated by Kleiner, *Chinese Snuff Bottles from the Collection of Denys and Eithne Cowell*, p. 5, no. 5.

The same remarks regarding the possibility of this bottle being a conversion from a fondling piece that were laid out in the previous entry in this publication, No. 19, apply here. However, in this case there appear to be more indicators suggestive of original bottle use. Again the bottle stands un-aided as illustrated, fits well in to the 'naturalistic' school of snuff bottles, though large is not cumbersome, and in this case has a well cut mouth and is quite deeply hollowed to the interior. Surprisingly, the palm, so to speak, of the Buddha's hand is not finished as superbly as the exterior.

The carving of the undulating surface, gently curved finger tendrils, overall formal integrity, use of a wonderful stone with clever enhancements of staining all point to an eighteenth century production date. However the large, though not cumbersome, size may be indicative of very slightly later manufacture.

(CBL C 756)

20 (two views)

21

Nephrite, modeled as a shell wrapped in a lotus leaf with delicately carved low-relief veins, stalks, and a small lotus pod, a mouth opening at the terminus of the stalks, an extremely well hollowed interior, the stone of celadon tone with small areas of natural russet colour remaining throughout

1750-1820

Height: 6.2 cm
Mouth: 0.7 cm
Neck: No neck

The subject is quite an unusual one. The shell, which at first might be mistaken for part of the lotus rhizome, probably represents a snail or other aquatic mollusk, so often found in muddy lotus ponds. As a subject the snail is quite rare other than as an auxiliary motif. Snuff bottle stoppers of this subject certainly exist. A Yixing teapot illustrated by Bartholomew, *Hidden Meanings in Chinese Art*, p. 49, no. 2.16.8, in the form of a lotus rhizome, has a snail lid; and an agate snuff bottle illustrated by Moss, Graham, and Tsang, *A Treasury of Chinese Snuff Bottles: The Mary and George Bloch Collection*, Vol. 2, part 2, Quartz, pp. 404-407, no. 331, has a snail amidst other aquatic subjects within the design.

The snail shell also resembles a conch *(luo)*, one of the eight auspicious Buddhist symbols *(Ba jixiang)*, and represents the sound of Buddha's teaching spreading throughout the world. In this bottle, the symbolism of conch and lotus being paired together would be clear.

In the pictorial and decorative arts the lotus is a potent, almost omnipresent, symbol. Its meanings are manifold but foremost it is a symbol of purity, emerging as it does unstained from the mud and a lotus flower often supports the seated figure of Buddha and other bodhisattvas.

As in the two previous examples this bottle may have originally been carved as a fondling piece. This might be indicated by the fact that the carefully delineated veins, which run on the back of the large lotus leaf that surrounds the shell, actually extend across the mouth. If the carving had originally been created as a bottle this would presumably not be the case. The regular hollowing, neither well nor less well hollowed than one might expect, does not really act as an indicator in this example.

For another rare nephrite bottle of this form illustrated with its original stopper see Sotheby's Hong Kong, 5 May 1994, lot 1489, where the stopper is catalogued as 'part of the shell'. Unfortunately from the illustration it is impossible to see exactly what form it takes. For a brown-lacquer bottle possibly from Fuzhou depicting a conch shell, see Hall, *Chinese Snuff Bottles XI: The Snowy Peaks Collection*, no. 121.

(CBL C 757)

22

Nephrite, carved as a three-legged toad, squatting and holding a leafy five-petal flower spray in its mouth, the third leg curling from the rear to one side, the head cut with simple dimples, representing warts, bulging eye sockets inlaid with pink hard stones, the toads mouth drilled for the spoon, a well hollowed interior

1770-1860

Length: 6.8 cm
Mouth: 0.55 cm
Neck: No neck

The three-legged toad of the Daoist immortal Liu Hai became so popular an image, that its meaning would be understood independent of the immortal himself. Such is the case with our bottle here. For a discussion of the strangely three-legged toad (two at the front and one at the back) and his association with Liu Hai see Bartholomew, *Hidden Meanings in Chinese Art*, p. 150, no. 6.24. Liu Hai is usually depicted as a boy or a young man wearing bangs across his forehead and wearing a robe that is drawn open across his chest. He carries a string of cash with which he is often depicted teasing the three-legged toad. He is revered as a god of wealth and according to tradition was a historical figure from the Han dynasty (206 BCE-CE 220) who was once prime minister. His former name was Liu Yuanying but he is/was also known as Haichanzi hence the combined Liu Hai.

For a porcelain snuff bottle depicting this figure with his three-legged toad see Hughes, *The Blair Bequest: Chinese Snuff Bottles from the Princeton University Art Museum*, pp. 221-222, nos. 302 and 303.

Why the toad carries a five-petal flower in his mouth is uncertain. Generally he is depicted with a string of cash, however blooming flowers can be interpreted as prosperity, which in combination with the toad would make for an auspicious symbol.

This bottle almost certainly did not start life as a bottle but as a fondling piece. The hole is rather crudely drilled and no attempt has been made to soften the edges around the opening, so that it might even appear as an original mouth. Paradoxically, the hollowing to the interior is quite thorough and it is successful as a snuff container. Whilst the eye sockets of this carving where always bulging, the pink hard-stones that now serve as eyes may well be later replacements. Technically the carving is of a very fine quality with subtle undulations to the body of the toad that seem to mirror the 'ugly' warts that are cleverly drilled and cut to the face and head.

(CBL C 823)

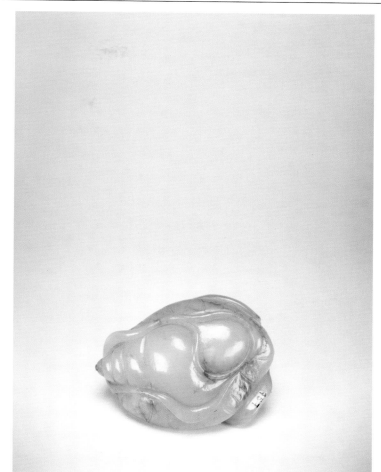

21 (two views)

23

Nephrite, one main face with a neatly engraved 16-character seal inscription, *zhuanshu*, the other side with a single-horned beast with bifurcated tail, modeled as a seal, the stone of even tone throughout with a few minor inclusions, a short cylindrical neck, regular mouth and a very well hollowed interior, the base is cut as a shallow oval depression

1750-1800

Stopper: Coral carved as a *chilong* on a turquoise collar, possibly original

Height: 6.6 cm
Mouth: 0.75 cm
Neck: 2.35 cm

The inscription, in four four-character lines, reads:
Wei fan tian di
You zan shen ming
Bao he tai he
Wan shou wu jiang

This translates as:
Place including heaven and earth
Admire the gods
Bao He and Tai He (two palaces in the Forbidden City)
10,000 Shou (Longevity) endless

This outstanding bottle is made from a glorious even 'yellow' jade.
See the entry for No. 18 in this publication for a discussion of this particular type of stone.

The beast, which forms the upper portion of a seal on one side, has a furry mane and bifurcated tail, flame-scrolls at front and rear haunches, and claws on the three visible claws on each foot. The long snout has flaring nostrils and is centered by a *wang* (king) character. A single horn rises from its head. Simple lines in perspective indicate the square seal form under the beast. The script on the other side of the bottle is not in reverse as you would find on a true seal but the top and right edge have additional lines in perspective that show the artist was attempting to show the underside of a seal. This delightful trompe l'oeil may well have been made for an official, perhaps even based on a seal owned by an official. All officials possessed a seal that came with his preferment of rank.

According to Moss and Tsang, *Arts From the Scholar's Studio*, p.152, no. 125, the use of seals for official and personal use may have made an appearance as early as the Shang dynasty, but certainly by the Spring and Autumn period of the Zhou dynasty, they were in use and called *xi*, seals and in some cases *guxi*, archaic seals, suggesting that some already had some antiquity. Under the Qin dynasty the term *xi* was reserved for official seals and *yin*, the name they now called, was used for other types. The early seals were mostly made of bronze and by the Han the official seals were rigidly controlled, with Imperial seals made in jade, those of princes of gold, and the rest in bronze. In the Tang and Song dynasties, according to the authors, an important change took place in seal culture, " they evolved from their primary functional, identifying and authoritative role into objects of art, not only in the carving of the seals and seal knobs but in the use of the seal text. Seals of collectors, studio names and other fanciful names, poems and enigmatic phrases or passages and so forth were developed and the seal became an indispensible appurtenance of the scholar"

By the mid Ming period the use of ivory, rhinoceros, wood, and bamboo was supplanted by the use of soapstone. The soft surface of this material, allowed the scholar to be directly involved in carving the seals with the use of a metal blade to replace his brush, and hence the term 'iron-brush' used in seal carving. A distinctive style of writing for stone thus evolved.

The majority of Imperial seals are surmounted by dragons and our beast may well represent one, albeit more leonine. There seems to be a very good reason to link our bottle with the Court, if not directly with Court workshops then by Imperial order. The inscription on our bottle mentions two palaces in

the Forbidden City, The *Baohedian* (Hall of Preserving Harmony) and *Taihedian* (Hall of Supreme Harmony). The palace grounds are divided into two parts: the Front Palace, *Qianchao*, to the south and the Inner Palace, *Neiting*, to the north. The Front Palace consists chiefly of three great halls, the two aforementioned, and the *Zhonghedian*, Hall of Central Harmony. Here important ceremonies, such as the accession of a new emperor to the throne and the emperor's birthday and wedding, were held. The Inner Palace was the residential area of the emperor and the imperial household. See *The Forbidden City*, 1993, no. 20 for a view of the Hall of Supreme Harmony and no. 35, for an interior view of the Hall of Preserving Harmony.

Whilst the large size of the bottle, the lack of handles or a foot might also suggest a possible link to the Suzhou workshops where these features are common, the stone is an uncommon one for the school. However, the stone is of a kind preferred at court; the hollowing is of the highest order; the inscription is technically unsurpassed; and the subject would have been an appropriate one for the Court.

A comparable white nephrite bottle of near identical shape with a mythical beast seal carved to one side and an almost identical seal inscription, *zhuanshu*, is illustrated in an exhibition catalogue by Randall, *From the China Trade to the Imperial Court*, no. 27. Another, perhaps the same one, with the addition of red pigments to highlight the *zhuanshu* seal script and gold pigments to highlight an additional song-style *kaishu* inscription (not present on our bottle), is illustrated by Sotheby's New York, 17 March 1997, lot 256, where part of the *kaishu* inscription is translated as 'Precious Imperial Seal of the Song Dynasty' *song ding ming bao xi*.

A blue glass overlay example carved with lion seals on each side from the Gerry P. Mack Collection was sold at Sotheby's New York, 25 October 1997, lot 1. A red overlay glass bottle similarly decorated was exhibited at the Special Exhibition Galleries at the Suzhou Museum, March-November, 2009, and illustrated in the exhibition catalogue *'A Special Exhibit of Collections from Mr. Robert Chang's Studio of Lotus Fragrance'*, no. 128.

(CBL C 743)

23 (two views)

24

Nephrite, carved as a bulging-eyed dragon-headed carp, the fish curling very slightly to one side, the mouth simply drilled between the lips of the fish, a well hollowed interior, the grey stone with brown inclusions one running horizontally along the length of the fish, some pitting to stone

1720-1800

Length: 8.0 cm
Mouth: 0.5 cm
Neck: No neck

This unusual bottle, which is remarkably sculptural in form and uses an ancient-looking material, probably did start life as a bottle but there is the possibility that it may be a conversion from an earlier fondling piece or paperweight from a scholar's table. Certainly the material itself, a grey stone with brown markings and random pitting to the surface reminiscent of well-worn leather, is of a kind that can be found in early jade carvings of the Yuan and Ming period, see *The Complete Collection of Treasures of the Palace Museum, Jadeware II*, pp. 234-235, no. 184, for a Ming dynasty rhyton cup in the form of a dragon-headed fish and p. 142, no. 115, for a Yuan fish pendant, each using a similar stone.

Whilst the mouth details are handled rather peremptorily for a bottle, the large size of the opening suggests it was probably always meant for insertion of a spoon and stopper. The interior hollowing is extremely well carved which one might not expect to see with a conversion. The ill-fitting coral stopper with a stained ivory collar imitating brass which is stored with this bottle is not the original one and we have taken the liberty of removing it for photography.

For a green nephrite vessel of two fish, which resemble dragon-fish rising from waves, see Bartholomew, *Hidden Meanings in Chinese Art*, p. 92, no. 4.11.2. The carp is the fish associated with motifs for passing the civil service examinations. The story goes, according to tradition, that carp swimming up the Yellow River, fighting the opposing current, must leap the rapids of Dragon's Gate (Longmen) falls; the first to succeed transforms itself into a dragon. This story is a metaphor for a poor scholar who, by passing the civil services exams, raises himself to the status of high official.

Clearly the carp in our image is in the throws of his transformation to a dragon.

(CBL C 749)

25

Nephrite, carved as a fat scaly goldfish, the creamy white stone with black-brown inclusions, used on one side to depict a water beetle just behind the fish's gills, and on the other side as a brown patch, the entire body carefully carved with fine scales but the surface left plain to the face and gills, the eyes set low in the head, the mouth quite wide, very well hollowed

1730-1820

Length: 7.0 cm
Mouth: 0.8 cm
Neck: No neck

For a goldfish jade bottle of similar shape and proportions, i.e. bulbous rounded body and down-flicking tail see Moss, Graham, and Tsang, *A Treasury of Chinese Snuff Bottles: The Mary and George Bloch Collection*, Vol. 1, Jade, pp. 132-133, no. 52. Like that example, though to a slightly lesser extent, the fish is laid out symmetrically and very formally, with the body in a straight line and the two outer tail fins balancing each other exactly on either side of the central tail fin. The two outer fins also act as a supporting foot, so to speak, when the bottle lies flat. The eyes of both bottles appear to be carved in a very similar fashion, also being a central boss within a hollowed but raised circular rim. A number of features do not correspond, in particular the treatment of the mouth, which in our example follows the more traditional method of a simply drilled hole between the fish's lips, whereas the Bloch bottle has the rare feature of a regular snuff bottle mouth of a short cylinder with a flat lip and cylindrical mouth. The other obvious difference is the carving of the scales in relief albeit shallow, on our bottle, rather then being simply incised as on the other. Moss et al, op cit, p. 133, also argue persuasively that the fish-form bottles were made at the Imperial workshops.

Clearly the shape of our bottle was to a major extent dictated by the shape of the original pebble that it was carved from. The lapidary has cleverly used the skin on one side to leave a large water beetle clinging to the fish, whilst leaving just a token of the skin on the other side. The beetle is also useful as a place to hold the thumb when removing snuff, acting in effect as a handle would on a regular form bottle. The long-standing and more highly valued traditional source of jade was, of course, riverbeds, which presumably became more beloved as this source was supplanted by the introduction of quarried material. Therefore in addition to the rebus allusions listed below, the depiction of a fish and a water beetle would also be read as a reminder of the jade source itself.

As we have mentioned in an earlier entry, the fish is an extremely popular subject in Chinese art. This example almost certainly depicts a goldfish, *jinyu*, which is homophonous with the term meaning 'gold and jade', i.e. wealth. The second sound, *yu*, also represents abundance or plenty.

(CBL C 750)

24

25

26

Nephrite, of triangular pebble shape, possibly suggesting a peach form, a large bat on one side carved from the pale russet inclusions with a veined long leaf alongside carved from a branch stem to the bottom edge of the bottle, a further leaf rising to the other side, extremely well hollowed

1730-1820

Height: 6.5 cm
Mouth: 0.65 cm
Neck: No neck

This extraordinary little bottle, delicately carved from the skin of a small pebble, has an exceedingly silky polish to the surface. It has been illustrated in a vertical format but ideally should be placed flat in the hand and viewed horizontally. The lower underside at the bulbous end is formed from the branches of a lovely fruit-form shape of undetermined species but suggestive of a peach. Leafy branches spread up and around the bottle on both sides. The motif of a bat is a typical and popular feature in combination with a peach, which further confirms that this is indeed the fruit represented on this bottle. Its unusual shape can probably be best explained by the dictates of the original pebble, which may have contained unforeseen flaws. The rendering of the bat is particularly masterful, with extremely well balanced wings forming a sweeping s-curve, reminiscent of a *yinyang* symbol, formed by the forward arching left wing and the backward curling right wing. The general swooping motion of the bat, whose head is turned upward to echo the curves, further enhances this. Even the minutest details of the bat are picked out from the mouth, eyes, and ears to fur running down the back.

The Chinese name for bat (*fu*), has the same sound as the word for blessings (*fu*). The peach (*shoutao*) is a symbol of longevity and is the symbol of the venerable god of longevity, Shoulao. The bat and the peach together form the rebus, *fushou shuangquan*, 'May you possess both blessings and longevity.'

(CBL C 758)

27

Nephrite, artificially stained to suggest russet colouring, modeled as a two-horned seated beast, *qilin*, with ribbed chest and three claws on each foot, furry tufts on each back leg, and a tail tucked to one side, wearing a large saddle-cloth and caparisons on the hindquarters, below a pear-shaped vase supported on the back with a dragon coiled around the neck, the neck with a very wide mouth and a thin lip, the interior fairly well hollowed, added russet staining

1760-1860

Height: 6.0 cm
Mouth: 0.9 cm
Neck: 1.0 cm

Whilst initially having the appearance of the ancient-looking material seen in No. 24 in this publication, this is instead a Qing archaism. The original stone is in fact a grey-white jade and has been artfully stained to resemble either pebble material or the archaic appearance of early jade.

The artificial staining on the surface of this bottle is clearly visible in the flaw lines that run down the neck. Here the brown stain has crept into the cracks. This would not be the case if this were the original skin of the jade. The staining is also at its darkest in the carved channels of the design (the beast's mouth, toes, and chest ribbing, for example). Again an original skin would sit proud of the surface not below the surface. Nevertheless, we still have a most attractive archaism which here follows the form of an archaic bronze vessel. For a lengthy discussion on the staining of jades, particularly after the 1760s when quarried jade became plentiful, see Moss, Graham, and Tsang, *A Treasury of Chinese Snuff Bottles: The Mary and George Bloch Collection*, Vol. 1, Jade, pp. 136-137, no. 54.

For further discussion on the Qianlong emperor's involvement with archaic design on jade production in the eighteenth century and illustrations of archaistic jade vessels alongside their Bronze Age counterparts, see *The Refined Taste of the Emperor: Special Exhibition of Archaic and Pictorial Jades of the Ch'ing Court*, pp. 47-104. The catalogue, illustrates a number of Qianlong period jade vessels that depict mythical beasts supporting vases and other vessels on their backs, a common early theme in bronze production; see pp. 92-93, no. 18, for a leonine beast with a vase on its back; pp. 70-71, no. 8, for a bear with a cylinder rising from its back; and pp. 76-81, nos. 10 and 12, for archaic bronze beaker vases with dragons crawling around the necks. Such imagery from early bronzes made its way into various areas of the arts including ceramic, bronze, iron and stone and jade tomb sculptures of the later Han and Tang dynasties where the depictions tend to be conspicuously dramatic. By the Song dynasty however, the features become softer and with a degree of formality. It would seem that our bottle is based on a Song or perhaps Ming archaism rather than directly copying an ancient bronze.

(CBL C 760)

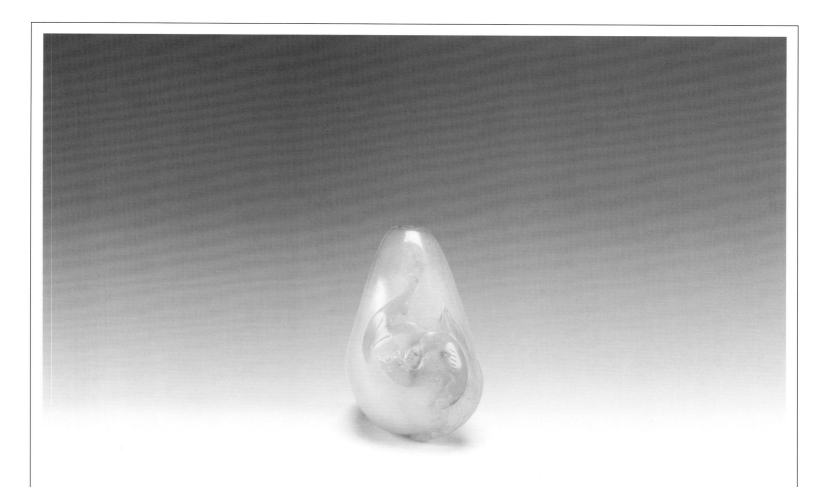

26

27

28

Nephrite, each main face carved with a single character sitting proud within a recessed rectangular panel, one reading *Shou*, the other *Fu*, each character is highly polished on a slightly uneven and unpolished ground that silhouettes it, the narrow sides with exquisitely carved lion-mask ring-handles, the shoulder flat and the cylindrical neck with a flat lip and a relatively small opening, a well hollowed interior, the wide rectangular foot-ring shallowly cut at its centre

1750-1820

Stopper: Green glass imitating emerald or jadeite

Height: 5.9 cm
Mouth: 0.5 cm
Neck: 1.85 cm

There are basically three ways that the Chinese depict a wish for blessings on their works of art. The first is to simply depict the characters themselves, as here, using the calligraphic strokes of the words for blessings or good luck, *fu*, and the character for longevity, *shou*. These, and two others, *lu*, official salary, and *shuangxi*, double happiness, often appear as popular motifs. The second method is to depict well-known good luck symbols such as pine and crane for longevity, the dragon for power and authority and coins or ingots for wealth. The third method uses rebuses (pictorial puns); the Chinese language is rich in words that share the same sounds and tones; such as a bat, *fu*, for blessings, *fu*, or a depiction of Shoulao for longevity, *shou*.

The *shou* character can be written one hundred ways, making it a very versatile decorative motif. Combined with the word *fu*, as it often is on decorative jades and textiles, it forms the wish "May you have blessings and longevity, *fushou*.

It is remarkable that the fluid characters on each face of our bottle could possibly be carved out of a stone as hard as jade. The beautiful swirling calligraphy almost appears as if it had been painted by a brush rather than polished through abrasion. The carver has even captured the untidy ends of calligraphic brushstrokes. Similarly, the lapidary has magically conjured exquisitely finished lion masks with simple-ring handles on the narrow sides that are carved in extremely shallow relief and which extend more than halfway down the bottle. The stone is of a pale celadon or off-white colour and the ground of the calligraphic panels has been left relatively un-polished to contrast with the polished raised surface of the two characters.

(CBL C 771)

29

Nephrite, carved in low relief on each of the main faces with six distinct seal-script *shou* characters within a rounded rectangular panel, the shoulder flat, the neck cylindrical, the stone of even white tone with some pale inclusions, a small flaw runs through the stone visible as a crack to either side of the neck, a quite well hollowed interior, a rounded rectangular foot which is deeply cut

1780-1860

Stopper: Green glass imitating emerald or jadeite

Height: 6.45 cm
Mouth: unknown (stopper not removable)
Neck: 1.8 cm

The overall quality of the colour of this stone is very good, being a particularly even-toned white, unfortunately there are some pale inclusions, particularly visible at the neck and a flaw line runs through the stone mostly visible as a crack on either side of the cylindrical neck. The *shou* characters have been carved acceptably, though rather mechanically and at some point in their history treated with a red wax or pigment to highlight them.

See another white nephrite example of similar design but with the addition of *xi* (joy or happpines) characters to the narrow sides illustrated in *Snuff Bottles: Little Gems of Delight*, p. 22, no. M 16 from the Richard Baey Collection.

The presence of bottles in the Palace Collection today, that are of similar basic rectangular shape, standing on rounded rectangular feet and with cylindrical necks, and carved in low relief with auspicious characters might suggest that such bottles were ordered by the Court and at worst indicates that they were received as gifts and deemed worthy enough to enter the collection, see *Snuff Bottles in the Collection of the National Palace Museum, Taipei*, p. 174, nos. 186-187 and p. 146, no. 116 for a boxed set of ten of similar outline.

See Bartholomew, *Hidden Meanings in Chinese Art*, p. 221, 7.56, for a discussion of the use of a *shou* character in Chinese art. The character represents the word 'longevity' and is itself a symbol of longevity. The calligraphic motif of the *shou* character can be written in one hundred ways each with distinct and different combination of strokes, and often decorates birthday gifts.

(CBL C 770)

30

Nephrite, each main face is slightly convex in shape and carved in low-relief seal script with four distinct characters, the semi-opaque misty grey-white stone with vertical 'turnip-like' inclusions, standing on an ogival foot ring, the base deeply cut

1750-1850

Stopper: Green glass imitating emerald or jadeite

Height: 5.9 cm
Mouth: unknown (stopper not removable)
Neck: 1.8 cm

The two four-character lines read:
Ban ke gu qin
Ming yue hua wu

This translates as:
Play qin with guest
in a beautiful house under a bright moon

The inscription evokes the extremely high status accorded music in the life of the literatus or lofty gentleman. The *qin*, also known as the *guqin*, or 'ancient qin', was the instrument most closely associated with the influential minority for thousands of years. According to Moss and Tsang, *Arts from the Scholar's Studio*, p. 34, no. 1, where they illustrate a Yuan dynasty example, the *qin* was equated with the refined mind and its search for self-realization and musical mastery symbolized by this instrument was synonymous with enlightenment. The inscription would also appeal to the scholar gentleman who wished to escape the reality of metropolitan life for the more peaceful, country existence with pleasant musical evenings set under clear skies.

The 'emphasized' ogival shape of our bottle, rather than merely a rectangular bottle with lighted canted corners, whilst not unique, is certainly unusual particularly so as the foot is carved to mirror the bottles outline. The foot might also be read as a stylized begonia flower-head. Other bottles of the more rectilinear type carved with auspicious characters can be found in the Imperial collections, see *Snuff Bottles in the Collection of the National Palace Museum, Taipei*, pp. 172-174, nos. 180 and 186. See also the previous entry in this publication.

Due to an un-removable stopper we are unable to ascertain if the interior is well hollowed or not, nor if the mouth is small or large. The weight alone however suggests that the hollowing is regular.

(CBL C 776)

28 (two views)

31

Nephrite, twin bottle, one rectangular, the other gourd-shaped, a simple rectangular panel carved on each main face of the canted rectangular bottle which stands on a flat rectangular base, the gourd bottle softly polished and standing on simply cut flat oval foot, both bottles with 'turnip-like' inclusions to the even-coloured stone, both quite well hollowed

1750-1820

Stoppers: One jadeite twig form with rich emerald inclusions, the other glass imitating jadeite

Height: 5.4 cm (rectangular), 4.65 cm (gourd)
Mouth: 0.45 cm (rectangular), 0.5 cm (gourd), both slightly funnelled
Neck: 0.95 cm (rectangular), 0.9 cm (gourd)

In much Chinese art, paired subjects—such as twin-fish, two-bats, two boys, two ducks, yin and yang, and others—are extremely popular as a designation for harmony, togetherness, and conjugal bliss. Conjoined bottles, whether decorated or plain, would clearly convey the same message and this little masterpiece would have been very fitting as a wedding present: the delicate curves of the gourd bottle alongside the more masculine profile of the other, conjoined for eternity.

Both forms are highly satisfactory and have been well hollowed to the interior making them unusually light in the hand. The hollowing also allows for a slight transparency to the stone, particularly visible at the neck of the gourd bottle. Interestingly, though the neck of the gourd bottle is actually of a slightly smaller dimension than the other neck, the mouth size is actually larger. This was probably necessary to allow the lapidary access for hollowing. The stone has a soft attractive polish over the entire surface.

For a similar twin bottle see Moss, Graham, and Tsang, *A Treasury of Chinese Snuff Bottles: The Mary and George Bloch Collection*, Vol. 1, Jade, pp. 211-212, no. 87, where the authors note that the unusual grouping is typical of court production which had to satisfy a patron for whom vast numbers of bottles were made and for whom artistic novelty became a necessity to command attention. The Bloch example also has oval panels on one of the bottles that the authors suggest are integral snuff dishes. However the lack of a concave surface on which the snuff could sit safely, probably negates that theory on our example.

(CBL C 775)

32

Nephrite, very neatly carved with bamboo basket-weave from just above the foot to just above the shoulders at the lower part of the neck and wrapping entirely around the bottle, a short neck with flat lip and a small mouth and a well hollowed interior, a flat oval foot ring and regularly cut base

1780-1850

Stoppers: Jadeite with coral collar

Height: 6.45 cm
Mouth: 0.45 cm
Neck: 2 cm

The basket-weave decoration on this rectangular bottle is a form of trompe l'oeil conceit intended to represent the ubiquitous woven material wrapped around a wide range of functional vessels across China since Neolithic times. The function was three-fold: to protect the vessel from damage, to augment carrying, and to insulate.

There was no particular formula, it seems, amongst the lapidaries for depicting the woven material, though the particular bamboo-like depiction used on this bottle does seem the most popular. However the actual size of the grain-like elements that make up the whole seems to vary enormously, as does the

point on the body, shoulder, or neck where the material ends and indeed how this is truncated by a border or without. As a motif it was also popular with the makers of glass snuff bottles.

For other jade examples that show the range of this group, see Hughes, *The Blair Bequest: Chinese Snuff Bottles from the Princeton University Art Museum*, p. 41, no. 6; Kleiner, *Treasures from the Sanctum of Enlightened Respect: Chinese Snuff Bottles from the Denis Low Collection*, p. 49, no. 37 bearing a hallmark of the fifth Prince Ding, Zaichuan who died in 1854; Moss, Graham, and Tsang, *A Treasury of Chinese Snuff Bottles: The Mary and George Bloch Collection*, Vol. 1, Jade, pp. 386-389, no. 149 bearing a studio mark of the Jiaqing Emperor; Moss, Graham, and Tsang, *The Art of the Chinese Snuff Bottle: The J & J Collection*, Vol. 1, p. 109, no. 50, which, like ours, and the majority of the group, is unmarked. We can deduce from the marked examples of this group that this type of jade bottle was in production at least between 1820, the end of the Jiaqing reign, and 1854. The strong likelihood however, based on other factors including the quality of the often flawless jade, impeccable carving, and degrees of hollowing are that production began as early as the last quarter of the eighteenth century.

A single flaw line not visible in this illustration runs down and across one of the main faces of the bottle.

(CBL C 777)

33

Nephrite, carved in a very low and fine relief on each of the main faces with stylized archaistic confronted dragons with complex key-pattern bodies with C-scrolls and rice-grain dots, the narrow sides plain, the neck slightly everted, a small mouth and quite well hollowed interior, a flat oval foot ring with regularly cut base, the muddy-white stone with some paler inclusions

1750-1850

Stopper: Jadeite

Height: 6.95 cm
Mouth: 0.4 cm
Neck: 1.8 cm

The remarks regarding archaism in entry No. 11 in this publication also apply to this bottle. However, in this case it is the decoration rather than the shape that is archaistic. The decoration on ritual bronze vessels and jades was the inspiration for the carver. For examples of other eighteenth-century jades that derive their decoration from such sources, see *The Refined Taste of the Emperor: Special Exhibition of Archaic and Pictorial Jades of the Ch'ing Court*, pp. 94-115, nos. 19-28.

The formalized dragons are impeccably carved with extraordinary gradations of depth between the outlines, which rise to form a ridge at their edge, and the more shallow and sometimes concave channels that form part of the design. The even polish is typical of the finest small jade carvings made for or at the Court during the Qianlong period.

Confronted dragons are a popular motif representing a happy reunion and can be found in numerous bottle media including nephrite, glass, and quartz, some of which have Palace workshop attributions. For another example in white nephrite which is of less compressed shape, but also has an unusual everted neck, see Lawrence, *Miniature Masterpieces from the Middle Kingdom, The Monimar Collection of Chinese Snuff Bottles*, p.163, no. 75. The Monimar dragons are a little more fluid than those on this example, which are more in keeping with the archaic bronze prototype.

(CBL C 778)

31

32

33

34

Nephrite, of compressed spade shape with a widely spreading neck with vertically beveled edge, each main face carved with a shield-shaped panel engraved with rows of *fu* characters partially hidden by a brocade cloth with a swastika cell ground that wraps around the bottle from one shoulder and unusually continues on the flat oval foot, the stone with various inclusions and a russet flaw line on one shoulder, poorly hollowed

1740-1780

Height: 6.0 cm
Mouth: 0.8 cm to 2.0 cm
Neck: 2.4 cm to 2.5 cm

The motif of a cloth or brocade tied around a snuff bottle was a popular one during the reigns of the Yongzheng and Qianlong Emperors. A large number of examples appear to have been created in enamels on copper in Beijing and Guangdong. However examples in other media, in particular porcelain and jade made at or for the Court or other private workshops, are recorded but are far fewer.

A cloth tied around a vessel, be it a snuff bottle or otherwise, was a decorative device indicative of a gift. The practice followed the traditional custom at court of presenting any gift wrapped in precious brocade. According to Moss, Graham, and Tsang, *A Treasury of Chinese Snuff Bottles: The Mary and George Bloch Collection*, Vol. 1, Jade, pp. 76-81, nos. 26-28, the word for this kind of cloth, commonly used in ancient China for wrapping, carrying, and protecting a variety of objects, is *fu*. How appropriate then that the characters partially hidden beneath should also read *fu* (good luck or happiness), albeit a different character?

A popular depiction is two portray 100 longevity symbols, *bai fu*, for many blessings. Here the cloth sash hides the full number. The word for sash, *shoudai*, can also signify longevity, thus adding to the multiple layers of meaning such a subject can convey.

In our example the brocade is magnificently rendered with a long-life Buddhist symbol, the swastika, carefully placed on an octagonal cell ground with smaller diamond-shaped cells dividing these, all running at a forty-five degree angle across the bottle, but nicely juxtaposed against the partially hidden horizontal running *fu* characters beneath it. Additional to this is the extraordinary carving highlighting the folds in the cloth by cleverly breaking up the design, by the simple offsetting of the cells, somewhat like a 'geological fault line' on both sides of the bottle. The manner in which the cloth also extends across the base itself is highly unusual and suggestive of a master craftsman at work.

This bottle is in many ways a masterpiece, yet in one glaring instance it fails rather dramatically. Fortunately, the failing is not immediately apparent as it concerns the degree of hollowing. The interior is simply very poorly finished. Additional to this is the rather jarring treatment of the mouth, which is not drilled, as one would expect, with a circular hole that widens to the interior, but instead becomes narrower. The mouth edge is 2.5 cm across whilst the interior neck reduces to 0.8 cm across before it opens up again to the interior. The lip is also slightly uneven in not being perfectly circular, though it varies only by 0.1 cm.

The jade itself is also not the finest quality. It seems likely that a master carver was at work on this particular bottle but that at some stage in its production, the various flaws in the stone became more apparent as the bottle form revealed itself (there are pale and dark inclusions within the matrix of the stone and a russet flaw at the shoulder which extends in to the neck) and that by the time it came to hollow out the interior the lapidaries had lost heart.

For other examples in jade with cloth or brocade wraps, many of which are characterized by a preference for a spade or shield shape with a flaring neck, see Hughes, *The Blair Bequest: Chinese Snuff Bottles from the Princeton University Art Museum*, p. 41, no. 7; Moss et al, op cit, pp. 76-81, nos. 26-28; Sotheby's, Hong Kong, The Eric Young Collection, Part IV, 28 October 1993, lot 1188; Hui and Lam, *The Imperial Connection: Court Related Chinese Snuff Bottles*, nos. 61-62.

(CBL C 780)

34 (two views)

34 (detail)

35

Nephrite, carved in low relief with a bust-length profile portrait of a woman smelling a flower beneath curtains within a ribbed circular panel to one main face and with four characters within a ribbed circular panel divided in to quadrants on the other, the narrow sides with lion-mask and mock-ring handles, the cylindrical neck with a slightly concave lip and a small mouth, a well hollowed interior, a short foot and flat oval foot ring with shallow cut base, the stone of very pale celadon white colour with some pale russet colour at the centre

1750-1830

Height: 5.3 cm
Mouth: 0.5 cm
Neck: 1.7 cm very slightly concave

The four characters on the circular panel read:
Zhi chang ren yi

This translates as:
You can be (it) very kind, fruitful, friendly

The extremely unusual and rare portrait on one side is beguiling and baffling. It does not seem to fall in to the category of 'coin' bottle, despite the ribbed circular panel that frames it. More likely it is taken from some other Western source. Perhaps it copies a European print or perhaps even a Western drawing. The subject reminds us of some found on enamel snuff bottles produced for the Imperial court during the Qianlong period. For example see Moss, Graham, and Tsang, *A Treasury of Chinese Snuff Bottles, The Mary and George Bloch Collection*, Vol. 6, Arts of the Fire, pp. 152-160, nos. 1076-1078; and also pp. 243-245, no. 1112, where elegant European ladies, some holding flowers and with elaborate hairdos are depicted.

The lady in our example holds a single flower spray in her hand, possibly an orchid or lotus and has a long pointed nose. Perhaps this is an illusion to the sense of smell, one of the five senses. Her pursed lips are most unusually represented, the cartoon-like grimace almost comical. What appears to be a large peony is placed in her hair, flower-drop earrings dangle from pendant ears, and a rather unusual object, perhaps a diadem or tiara, is centred above her forehead. A curtain drawn open behind her frames the scene. Whilst a European source seems most likely, an Eastern source, perhaps Indian, cannot be ruled out. If this is the case it might represent an elegant princess (or even a prince), bejeweled with earrings and flowers.

As yet the relationship between the inscription on one main face and the portrait on the other has not been determined, and indeed there may not be one, though this seems unlikely, given that the majority of inscriptions on bottles do tend to refer in some way to the subjects depicted. The layout of the calligraphy imitates a Han dynasty terminal roof tile, *wadang*, which were used to cap the ends of semi-circular tubular tiles under the eaves of roofs (see No. 70 in this publication). However, this type of an inscription would not have been placed on a roof tile. The ground of both circular panels has been left slightly 'un-finished' or under-polished, presumably a device to highlight the more polished finish of the subject and calligraphy.

(CBL C 790)

36

Nephrite, one main face carved with a more convex surface than the other and centred with a roundel depicting two lions moving in a circular motion contesting a ribboned-ball, the other side carved in low relief with a phoenix with out-stretched wings on rockwork surrounded by peony sprays, the neck cylindrical, the lip flat, a small mouth and a quite well hollowed interior, the celadon stone with some russet and cream inclusions mostly hidden within the lion roundel, some black flecks dispersed around the body, a simple flat oval base

Possibly Suzhou, 1770-1850

Height: 7.4 cm
Mouth: 0.6 cm slightly off centre
Neck: 2.4-2.5 cm

It is quite unusual for a jade bottle to be markedly more convex on one main face than the other, as with this example. When this occurs in other jade bottles it appears primarily in the Suzhou School workshops. However the carving of our bottle does not meet the high standards expected of the school. This suggests a later workshop working within the traditions of the earlier school or simply a less fine example, perhaps late in the school's production period. The reverse side of the bottle, or at least the side carved in more low relief bears some resemblance to the carving found on other hard-stones in particular jadeite and quartz and a date in the nineteenth century would seem more appropriate based on the quality. Again it would seem that the appearance of black spots within the matrix of the otherwise 'clean' stone was a misfortunate unexpected occurrence.

According to Bartholomew, *Hidden Meaning in Chinese Art*, p. 35, no. 1.7.1, the subject of two lions chasing a ribboned ball, *ershi gunxiuqiu*, is an auspicious design to bring blessings and joy. It was believed that when lions mate, their hair forms a ball, from which emerges a baby lion. Thus the motif arose, but with silk ribboned balls replacing the hairballs. The same author later notes p. 117, no. 5.17.2, that the depiction of two lions, one larger than the other, playing with a ribboned ball, can also be read as 'may you and your descendants achieve high rank'. In regard to the depiction of the phoenix (*feng*) in combination with the king of flowers, the peony (*fuguihua*) she notes, p. 160, no 6.37.1, that the rebus may be read as 'may there be wealth, rank, and good fortune' (*fugui jixiang*). The combination of both auspicious subjects on each main face of the bottle augers great blessings.

(CBL C 793)

35 (two views)

36 (two views)

37

Nephrite, one main face carved in low and fine relief with a figure paddling a boat in a ravine with a mountain backdrop, a small pavilion on one bank and other buildings connected by a bridge on the other bank, the other main face carved in slightly higher relief with gnarled pine rising from rocks and a vertical four-character inscription alongside, the neck everted, the rim slightly concave, a small mouth and well hollowed to the interior, flat oval foot ring with shallow cut base

Possibly Suzhou, 1770-1850

Height: 5.5 cm
Mouth: 0.5 cm
Neck: 1.95 cm

The four characters read:
Yi po cheng chun

This translates as:
One cypress (pine) forever Spring (always green)

The inscription refers to the fact that the pine and the cypress are evergreens remaining vital through even the harshest winter. Thus they have become one of the most evocative icons of longevity. A depiction of the pine and cypress together also symbolizes friends who remain constant in adversity.

The carving and placement of the inscription on one side of this bottle has a rather clumsy appearance, which is odd as the remaining carved decoration of the pine alongside it and the low-relief carving on the reverse side, which is in lower relief, is far more successful, particularly in its depiction of perspective and the successful transition of various planes.

In some respects our bottle is reminiscent, though without quite the high degree of quality required, of some eighteenth century Suzhou workshop bottles. For a number of comparisons see Moss, Graham, and Tsang, *A Treasury of Chinese Snuff Bottles: The Mary and George Bloch Collection*, Vol. 1, Jades, pp. 296-303, nos. 119-121. Perhaps our bottle is a later phase of the school when standards had fallen and when the use of rote imagery had become prevalent. Indisputably, certain features on our bottle such as the slanting bridge connecting the banks of a river, the gradation of surface planes between foreground and backdrop, and even the 'drilled' dots on the pine bark are unmistakable borrowings from eighteenth century and early nineteenth Suzhou output. It is really only the rather compressed spade shape with flaring neck that prevents a more conclusive attribution.

(CBL C 794)

38

Nephrite, of fruit shape, carved in very low but extremely fine relief with leafy branches around the entire body, one narrow side with a pendant pomegranate hanging from one branch and revealing interior seeds, whilst on the narrow side opposite is depicted a cluster of bursting 'seeds' which form part of the entire fruit form bottle, the stone of fine white colour with some small very pale brown inclusions mostly to one side and with a delicate soft polish, a spreading cylindrical neck, small mouth and very well hollowed interior, a flat oval base

1740-1800

Stopper: coral and brass

Height: 5.4 cm
Mouth: 0.5 cm
Neck: 1.8 cm

A cluster of 'bursting seeds' is carved on one of the narrow sides of the bottle and forms part of the design of the very subtly carved pomegranate-shaped bottle. It is a form of conceit with the bottle forming a large stylized pomegranate, which is itself surrounded by the branches of another pomegranate, which form the main design. Thus re-iterating the wish for numerous progeny. The seeds that effortlessly spill forth from the fecund pomegranate are an obvious metaphor of fertility. According to Bartholomew, *Hidden Meaning in Chinese Art*, p. 76, nos. 3.23 and 3.23.1, the flower of the fruit symbolizes the fifth lunar month and the fiery red colour of the fruit was believed to ward off evil. The splitting open of the pomegranate (*shiliu*) to reveal the seeds inside can form the rebus 'pomegranate revealing one hundred sons' (*liukai baizi*).

This is one of the real gems of the collection if not indeed of lapidary art in general. The sheer quality of the carving is unsurpassed. The bottle has a 'silky' quality to the surface and a soft polish that highlights the remarkable but subtle carving of life-like details of the knots and gnarls in the branches, the veins in the leaves, the bending of leaf tips and the drooping of heavy fruit. Whilst the stone is not entirely flawless and the pale brown 'stain' that runs horizontally across one main face and down one narrow side has not exactly been hidden in the design, it has been cunningly manipulated to form a vague shadow which at least follows, or rather dictates, the direction of leaves and branches within the design. Another feature that suggests an Imperial workshop is the masterful degree of hollowing achieved through a fairly tiny mouth.

See Moss, Graham, and Tsang, *A Treasury of Chinese Snuff Bottles, The Mary and George Bloch Collection*, Vol. 1, Jade, pp. 154-157, no. 62, for a discussion of a series of fruit-, flower-, and vegetable-form bottles, mostly of white or greenish-white nephrite and sometimes with areas of brown skin, which form a large and well-known group. Moss suggests that the entire oeuvre might best be termed as 'naturalistic' thus embracing all forms dictated by nature, be it flora or fauna. He further argues that whilst many of the group were certainly made at a number of different centres, there seems to be evidence that they were popular at Court and that a fair number of them might have been made in the Imperial workshops. Their popularity at court cannot be in doubt since they still form a large proportion of the published nephrite bottles from the Imperial collection.

(CBL C 795)

37 (two views)

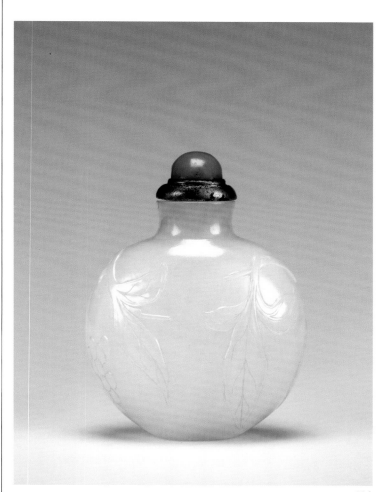

38 (two views)

39

Nephrite, both main faces carved with a raised circular panel simply delineated by a deep channel, one with a low relief river landscape scene with a bridge in the foreground with a pavilion at the water's edge near willow and maple, the other with a ten-character poetic inscription, the neck tapering slightly, a small mouth and very well hollowed interior the base cut as a flat oval, some pale cream inclusions and a flaw at the left shoulder above the landscape scene

Suzhou, 1730-1820

Stopper: Glass with rose quartz imitating tourmaline

Height: 5.2 cm
Mouth: 0.5 cm
Neck: 1.5 cm

The ten characters read:
Yuan Xiang
Lai ji fu
Jing zhi lao xu ting

This translates as:
Frequently comes from far away
Very clear, very clean, (air) around the pavilion

The exact meaning is uncertain though the inscription might be a metaphor referring to 'a sense of clarity' in this place or pavilion.

This magnificent bottle is of the highest possible quality despite some imperfections in the stone and, like the previous bottle, it is one of the gems of the collection. Though understated in the simple very low-relief decoration, the combination of a peaceful bucolic riverscape on one side and an elegant un-crammed inscription on the other create a calm dynamic that pervades the bottle. Along with the slightly bulbous but elegant spade shape with tapering neck, the simple flat foot, and fair degree of hollowing, these elements create a quietly distinguished masterpiece.

This bottle might be a candidate for early Suzhou production. For a discussion of the school see Moss, Graham, and Tsang, *The Art of the Chinese Snuff Bottle: The J & J Collection*, vol. 1, pp. 62-65, no. 21, where the authors lay out their reasoning for such an attribution, which though largely circumstantial, seems plausible. The groups stylistic evolution can be traced back to a group of late Ming and early Qing jade carvings which bear the signature, rarely genuine, of Lu Zigang, the famous sixteenth-century jade carver from Suzhou. Central among these is a series of generally rectangular plaques with low-relief decoration and frequently bearing inscriptions, which have highly literary subjects. It seems that two styles evolved in the Suzhou workshops. The first involved rather low-key decoration, like our example, whilst the later style with multiple relief planes, contrasting colours, and more bombastic tendencies became the more popular. However, despite the popularity of the later style, it appears that for while at least both styles were produced concurrently. Interestingly, a number of bottles carved in the later style have necks cut unusually, like our example, with a tapering neck, see Moss, Graham, and Tsang, *The Art of the Chinese Snuff Bottle: The J & J Collection*, Vol. 1, pp. 62-68, no. 21-23 suggesting that tapering necks were in use from the early days of Suzhou production.

(CBL C 796)

39 (two views)

40

Nephrite, carved in very fine low relief in a continuous landscape scene around the body, though split in to two separate vignettes, one with an elderly gentleman and his assistant holding a pot of chrysanthemums, amongst rockwork and below pine and another tree branch, the other vignette with another (or perhaps the same) elderly gentleman gesticulating to his assistant between tall rocks, the short neck very slightly spreading, a small mouth and an exceedingly well hollowed interior, the foot simply cut as a flat oval with some engraved continuation of the rock design from the main scenes

Suzhou, 1730-1820

Stopper: Rose quartz

Height: 6.4 cm
Mouth: 0.6 cm
Neck: 2.3 cm

This bottle, like the previous one, must also be a candidate for Suzhou production. It certainly resembles quite closely the late Ming and early Qing pendant carvings that gave rise to the so-called Suzhou school. It has a literate subject matter and low-relief carving which includes various planes of rockwork, so beloved of the school. It also has a flat foot so often seen in bottles from the workshop with a design of rocks that continues from the main faces to the underside. For a discussion see the previous entry.

In many respects other than weight (our example is unusually light for such a bulbous shape), this bottle can be favorably compared with a number of published Suzhou bottles in the use of subject matter and quality of carving, albeit in a lower relief, see Moss, Graham, and Tsang, *The Art of the Chinese Snuff Bottle: The J & J Collection*, Vol. 1, pp. 62-68, no. 21-23. Like all of these our bottle has a formal integrity that is synonymous with the group. The symbolic genre subject matter is also typical of Suzhou, which attracted cultural aesthetes like scholar poets, painters, calligraphers, and musicians to the province and which unsurprisingly made its way in to the decorative repertoire. On this bottle we see the scholar with his ever-present assistant, engaged in pleasant activities within a relaxed idyllic rural setting, far from the stresses of cosmopolitan city life and contemplating nature. The subject on this bottle could well be the famous Jin dynasty poet Tao Yuanming (real name Tao Qian, died 427) who was famous for composing poems about chrysanthemums and who planted them in profusion after his early retirement.

The carving, whilst not typical of the more favored high-relief decoration of most of the school's output, is still of an extremely high calibre.

The even coloured white stone does have some paler white inclusions in some areas and the upper third of the bottle, due to the degree of hollowing, is more opaque.

(CBL C 797)

40 (two views)

41

Nephrite, carved on each main face in low relief with six lotus pods, each with six or seven seeds, conjoined by their stems around a *Xi* character, the narrow sides rounded, the stone of yellowish off-white colour, the neck slightly spreading, a regular mouth and a well hollowed interior, a shallowly-cut oval base

1770-1830

Height: 6.6 cm
Mouth: 0.55 cm
Neck: 2.05 cm

The strokes of the *Xi* character are 'channeled' to highlight them and the centre of the pods have been scooped out and drilled with seeds, adding subtle light shifts to the surface. The character *Xi* can be read as joy or happiness and is generally associated with happy events such as weddings. When it is shown twice it represents double happiness, *shuangxi,* and is even more appropriate in a wedding setting, as good things come in pairs. In combination with lotus seeds, *lianzi,* which is a pun for 'continuous sons' *lianzi,* we can be fairly confident that this bottle was given as a wedding gift, see Bartholomew, *Hidden Meaning in Chinese Art*, p. 57, no. 2.27.

The compressed spade shape or oblate form was a popular one throughout snuff bottle production and is not enormously helpful as a dating tool in this particular case other than stating the obvious that it might be an eighteenth or nineteenth century form. The stone itself however is a slightly off-white almost yellow colour of not the finest quality that might suggest a later production date. The formalized decoration does however have some lyrical touches in the scooping out of the lotus pods and the channeling of the xi characters and an integrity in composition that is reminiscent of late eighteenth century carving. These observations combined with the well-hollowed interior hint that our bottle bridges the last decades of the eighteenth with the first of the nineteenth century

(CBL C 798)

42

Nephrite, of *meiping* shape, unusually carved around the body with 'loose-sprays' of pine, bamboo, and prunus in a very high quality low relief, the neck cup-shaped, the rim flat with quite a wide mouth opening and very well hollowed interior, a wide flat circular foot ring and shallowly cut to the base

1750-1830

Height: 7.2 cm
Mouth: 0.9 cm
Neck: 1.5 cm

The loose sprays of pine, bamboo, and prunus are not growing from a branch of a tree or from rockwork but begin arbitrarily around the sides of the bottle. This unusual feature must simply have been an artistic choice as the shape and size would certainly allow for a more conventional depiction. Possibly the artist was just playing with the meaning that the shape of the vessel, *meiping,* conjures. *Meiping* literally means 'prunus blossom vase' and was intended to hold a sprig or two of the blossom. Perhaps the artist was copying an earlier painted pottery *meiping* form. The shape, with narrow foot and high rounded shoulders, is certainly very reminiscent of the Song forms and the arbitrary loose sprays would be in keeping with the carver following a painted example such as a Cizhou vase.

A small group of Imperial jade bottles, many of yellow jade, that use the *meiping* form are published and it is indeed possible that our bottle is related in some way to them. Like ours, they usually have a form of cup-shaped mouth, they are weighted towards the foot, and have a simple flat quite wide circular foot ring with a shallow cut base. Generally, however, they do not have naturalistic decoration but are either plain or copy archaistic bronze vessel decoration. Unlike this example, some are inscribed with an Imperial Qianlong mark. For examples of basic *meiping* shape, see Moss, Graham, and Tsang, *A Treasury of Chinese Snuff Bottles: The Mary and George Bloch Collection*, Vol. 1, Jade, pp. 200-209, no's. 81-85; Moss, Graham, and Tsang, *The Art of the Chinese Snuff Bottle: The J & J Collection*, Vol. 1, p. 91, no. 36.

The carving on our bottle is subtle in the extreme, which only adds to the allure of this understated treasure. No part of the decoration is unessential and every stroke serves a purpose. The delicious white stone has some grey flecks within its matrix and does shade to a pale brown colour at the neck where the stone is thinnest, but the viewer is never disappointed.

The subject of pine (*song*), bamboo (*zhu*), and prunus or plum (*mei*), is commonly known as 'Three Friends of Winter' (*suihan sanyou*). The three are models of fortitude and uprightness in adverse conditions, as the pine and bamboo remain green through harsh winters whilst the prunus is the first to bloom each year.

Each is also a symbol of longevity as all three plants have long life spans.

(CBL C 801)

41

42

43

Nephrite, of aubergine shape, the fruit carved from a white pebble and shaped with a distended belly and pointed end, the leafy calyx (collar) separately attached and cut from a spinach-green nephrite with small black flecks, carved with four leaf extensions pointing away from the neck and down the fruit, the mouth not centred but cut at a slight angle, a well hollowed interior

1730-1800

Stopper: Probably ivory stained red

Height: 7.5 cm
Mouth: 0.45 cm-0.8 cm (countersunk)
Neck: no neck

This bottle belongs to a well-documented group of white nephrite bottles with a separately cut calyx made from a spinach-green nephrite, which were clearly made in some quantity possibly in the Palace workshops but almost certainly for Imperial use. The collar on our example fits snuggly like a glove over the neck and the superbly rendered leaves delicately follow the ample form of the fruit that widens before tapering to a pointed tip that is slightly turned in one direction. The weight of the bottle in the hand is very satisfying, being heavy but not overtly so, and remarkably sensual due to the smoothly polished and lovingly crafted fecund shape.

For nearly identical examples, see Hughes, *The Blair Bequest: Chinese Snuff Bottles from The Princeton University Art Museum*, p. 39, no. 4; *Snuff Bottles In the Collection of the National Palace Museum*, no. 115, a boxed set of ten; and nos. 160-161 for single examples from the royal collection; and Hui and Sin, *An Imperial Qing Tradition*, p. 67, no. 67. The group as a whole varies in both the quality of carving and the stone used. For further discussion see Moss, Graham, and Tsang, *A Treasury of Chinese Snuff Bottles: The Mary and George Bloch Collection*, Vol. 1, Jade, pp. 174-175, no. 70. Like that example, the mouth of our bottle is of a kind described as 'countersunk' by which they mean it matches, in negative, the underside of the head of a screw. This may have been the standard way this type of bottle was carved to match a now missing original stopper, which was most likely twig-shaped.

Though superbly carved, the white stone does have some paler opaque inclusions and a small flaw line to one side of the fruit. One leaf on the collar is also chipped

(CBL C 805)

44

Nephrite, of aubergine shape, the calyx (collar) of the fruit neatly delineated in low relief, the rest of the bottle in high relief with leafy branches, five-petalled flower-heads, several smaller aubergines and a beetle, the mouth drilled at the calyx and very well hollowed, the white stone with a faintly discernible pale celadon tone

1730-1790

Height: 6 cm
Mouth: 0.5 cm
Neck: no neck

Whilst some features suggest this bottle may have originally been a carving or fondling piece, there is a much greater chance that it was indeed originally intended as a snuff bottle. Looking first at those features that indicate the bottle was adapted from another use, we must note that it does not stand un-aided. This in itself is not conclusive as the aubergine (eggplant) group as a whole, as discussed in the previous entry, is well recorded and do not stand un-aided. Whilst it is true that most have separately-cut calyx, examples carved from a single piece of stone like ours are known, see Moss, Graham, and Tsang, *A Treasury of Chinese Snuff Bottles: The Mary and George Bloch Collection*, Vol. 1, Jade, pp. 180-181, no. 72. The mouth shape, as discussed in the previous entry, is very slightly countersunk, but admittedly not of the finest cutting. The additional carving of fruit, flowers and a beetle appears unique and inconsistent within this particular group. However it does fit more comfortably in the 'naturalistic' group discussed in the entry for No. 38 in this publication. It is instructive here to read comments by Moss, Graham, and Tsang, ibid, p.155, no. 62, regarding another aubergine (eggplant) bottle, called 'The Castiglione of Jade Carvers Gourd' where the authors note, 'We have made the case for ascribing the eggplants with separate calyxes to Imperial workshops and it is perhaps no coincidence that of the above-listed fruit- and vegetable-forms in the Imperial collection which do not have separate material for the calyx, at least six are of eggplant form.'

The stone in our example is almost a perfect white with just a barely discernable pale celadon tone, wholly consistent with the finest jade used for the court and in the Imperial workshops. The quality of the carving is no less extraordinary. The beetle appears to scurry across the swelling bulb of the fruit and the smaller fruit that adorn the sides hang with a delicious fullness in counterpoint to the paper-thin flower heads, twisting branches, and curling leaves.

For another white neprite example of an aubergine similar to ours from the Imperial Collection, see *Snuff Bottles in the Collection of the National Palace Museum*, p. 159, no. 146.

(CBL C 808)

43

44

45

Nephrite, of bamboo shoot shape, the body of the shoot carved from a single piece of white nephrite and carved with overlapping petals which radiate from the mouth around the swelling shoot and down to the pointed tip, the mouth and collar formed from a separate piece of grey-brown nephrite, a spinach-green nephrite branch of leafy bamboo cut from several pieces of stone and 'jig-sawed' together to extend down and around the shoot, a well hollowed interior

1750-1830

Height: 6.5 cm
Mouth: 0.4 cm
Neck: 0.3 cm-0.4 cm

The bamboo shoot, *sun*, is a pun for the word grandson, *sun*, which is pronounced identically and according to Bartholomew, *Hidden Meanings in Chinese Art*, p. 60, no. 3.1, because it is evergreen and has a straight exterior and hollow culm, symbolizes fidelity and humility; and because it bends but does not break, exemplifies integrity. It is also considered one of the 'Four Gentlemen among Flowers', one of the 'Three Friends of Winter', and an important symbol of peace.

For a similar bottle that is, in the words of the authors, 'sensibly, if not entirely convincingly' attributed to the Palace workshops, see Moss, Graham and Tsang, *A Treasury of Chinese Snuff Bottles: The Mary and George Bloch Collection*, Vol. 1, Jade, pp. 172-3, no. 69. The attribution is based on the colour of the jade, including typical white flaws found in much jade used at court (also found in our example), the auspicious symbolism, and especially the use of the spinach-green embellishments which link the group to the aubergine (eggplant) bottles which were unquestionably made for the Court, see No. 43 in this publication. The carving of the shoot leaves on our bottle is rather formal with simple shallowly-cut incisions representing the layers of folded twisting leaves, and is identical to that of the Bloch bottle noted above, but quite different from two other nephrite bamboo shoot bottles (without embellishment) in the Bloch collection which are worthy of comparison, *ibid*, pp. 168-171, nos. 67 and 68, but depicted with finely ribbed twisted leaves which are convincingly realistic. Another is illustrated in *Zhongguo biyanhu zhenshang* (Gems of Chinese Snuff Bottles), p. 225, no. 264.

Interestingly, another plain bamboo shoot bottle (without embellishment) was offered at Christie's Hong Kong, 1 April 1992, lot 1555 and catalogued as having the original nephrite stopper. Though no good reason was given for the stopper attribution (one assumes it fitted exceedingly well; must have appeared to have had considerable age, and was carved as a bamboo node) it was made from a brownish-beige nephrite that matches the colour of our collar and might therefore have been similar to one that our bottle originally donned. The grey/brown jade collar that forms the neck of our bottle was at first thought to be a later replacement because of slight inconsistencies in the alignment and quality of the engraved decoration. However it seems unlikely that a restorer would add a quite unremarkable and dull coloured stone that appears out of place in the colour scheme, when spinach-green nephrite matching the embellished bamboo was readily available. More likely it was the original neck. The quality of the remaining spinach-green nephrite branches and leaves that adorn the one side of the bottle are of a very high quality and cleverly comprised of various separate pieces of conjoined spinach-green stone inserted in to the sides of the bottle by means of small (0.3 cm-0.4 cm) diameter shallow drill holes (as evidenced on the other side where a large bamboo branch is missing and two such holes are clearly visible where the jade appliqués could be attached).

A small area of artificially stained russet on the surface of the white nephrite shoot tip might suggest that the missing portion may have originally been a colour other than spinach-green to match it. As staining was very popular at the Palace workshops, it is also another possible indication of Imperial provenance.

(CBL C 811)

45 (two views)

46

Nephrite, of compressed gourd shape, carved in extremely high-relief with twisting tendrils and curling leaves trailing down from the neck of the bottle and wrapping around the entire body, a further smaller gourd to one side, the wider end of each gourd beautifully finished with superbly executed blossom ends, a well hollowed interior

1730-1790

Stopper: Glass of twig form imitating jadeite

Height: 8 cm
Mouth: 0.5 cm
Neck: no neck

This is yet another masterpiece of jade carving and, like Nos. 38, 43-45 and 47 in this publication, fits comfortably in the 'naturalistic' group discussed in the entry for No. 38. Like most of these examples, this bottle does not stand unaided suggesting that it too may once have been a fondling piece; although free standing was not a necessity of a snuff bottle it is the rule rather than the exception. However it might just be that the entire group of 'fruit-shaped' bottles, by mere fact of their unusual shapes, could simply not conform to the accepted norm for bottle shapes and were therefore made as pieces to be held primarily in the hand. Certainly the execution of the mouth of this bottle is unusual, 'hidden' as it were beneath the vine tendrils that burst from the top of the gourd and making insertion of the stopper and spoon aesthetically displeasing. Of course the original stopper may have been of a different scale and form. Once again we have good reason to believe that the carving was made for the court and was possibly even a product of the Palace workshops. The popularity at court of the 'naturalistic' group cannot be in doubt since they comprise a large percentage of the published nephrite bottles from the Imperial collection. Primarily we must base our attribution on sheer quality alone. The genius of this particular lapidary is self-evident in the manner in which the fruit has been brought to life. No aspect has been overlooked. Every tendril and leaf that curls and twists around the body has been miraculously undercut and softly polished; subtle gradations in the skin's surface have been lovingly wrought; the blossom ends, which terminate the lower bulbs of all the gourds, are painstakingly detailed; the smaller but weighty fruits hang deliciously to the sides and are almost unbearably heavy; the tendrils coil and twist in so realistic a manner it is hard to believe that this bottle started life as a menacingly hard pebble. Finally, the pure white stone is of the most magnificent quality.

See Moss, Graham, and Tsang, *A Treasury of Chinese Snuff Bottles: The Mary and George Bloch Collection*, Vol. 1, Jade, pp. 154-159, no. 62 and 63; pp.164-165, no. 65, for three other examples of extraordinary nephrite fruit-form bottles that bear comparison.

See Bartholomew, *Hidden Meaning in Chinese Art*, p. 61, no. 3.3, for an explanation of the gourd as an important auspicious symbol. It is a natural symbol of fertility because of its numerous seeds. The plant can produce large gourds, *gua*, and small gourds, *die*, and when depicted as such (as in our example) can form the rebus *guadie mianmian*, meaning 'ceaseless generations of descendants'. The string-like vines and tendrils, *mandai,* can be read as a pun on *wandai*, 'ten thousand generations' further solidifying the reading of the previous rebus.

(CBL C 814)

46 (two views)

49

Nephrite, modeled as two well-defined lotus pods wrapped in a large lotus pad finely delineated with veins, which forms most of one main face, whilst the two pods form the other face, one narrow edge carved with a small long-tailed bird, the stone with a faint pale celadon hue with some russet inclusions and a few flaws cleverly used in the design

1750-1820

Stopper: nephrite probably original

Height: 6.0 cm (6.4 cm with original stopper)
Mouth: 0.4 cm
Neck: no neck

At first it is quite difficult to reconcile the elements of this rather unusual bottle, but as it is turned in the hand, the various parts reveal themselves. The carver has cleverly softened the extremities of the bottle so that the different elements do not interrupt the elegant shape or compromise the form, particularly the precariously balanced magpie. Even the stopper which appears to be original and of flower head form is cleverly slipped in to place and nestles snuggly in to the contours of the mouth, whilst protected at its lower edges by the lotus pad on one side. The bottle is remarkably well hollowed for a mouth of such small dimension. Russet flaw lines within the matrix of the stone have been engineered to form natural breaks in the design particularly along the edge of the lotus pad and between the two seedpods.

The subject of a magpie (*xique*) eating lotus seeds (*lianzi*) is recorded by Bartholomew, *Hidden Meanings in Chinese Art*, pp. 95-96, 4.17-4.18.1. This unusual and uncommon subject forms the rebus 'May you joyfully pass your exams, one after another', *xide lianke*. The magpie, because of its name, symbolizes joy, *xi*.

Another example of a nephrite lotus pod bottle is illustrated by Low, *Chinese Snuff Bottles from the Sanctum of Enlightened Respect III*, p. 61, no. 42, where the author notes that the lotus normally represents purity, but when in the form of a lotus pod, is a symbol of fertility and that a special characteristic of the plant is that the seedpod is already formed when the lotus flower blooms and as such represents a good omen of the early arrival of sons.

See also *Snuff Bottles: Little Gems of Delight*, p. 22, no. M 17 for another with russet inclusions from the Richard Baey Collection.

(CBL C 818)

50

Nephrite, of pomegranate shape, the calyx (collar) forming the neck of the bottle and drilled with a small mouth, the interior well hollowed, the foot formed from leafy branches which climb up and around the body of the fruit, one smaller pomegranate and a butterfly or moth to one main face, and an area of 'bursting' seeds and leaves on the other

1730-1800

Stopper: buffalo horn

Height: 5.2 cm
Mouth: 0.4 cm
Neck: 1.0 cm

This bottle is another gem of the 'naturalistic' bottle group. Superb carving and technical mastery renders this as a highly likely candidate for Imperial production. As with many of this group, the pure white stone is of an even colour throughout but with the addition of minor creamy inclusions typical of the jade used at court, whilst not wholly exclusive to it. The realism of the curling leaves; the remarkable 'splitting' of the flesh to reveal the bursting seeds; the clever manipulation of the branches that form a firm footing for the bottle are all exceptional features, that raise this bottle to the highest levels of achievement within the lapidary world.

According to Bartholomew, *Hidden Meanings in Chinese Art*, p. 76, no. 3.23 and 3.23.1, the splitting open of the pomegranate (*shiliu*) to reveal the seeds inside can form the rebus 'pomegranate revealing one hundred sons, *liukai baizi*. Butterfly, *hudie*, or groups of butterflies can form the rebus, 'may you have an accumulation of blessings', *fudie*, thus further highlighting the good fortune such a gift was intended to bestow on its recipient.

See Moss, Graham, and Tsang, *A Treasury of Chinese Snuff Bottles: The Mary and George Bloch Collection*, Vol. 1, Jade, pp. 154-157, no. 62 for a discussion of a series of fruit-, flower-, and vegetable form bottles, mostly of white or greenish-white nephrite that form this large and well-known group and ibid, pp. 160-163, no. 64 for another superb pomegranate bottle, which interestingly has a similar calyx at the neck albeit slightly more sculptural.

See also the entry for another pomegranate bottle, No. 38, in this collection.

(CBL C 819)

49 (two views)

50 (two views)

51

Nephrite, twin-fish bottle, modeled as two conjoined fish unusually lying head to tail, one modeled as a bulging-eyed dragon-headed carp, the eye simply formed by hollow drilling, two rounded horns extending back from the brow, the other fish of more slender form and without horns, both with simply engraved scales and well carved fins to the bodies, wide mouth openings of equal size, well hollowed

1750-1850

Height: 8.0 cm
Mouths: 0.55 cm
Necks: 0.9 cm

See Bartholomew, *Hidden Meanings in Chinese Art*, p. 44, no. 2.9.2 where the image of two fish is discussed. Double fish, *shuangyu*, forms the rebus 'May you be blessed with connubial bliss, fecundity, and an abundance of good luck', *shuangyu jiqing*.

In Chinese legend, as fish are reputed to swim in pairs, they also symbolize the joys of union. It is pertinent then that our example appears to depict a male and female fish. The horned fish appears to have a more ferocious 'male' aspect, whilst the more slender fish has a feminine quality, with softer features and rounded tail fin.

See also ibid, p. 92, 4.11.2, for a sculpture in green nephrite of two fish resembling dragons, rising from waves. The carp is the fish associated with motifs for passing the civil service examinations. The story goes, according to tradition, that a carp swimming upstream in the Yellow River, fighting against the opposing current must leap the rapids of Dragon's Gate; the first to succeed transforms itself into a dragon. This story is a metaphor for a poor scholar who by passing the civil services exams raises himself to the status of high official. In our case it would appear a different reading is required though clearly one of our fish is in the throws of his transformation to dragon though his partner is not.

The transition between the edges of the two fish is imperceptible and remarkably well achieved. Both bottles are very well hollowed and each fish's mouth is formed as a simple cylinder clearly intended for the insertion of stoppers. The scales whilst simplified are neat and well organized and the fins whilst small do have realistic movement implied by their subtle wavy edge. The eyes of both fish were somewhat crudely bored with a hollow drill head to forge a simple circular channel centred by a boss. While basic in its conception, it is a surprisingly effective in capturing the essentials.

The stone is of an unusual olive grey tone.

(CBL C 826)

52

Nephrite, modeled as a curled up dog, with large head, wide smiling mouth, simply delineated eyes below large brows and large curling ears, a single channel runs down the spine of the dog, the legs are tucked in and only three are visible, each paw with two claws, fire-scrolls or hair tufts emanate from the haunches of the animal which continue in low relief on the underside, adequately hollowed interior, the stone of superb even white tone

1730-1790

Width: 6.6 cm
Mouth: 0.5 cm
Neck: no neck

Here we have a bottle that unquestionably began life as a carving. The conversion is evident both in the lack of adequate hollowing to the interior and because the original engraved decoration to the rear of the animal has been compromised to allow for the hollowing and subsequent addition of the bottle mouth. The carving may have been intended as sleeve weight (its form would certainly be appropriate for that purpose), a scroll weight, or simply a cabinet piece for a scholar's studio.

Putting aside the question of its original purpose, the piece is still a magnificent little carving that is amongst the finest of its genre. The curling dog's form, though of distinctly pebble form, is not entirely dictated by the stone. In fact it positively breathes life. The legs are cleverly twisted to fit the shape and in fact only three are visible with each paw having two claw-like ends. The dog wears a capricious smile and the tufts of hair or fire scrolls that coil around the body are superbly under-cut and polished. The spine is cut with a single channel that runs the entire length of the body. The belly of the dog on the underside of the carving, has been subtly rendered by just a few simple strokes of the carver's tools and surrounded by an abstract pattern of the tufts and tail that envelope the sculpture from the other side. The stone is of the purest white with just a hint of inclusions.

The addition of claw-like appendages on the paws of the dog and the unusual tufts that emanate from the dog's body, reminiscent of fire scrolls when seen in the context of dragons, suggests that this seemingly innocent puppy dog might in fact represent a mythical dog beast. See Williams, *Outlines of Chinese Symbolism and Art Motives*, pp. 124-126, where the author muses on the origin and evolution of the so-called 'Pekingese' dog. 'Short dogs' are mentioned in the records of the Zhou dynasty (c. 1000 BCE) as part of the annual tribute from Shansi and by the Christian era were labeled as a breed apart under the name *Pai*. It was however the Manchus (Qing dynasty) who capitalized in their own interests the lion-like characteristics that indirectly linked the palace dogs with Buddhism, as the dynasty derived its name from the Manjusri Buddha who rides on a lion.

(CBL C 822)

51

52 (two views)

53

Jadeite, of compressed form, of extraordinary deep emerald-green colour and brilliance, a few small black flecks and an area of more apple tone to one side of the upper gourd, the neck is everted and the rim slightly concave, the mouth is small yet the interior is extremely well hollowed, the foot is simply cut as an oval dimple

1780-1850

Height: 6.1 cm
Mouth: 0.52 cm
Neck: 1.5 cm

This bottle is a jadeite masterpiece. The stone has been cut from a boulder of the deepest richest colour available to the carver. Its simple sensual form enhances the translucent qualities of the emerald-green hue. The form has been magnificently shaped with bulbous swelling body, when viewed frontally, or from the narrow sides. The degree of polish is unequaled and the extraordinary hollowing has created a partially translucent bottle. Though some parts of the stone reveal indistinct fibrous markings and a small area of more apple tone to one narrow side of the upper gourd, the overall impression is one of even rich colour. The bottle stands un-aided on a very carefully but simply cut oval dimple about 0.8 cm across.

See Moss, Graham, and Tsang, *A Treasury of Chinese Snuff Bottles: The Mary and George Bloch Collection*, Vol. 1, Jade, pp. 458-459, no. 181, where the author discusses the rarity of the finest jadeite in snuff bottle production. Due to the amount of wastage during the interior drilling process, the best stones were generally saved for producing jewelry and rarely used for objects bigger than beads or rings. For a stone of this quality a palace workshop attribution must be entertained. The gourd shape, as previously discussed (No. 13) was a popular one at Court during the Qianlong period and onwards as evidenced by the examples in glass and enamel bearing the Qianlong emperors' reign mark. It is hard to imagine that an example of such brilliance would have been attempted anywhere except at the Imperial court. See also another gourd bottle, using a red jadeite, but of less pleasing form than our example, illustrated by Moss et al, ibid, pp. 466-467, no. 185, which they suggest is possibly Imperial and perhaps from the Palace workshop.

A plain gourd-shaped jadeite bottle of apple rather than emerald green from ther Imperial Collection is illustrated in *Snuff Bottles in the Collection of the National Palace Museum*, p. 189, no. 226 and another is illustrated in *Snuff Bottles: Little Gems of Delight*, p. 67, no. M 211 from the Joseph Grimberg Collection.

An almost identically shaped jadeite bottle with the addition of low-relief floral decoration is illustrated by Low, *Chinese Snuff Bottles from the Sanctum of Enlightened Respect III*, pp. 96-97, no. 75 and a paler carved jadite example from the Carl F. Barron collection, is illustrated by Moss, *The Barron Collection: Illustrated Handlist*, ICSBS Convention, Boston, 2008, p.1, no. 2734.

(CBL C 674)

54

Jadeite, with an unusual matrix of dark emerald and blackish-green 'chips' set within a paler apple-green ground, some chips with a highly reflective quality, a short cylindrical neck, slightly concave rim and small mouth, regular hollowing to the interior, a simple flat oval base

1790-1900

Stopper: glass imitating coral

Height: 5.0 cm
Mouth: 0.6 cm
Neck: 1.9 cm

This is an unusual and intriguing stone. The dark inclusions are more reminiscent of hard stones like puddingstone or fossiliferous limestone than they are of regular jadeite, where the inclusions tend to be more fluid within the stone, rather than 'fractured' or 'chip'-like as in this example. Some are almost like rutile needles found in quartz bottles that run more or less in regular flow pattern but with occasional anomalies that suddenly run counter to them. Many of the inclusions have a highly reflective quality reminiscent of 'tiger's-eye', which adds a pleasant sparkling quality to the highly polished surface. Various fractures or flaw lines in the stone can be found on close inspection.

The otherwise formal integrity of this bottle has been compromised by the rather shoddy angle at which the foot, a simple flat oval, has been cut. This puzzling mistake causes the bottle to lean very slightly to one side. The degree of hollowing is satisfactory.

For a similar example see Moss, Graham, and Tsang, *The Art of the Chinese Snuff Bottle: The J & J Collection*, Vol. 1, p.125, no. 62.

(CBL C 725)

53 (two views)

54 (two views)

55

Jadeite, of compressed melon shape with lobes, one main face carved with a butterfly above a finely veined lotus pad with curling edges, the other main face un-decorated but of richer apple-green colour, a simple raised band at the base of the slightly everted neck, a concave rim and a regular mouth, the interior very well hollowed, all on a narrow flat oval foot ring with shallowly cut concave base

1790-1880

Height: 6.4 cm
Mouth: 0.6 cm
Neck: 1.65 cm

The dark apple-green colour of the stone is rather evenly distributed throughout the bottle. The lapidary has attempted, with some degree of success, to include a few un-avoidable russet brown inclusions within the lotus pad decoration. The slightly transparent nature of the jadeite adds a rich buttery quality to the stone.

For a discussion on the subject of gourds (*gua*) and butterflies (*die*) see Bartholomew, *Hidden Meanings in Chinese Art*, p. 62, 3.3.4. The author notes that the gourd, melon, pumpkin, and squash were interchangeable as subjects when paired with butterflies, and that the rebus *guaddie mianmian* ('may there be ceaseless generations of sons and grandsons') applies to all. The addition of a lotus pad to the design on our bottle, whilst appearing arbitrary, almost certainly carries some hidden meaning.

For a slightly more squat jadeite bottle of less rich colour and carved with two butterflies on a melon, see Stevens, *The Collector's Book of Snuff Bottles*, pp. 280-282, no. 1012. See also Moss, Graham, and Tsang, *A Treasury of Chinese Snuff Bottles: The Mary and George Bloch Collection*, Vol. 1, Jade, pp. 472-473, no. 187, for a more naturalistic melon bottle of opaque paler colour.

Another lobed melon form jadeite bottle of paler colour from the Eric Young Collection sold at Sotheby's London, 3 March 1987, lot 131.

(CBL C 681)

56

Jadeite, the stone of pale yellowish apple-green tone with areas of emerald-green abstract inclusions, the rounded narrow sides with lion-mask fixed-ring handles, the oval foot ring rounded rather than flat and deeply cut to the base, well hollowed

1780-1860

Height: 6.2 cm
Mouth: 0.6 cm
Neck: 1.7 cm

It is rather difficult to date this bottle. Certainly the form could be from late in the eighteenth century but just as reasonably it could date to the second half of the nineteenth century. The satisfactory but not brilliant carving of the lion-mask ring handles does not seem to be an adequate indicator of date, although one does find the more elongated form of handle used on our bottle favored at an earlier date, whilst many from the late Qing dynasty tend to be cursory and small. The hollowing, however, may help date the piece. According to Moss, Graham, and Tsang, *A Treasury of Chinese Snuff Bottles: The Mary and George Bloch Collection*, Vol. 1, Jade, pp. 454-456, no. 179, the degree of hollowing suggests likely production dates, though it is not always definitive. They suggest that plain mid-Qing jade bottles tended to be well, if not extremely well, hollowed and that there was a tendency from probably the mid-nineteenth century onwards to more rudimentary hollowing. Therefore, given the very high degree of hollowing in our bottle, combined with reasonably well-carved elongated handles, its well proportioned shape, and a certain formal integrity, we can reasonably suggest an early nineteenth-century date of manufacture.

When held to the light, the abstract inclusions jump to life against the slightly fibrous 'turnip-like' matrix of the bulk of the stone.

(CBL C 683)

57

Jadeite, of compressed form, with vine tendrils, a lotus pad and a further smaller gourd carved in high relief trailing down from the cylindrical neck and across the smaller upper bulb to the larger lower bulb on one main face, an area of dark brown stone running through the upper half of the bottle on the other main face and towards one narrow side has been cleverly carved with a swooping bat with further small lotus pads, the stone of apple-green tone with various areas of darker emerald-green and also a russet brown and yellow, the rim flat, the mouth and interior with regular hollowing

1790-1900

Height: 6.0 cm
Mouth: 0.5 cm
Neck: 1.1 cm

This is a particularly distinctive bottle. The stone is of a rich and vibrant colour and the carving of very high quality despite the numerous inclusions in the stone suggesting that this bottle might be of mid-Qing production. However when we compare the basic shape of this bottle with the pure form of No. 53 in this publication, it becomes quite clear that the undecorated bottle has a more concise formal integrity and the upper and lower bulbs seem more naturally suited than the slightly elongated bulbs of the carved gourd. In addition, the waisted neck and everted rim of the former bring a lightness in keeping with a late eighteenth-century sensibility that is absent from the latter.

For a spinach-green nephrite example of a gourd-shaped bottle with smaller gourds in relief see Low, *Chinese Snuff Bottles from the Sanctum of Enlightened Respect III*, p. 73, no. 54, where the author discusses the symbolism of this double-gourd form, *hulu*, which is said to embody heaven and earth, and to contain spiritual energy that wards off evil spirits. One of the Daoist treasures, the gourd is also the vessel of magic elixirs, a symbol of mystery and necromancy, and the attribute of the immortal Li Tieguai.

(CBL C 682)

58

Jadeite, of compressed form, with a short cylindrical neck, the flat rim with a regular mouth, the interior regularly hollowed, the stone of a pale apple-ice green tone with very pale-emerald wispy inclusions, a more yellow area of stone at the centre of the stone on each main face, a flat oval foot

1820-1900

Stopper: rose quartz with metal collar

Height: 5.4 cm
Mouth: 0.55 cm
Neck: 1.65 cm

This rather icy-coloured jadeite is of a slightly unusual form being more rounded to the lower quadrants and with flat, almost square shoulders. It is most agreeable in the hand, however, and due to a fair degree of hollowing is of an attractive light weight despite a quite thick base. The wispy inclusions have a rather dreamy quality like chafe in the air or ethereal drifting smoke that is only enhanced by the gossamer-thin colour of the stone. A pale yellowish tinge to the heart of the stone merely multiplies the effect. Unusually the mouth is actually cut a little off centre. This would be distracting to bottle purists and there seems no obvious reason for this blunder.

(CBL C 688)

55

56

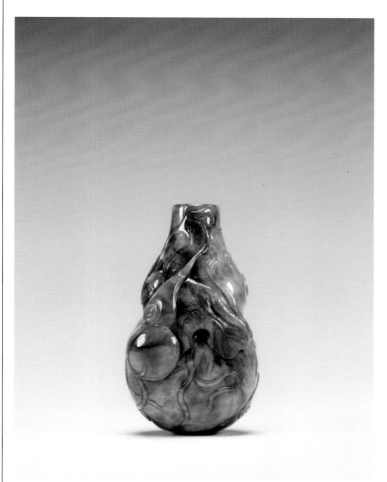

57

58

59

Jadeite, the body almost a perfect circle but truncated at the flat oval foot, the neck cylindrical and the rim slightly concave, the mouth small but the interior quite well hollowed, the stone of a very dense, almost emerald-green colour with some dark and light flecks throughout, a small area of white at the shoulder on one narrow side

1800-1900

Stopper: jadeite (not original)

Height: 5.9 cm
Mouth: 0.6 cm
Neck: 1.9 cm

Despite being slightly less than pure emerald-green in colour this bottle has an intensity rarely seen in jadeite bottles. It has been suggested that it may have received some colour 'enhancement' at some point in its lifetime but this theory can be easily dismissed. The areas of white dapples that dot the surface of the bottle throughout and which culminate in a rather large white patch at one shoulder could not have been avoided in a staining and heating process that would colour the entire bottle. The area of white at the shoulder measures about 0.9-1.5 cm across. The stone has a wonderful variegated surface of misty marble quality, with dark specks and swirling fibrous passages interspersed with paler areas.

In terms of its shape, this bottle is nearly a perfect circle. This fact, whilst interesting, possibly unique and certainly important in terms of formal integrity, is not especially helpful with dating the bottle. Rounded bottles of this form can be found in both the eighteenth and nineteenth centuries. However combined with the quite good degree of hollowing, these aspects might suggest an early nineteenth-century date.

For a shield-shaped bottle that appears to be carved from a very similar jadeite material, see Nicollier, *The Baur Collection*, pp. 208-209, no. H 81, which she dates 1800-1880.

(CBL C 680)

60

Jadeite of chloromelanite type, of rectangular shape with sloping rounded shoulders below a slightly oval neck, the mouth small and the interior regularly hollowed, a flat oval foot ring and deeply cut base, the stone of exceptionally deep emerald-green almost black colour, one main face of deeper tone than the other, areas of white veining and more subtle black inclusions to both sides

1800-1900

Height: 6.4 cm
Mouth: 0.4 cm
Neck: 1.5-1.7 cm across (oval)

Provenance: Possibly Roland N. Moore, New York, May 1913.

This fascinating form of jadeite, known as chloromelanite, is acknowledged as having been used for quite a wide range of bottles, mostly of rounded square or rounded rectangular outline. In 1993, Moss, Graham, and Tsang, *The Art of the Chinese Snuff Bottle, The J & J Collection*, p.132, no. 69, tentatively suggested that this distinctive material might be from the Tawmaw mines in Burma, which reportedly opened in the 1880s. However by 1995 and the publication of *A Treasury of Chinese Snuff Bottles: The Mary and George Bloch Collection*, Vol. 1, Jade, pp. 464-465, no. 184, the authors had revised their initial attribution based on the clear possibility that the forms themselves appeared to refute such a late dating. Based on this and the degree of hollowing through such a small mouth, an earlier date of production, perhaps as early as the 1780s, was proposed. The examples that the authors reference are, with only one exception (ibid, pp. 452-453, no. 178), of more broader form than the present example. The authors do add the caveat that the form and degree of hollowing may have continued un-interrupted up to twentieth century, citing as examples the broad range of crystal bottles of similar shape and high degree of hollowing that the inside-painted artists of the Beijing school utilized (ibid, p.464, no. 184).

The form of our bottle does actually more closely mirror the forms used by this school, rather than the broader examples cited by Moss et al. A wide ranging date of production, tentatively between 1800-1900, seems more appropriate for this bottle, despite the very narrow opening and good interior hollowing. With certainty however we can say that it was produced by a very competent workshop with an expensive and magnificent stone presumably for a significant patron.

For a very similar example cut from an equally dark stone, see Low, *More Treasures from the Sanctum of Enlightened Respect*, p. 85, no. 78 and another from the Gerry P. Mack Collection was sold at Sotheby's New York, 25 October 1997, lot 178.

(CBL C 675)

59

60

61

Jadeite, of chloromelanite type, carved with a bordered recessed circular panel on each main face with a *long* character formed from the entwined bodies of four stylized *kui* dragons, the narrow sides with vertical raised and grooved panels carved with low-relief stylized archaic *chilong* forming the handles, a tall circular neck with a concave rim and small mouth, the interior well hollowed, a short and narrow rounded oval foot ring and regularly cut base, the stone of deep emerald-green to almost black colour

1780-1880

Stopper: glass imitating jadeite

Height: 5.2 cm
Mouth: 0.5 cm
Neck: 1.5 cm

The comments on the material for the previous entry, No. 60, can also be applied to this bottle. However in this example, whilst the stone is the usual intense opaque emerald-green peppered with black spots and does have a few very small areas where white inclusions in the form of abstract patches no more than a few millimeters across are visible, the more usual network of fine white veins seen in most of the other bottles cited is absent here.

Regarding date, this bottle could well be earlier than the previous example; falling more in line with the parameters outlined by Moss. The form of this bottle is unusual for the group. Stylistically it aligns itself more with another well-known group of duan stone (shale) bottles often depicted on one side with the *long* character formed by dragons, which apparently date to late in the Qianlong reign and appear to have been made in the region of Guangdong. These were given to the Court as tribute. Both Moss (*The Art of the Chinese Snuff Bottle: The J & J Collection*, Vol. 1, p.152, no. 84) and Kleiner (*Chinese Snuff Bottles from Collection of John Ault*, p. 16, no. 20) argue they were then copied by the Imperial glassworks in Beijing. This leaves us with the intriguing question as to the likely date of production of the jadeite group. It is probably safe to assume that they do not pre-date the *duan* bottles. This particular compressed spherical form was a popular one in glass with various decorated and un-decorated examples recorded, some with elongated grooved panel handles on the narrow sides, see the *catalogue*, 'Snuff Bottles of the Ch'ing Dynasty, Hong Kong Museum of Art,' 1978, p. 70, no. 71 and Kleiner; *Chinese Snuff Bottles from Collection of John Ault*, p. 16, no. 20.

The addition of low-relief dragons on the handles on our example suggest that this might be the final step in a process of duplication and transformation, using the glass bottles as a template. This process might only take a few years from inception. Thus, in all likelihood, our bottle probably dates to no earlier than very late in the Qianlong period and perhaps as late as the 1880s.

(CBL C 676)

62

Jadeite, of chloromelanite type, carved in low relief with a continuous scene of pine, prunus (plum) and bamboo, *sanyou*, rising from a grassy knoll and rockwork, a large butterfly carved on one narrow edge of the shoulder, a large cylindrical neck, flat rim, a regular mouth and regular hollowing to the interior, standing on a rounded oval foot ring and with a regular cut base, the dark rich emerald green stone of quite even tone with a fine network of paler inclusions, white veins and some black spots

1800-1900

Stopper: glass imitating jadeite

Height: 5.2 cm
Mouth: 0.6 cm
Neck: 2.0 cm

Again, the remarks regarding the stone in entry No. 60 in this publication can be applied to this bottle as well. As already mentioned this type of jadeite, known as chloromelanite, is primarily carved into a rounded square or rounded rectangular outline, and this bottle is no exception.

The stone, like the previous two examples is an intense opaque emerald-green peppered with black spots and in this case does have the network of fine white veins generally associated with this material. These veins have actually dictated the flow of the design with various branches and leaves following the direction of the inclusions. The form of this bottle is slightly squatter and slightly heavier in weight than the examples illustrated by Moss et al. Combined with the large and somewhat cursory nature of the carving itself, we can comfortably assume that the bottle was probably made in the mid-to late-nineteenth century rather than earlier. The simplistic grassy knoll and peremptory rockwork suggest a carver in a hurry (or perhaps one with a blunt instrument!), and not one working on an imperial commission. Similarly, there appears to be little regard for scale. The regular hollowing, as opposed to the high degree of hollowing in the other examples in the collection also point to a late period of manufacture.

The subject of pine (*song*), bamboo (*zhu*), and prunus or plum (*mei*), is commonly known as 'Three Friends of Winter' (*suihan sanyou*). The three are models of fortitude and uprightness in adverse conditions, as the pine and bamboo remain green through harsh winters whilst the prunus is the first to bloom each year. The colour of the stone, being a vivid and fresh pine green further solidifies this reference. They are each also symbols of longevity in their own right due to long life spans, see Bartholomew, *Hidden Meanings in Chinese Art*, p. 210, no. 7.47.2. The butterfly is also an auspicious motif, symbolizing blessings and happiness as well as longevity, and therefore very appropriate in this setting.

(CBL C 678)

61

62

QUARTZ

63

Amethyst crystal, the main faces plain and almost flat, the narrow sides with unusual five-ring mask handles running the entire length of the sides, a cylindrical neck, a very slightly concave rim, a small mouth and a quite well hollowed interior, a flat oval foot ring and regular cut base, the stone of very rich even purple colour

1750-1850

Stopper: glass imitating amethyst

Height: 6.5 cm
Mouth: 0.65 cm
Neck: 1.6 cm

The closest comparable bottle to ours is a dark crystal example illustrated by Moss, Graham, and Tsang, *A Treasury of Chinese Snuff Bottles: The Mary and George Bloch Collection*, Vol. 2, Part 2, pp. 448-449, no. 346. It is almost identical in respect of height, neck and mouth size, type of foot, and more importantly has five rings suspended from a stylized lion mask that form the handles on the narrow sides. Both are also of basic rectangular shape that tapers to the foot, ours rather more obviously. The authors suggest that it might be Imperial. It is so close to our example in so many respects it is hard not to conclude that they come from the same workshop, one that not only specialized in hard-stones but also excelled in them. The importance of the ring handles at court is briefly discussed in the entry for No. 128, but is fully detailed by Moss et al in the literature cited above. The authors note that loose-ring handles appear in many Imperial jade pieces made for the Court during the eighteenth century which later developed in to the idea of linking these rings in to chains. This was not only a chance to display technical lapidary skills but it also echoed the reverence for antiquity, copying as they do the linked chains on bronze age vessels and covers. Clearly the real, loose-linked chains must have preceded the 'pseudo' loose rings of such bottles, and the authors believe this was unlikely before the middle of the century when the motif became popular.

A similar shaped amethyst bottle with simple mask handles is illustrated in the exhibition catalogue, *Chinese Snuff Bottles: Documentation of World Trade West to East*, The Oakland Museum, 1977, p. 17, no. 522.

(CBL C 564)

63 (two views)

64

Amethyst crystal, of pebble shape, one main face carved in low relief with a rocky winter mountain scene with figures, a small building and a leafless tree, the other side with an exquisite 14-character inscription including the artist's name, a small circular hole forming the mouth at the top of the bottle, the interior partially hollowed, standing an irregular oval foot, extremely vivid purple colour to the upper two-thirds of the bottle paling to a clear stone in the lower third

Signed : Shou He (Ju Shi-the Hermit), 1780-1880

Height: 4.2 cm
Width: 4.9 cm
Mouth: 0.5 cm

The inscription reads:
Liang gong zhu hu
Gong shu zhen ren
Shou he ju shi
Bao po

This translates as:
Good lapidary carved (engraved) bottles
Shrink real man in bottle
Shou He (artist name) Ju Shi (hermit)
Holding jade

It is difficult to be quite sure of the full meaning of the inscription. However, the first line is self-evident. This artist and workshop were confident and proud of their lapidary skills.

The second line, whilst referring to the two small figures dwarfed by the natural mountain backdrop carved on one side of the bottle, almost certainly has a second and important Daoist meaning. The double meaning is an integral part of Daoist duality. Pictorially we have a man shrunk to the size of a bottle: whilst metaphorically a gourd bottle, which is an important attribute of several of the Daoist immortals, symbolizes the joining of Heaven and Earth. For examples of two Daoist adepts, Zhongli Quan and Li Tieguai with their bottles, see Little, *Taoism and the Arts of China*, pp. 322-323, no. 119, and p. 331, no. 125.

The third line appears to be the artist's name, Shou He, followed by Ju Shi which can be read as 'hermit'. However, this is assuming the bottle is being read correctly. Unfortunately Moss, Graham, and Tsang, *The Art of the Chinese Snuff Bottle: The J & J Collection*, pp. 186-187, no. 104, translate a second bottle (brown crystal with a pale skin to one side) bearing the identical inscription differently. Their reading of the first two lines is in agreement, however, the third line is translated as '(while) the one who has attained the Way keeps (improper matters) in the dark' rather than as an artist's name. I am assured that our reading is correct, but in Chinese there is often more than one interpretation of a text. The inscription on the J & J bottle is followed by another artist's name, that of Youqin and a cyclical date corresponding to 1805 or possibly 1865. This might, understandably, be the reason for assuming Shou He (Ju Shi) is not in fact a name. However, I am again assured, that in all likelihood the maker of the J & J bottle was indeed Youqin, but that the inscription that precedes it was copied from another inscription, presumably on a bottle, and that bottle was made by Shou He (Ju Shi).

Fortunately for us the inscription on our amethyst bottle is identical to part of an inscription on another bottle, No. 69 in this publication. That bottle is a dark crystal of faceted pebble form carved in the style of the Rustic Crystal Master. It is dated 1817 (or possibly 1877), and bears the studio name 'Cave of Watery Brightness'. There is no question that both our bottles must be from the same workshop and presumably the same master. The 'Cave of Watery Brightness' is apparently recorded as being on the shore of Lake Tai at Huzhou or Wuxing. In all probability Shou He the hermit, was one of the leading carvers working in the style of the so-called 'School of the Rustic Crystal Master'. We can also be sure that a workshop near Lake Tai at Huzhou or Wuxing produced bottles in this style and lacking any further evidence may well be the centre of production.

The fourth line *Bao po*, literally reads as 'holding jade'. Whilst this refers to the magical properties that jade can transfer to its owner, it also has another possible Daoist connotation; that of 'Jade Purity' (*Yuqing*), the highest of the three purities that rule over the three celestial realms of the Daoist pantheon.

Once again this assumes we are reading the inscription correctly. Again Moss, Tsang, and Graham, *The Art of the Chinese Snuff Bottle: The J & J Collection*, pp. 186-187, no. 104, translate this differently (though they are splitting the lines in to different numbers of characters). Their reading of the last line is 'A recluse (always strives to) preserve his true nature'. The last character, *po*, is actually incorrectly inscribed on the J & J bottle, being mistakenly written with a 'wood' radical rather than the 'jade' radical.

The subject matter and carving style can be confidently attributed to the School of the Rustic Crystal Master, without any doubts. The rugged wintry mountain scene, with leafless trees with bare limbs is a classic feature of the school, as is the use of the crystal material. However, the delicate and balanced calligraphy of the poetic inscription is unusual and in contrast to the rugged landscape. It is extremely rare to find the artist's name on the bottle. This would certainly mean that he was the head of his particular workshop and might even suggest that he was the initiator of the style.

(CBL C 567)

64 (two views)

65

Macaroni agate, with attractive 'worm-like' inclusions throughout in shades of white, creams and grey within a pale yellow-brown transparent stone, the narrow rounded sides with lion-mask fixed-ring handles below a cylindrical neck, very slightly concave rim, small mouth and well-hollowed interior, the oval foot ring slightly rounded and the base shallowly cut

1820-1880

Stopper: agate

Height: 5.6 cm
Mouth: 0.65 cm
Neck: 2.0 cm

According to Moss, Graham, and Tsang, *A Treasury of Chinese Snuff Bottles: The Mary and George Bloch Collection*, Vol. 2, Part 1, Quartz, pp. 58-60, no. 201, the term 'macaroniagate' is confined to the snuff-bottle lexicon and not used by mineralogists. It refers to a group of agate bottles with clusters of pale markings that have the appearance of randomly sliced macaroni. Most examples appear to be close in colour to the present example, though darker stones do exist. In the case of our bottle the inclusions appear as squirming worm-like amoeba rather than macaroni, and at a stretch resemble rather jumbled Chinese characters. Under close observation the concentric banding within each worm-like marking is very evident, giving different and subtle hues of white, grey, and cream depending on the width of the rings and which actually properly identifies the material as agate. The swarming effect of these unusually large inclusions in our bottle is further enhanced by the transparent nature of the yellow-brown transparent ground. They also point out the odd anomaly that this most beautiful and intriguing stone was only used in the creation of snuff bottles. Not a single work of art in any other genre has been identified made of macaroni agate. Rarely is their carved decoration other than the occasional lion-mask ring handle, as in this instance.

Another macaroni-type bottle of similar shape but without handles and less defined markings from ther Imperial Collection is illustrated in *Snuff Bottles in the Collection of the National Palace Museum*, p. 238, no. 339 and another is illustrated by Kleiner, *Chinese Snuff Bottles from the Burghley House Collection*, no. 98.

(CBL C 632)

66

Chalcedony agate possibly jasper, the main faces plain but slightly bulbous, the narrow sides rounded, the stone of an unusual pale-honey colour with areas of pale orange-red markings mostly to one narrow side and continuing to one main face, around the neck and across the foot, steep shoulders below a cylindrical neck, slightly concave rim, a large mouth and regular hollowing to the interior, a rounded oval foot ring and regular cut base

1800-1900

Height: 6.7 cm
Mouth: 0.9 cm
Neck: 2.1 cm

This rather mysterious stone is certainly a chalcedony agate, possibly a jasper, a more specific type.

The markings in this bottle are extremely abstract and could be open to many interpretations. In profile from one narrow side one could see a dragon, facing the main face one could see a large tailed fish in the darker markings or alternatively a fat swooping bat, if concentrating on the negative space. It also has a resemblance to hornbill bottles, which often use the red skin for decorative effect on the narrow sides of bottles. For two hornbill examples in this collection, see Nos. 164 and 165 in this catalogue.

The stone is warm in colour but cold to the touch. It appears weighty but is in fact quite light. The foot is short, the base is shallowly cut and the interior hollowing only satisfactory. All point to a probable nineteenth-century date of production.

(CBL C 619)

67

Banded agate, the stone with creamy brown-beige colour in the upper half of the bottle above varying wavy bands of grey, white, and beige in the centre section, the lower third being of a more transparent misty tone, wide rounded shoulders and cylindrical neck, a slightly concave rim, large mouth and well hollowed interior, a flat oval foot ring and regularly cut base

1800-1880

Stopper: tiger's eye

Height: 5.9 cm
Mouth: 0.85 cm
Neck: 1.7 cm

For a discussion of banded agate, see Moss, Graham, and Tsang, *A Treasury of Chinese Snuff Bottles: The Mary and George Bloch Collection*, Vol. 2, Part 1, Quartz, pp. 50-51, no. 198, where they discuss the source of the banded agate material by cutting of cross-sections from the outer edge of large rock geodes.

The markings in this bottle are very attractive. The obvious interpretation is of waves lapping at a shoreline, though any land or seascape could be envisaged. Perhaps even serried rows of rice fields receding to the distance. The possibilities are endless and part of the enjoyment of owning such a mercurial bottle.

See Lawrence, *Miniature Masterpieces from the Middle Kingdom: The Monimar Collection of Chinese Snuff Bottles*, pp. 120-121, no. 54 for a very similar bottle, where the author notes that the symbolic division of the bottle into two parts by the use of a natural inclusion might refer to an ancient Chinese concept focused on the belief that the sky was circular and was draped like a canopy above the earth with a hole at its centre to allow entry to heaven.

(CBL C 625)

68

Banded agate, the stone with a wide central horizontal band of pale brown stone between thin opaque white bands dividing a slightly darker brown transparent stone in the upper portion and slightly misty but transparent section below, the neck very slightly waisted, the rim slightly concave, the mouth regular and the interior exceedingly well hollowed, a flat oval foot ring and slightly convex base

1800-1880

Stopper: malachite with metal collar

Height: 5.5 cm
Mouth: 0.75 cm
Neck: 2.1 cm

The bottle is remarkably light in weight due to the magnificent degree of hollowing to the interior. It is also given a lighter appearance because of the thinness of the walls and the gradation of tone within the matrix from misty transparent at the base to darker at the neck. This is further emphasized by the slightly waisted or pinched neck with slightly flaring rim, which has the effect of raising the bottle up, albeit subtly.

The reading of the inclusions leaves multiple choices, which might include waves lapping at the shore or even the conceit that the bottle is actually wrapped in a cloth. A cloth tied around a vessel, be it a snuff bottle or otherwise, was a decorative device indicative of a gift. The practice followed the traditional custom at court of presenting any gift wrapped in precious brocade.

For a more flattened agate example see Hall, *Chinese Snuff Bottles XI: The Snowy Peaks Collection*, no. 51.

(CBL C 628)

65

66

67

68

69

Quartz, of irregular pebble shape, with six facetted sides, the matrix of the stone a very dark brown, almost black, large grey and beige areas have been edited to resemble rockwork, these have then been engraved with calligraphy which has touches of a beige inlay that has been highlighted with gilt, the darker areas of the stone to the top and one side of the bottle have been engraved and carved in low relief in a continuous winter figural scene, some areas of the grey matrix are beige in tone and others are almost white, the entire flat foot has been very delicately engraved with waves which partially continue up the side of the bottle

Signed : Shou He (Ju Shi-the Hermit)

Studio name: Shui Jing Dong (Cave of Watery Brightness)

Dated: Ding Zhou year-1817 or possibly 1877

Height: 6.2 cm
Mouth: 0.6 cm-0.8 cm (tapering)
Neck: no neck

Published: Chapman, 'The Chester Beatty Collection of Snuff Bottles', *Arts of Asia*, March-April, 1988, p. 60, fig 7.

The larger inscription engraved across five facets of the bottle reads:
Liang gong zhu hu
Gong shu zhen ren
Shou he ju shi
Bao po

This can be translated as:
Good lapidary carved (engraved) bottles
Shrink real man in bottle
Shou He (artist name) Ju Shi (hermit)
Holding jade

The second inscription engraved on one facet reads:
Ding chou zhong qiu zhi yue
Shui jing dong zhi

This can be translated as:
Ding chou year (1817 or 1877), middle autumn, 8th month
Cave of Watery Brightness or Made in the Crystal Cave (Studio name).

The Cave of Watery Brightness is apparently recorded as being on the shore of Lake Tai at Huzhou or Wuxing

For a full discussion of the reading of the first inscription on this bottle see the entry for an amethyst bottle No. 64 in this publication (which bears the identical inscription). This bottle has the addition of a date and a studio name. There is no question that both our bottles must be from the same workshop and presumably the hand of the same master. In all probability Shou He the hermit, was one of the leading carvers working in the style of the so-called 'School of the Rustic Crystal Master'. We can also be sure that a workshop near Lake Tai at Huzhou or Wuxing produced bottles in this style and lacking any further evidence may well be the centre of production.

Moss et al mention another similar bottle in the collection of the Marquess of Exeter, with similar calligraphy and cutting as well as the use of the same material that Moss assumes must come from the same workshop and probably the same hand. It is illustrated by Kleiner, *Chinese Snuff Bottles from the Burghley House Collection*, no. 83 but unfortunately the inscriptions and seals are not translated. The stone however appears like ours to be a quartz-like material wrapped around a darker core.

The subject matter and carving style on our bottle can be confidently attributed to the School of the Rustic Crystal Master. The rugged wintry mountain scene with a single figure holding a staff standing on rockwork and gazing across the mountains carved with pine, other trees, a small building and wispy clouds is a classic feature of the school. The wonderful and clever use of the crystal material, another feature of the school, must be applauded. In the hands of a lesser master, the inclusions could have proved unusable, but here the grey and beige inclusions have been cleverly utilized to form rocky outcrops that rise and fall in height in a naturalistic manner and which are the perfect vehicle for the calligraphic passages.

(CBL C 584)

69 (four views)

70

Agate, the main faces carved with circular panels derived from Han dynasty roof tiles (*wadang*), with a seal script character in each quadrant, the narrow sides rounded, the neck cylindrical, the rim slightly concave, a small mouth and regular hollowing, the stone graduating in colour from a dark brown at the neck to almost black at the simple flat oval foot

1800-1900

Height: 5.15 cm
Mouth: 0.5 cm
Neck: 1.7 cm

The four characters on the Han roof tiles are longevity symbols and read: *Yong Shou Wu Jiang*

Terminal roof tiles, *wadang*, were used to cap the ends of semi-circular tubular tiles under the eaves of the roofline. Tiles with molded designs were made as early as the Zhou period, but those with stylized characters are more readily associated with the Han dynasty (206 BCE-220 ACE). By this time these baked clay tiles, which probably started life as terminals on the roofs of temples and court structures, could be found on private residences as well. In particular Western Han tiles are typically divided in to two or four sections and the simplified calligraphy is adapted to fit the quadrants of a circle.

The interest of Qing scholars with the 'antique' has already been remarked upon in the entry for No. 11 in this publication, and this is yet another example of the interest and reverence for the past displayed on the miniature world of the snuff bottle.

The stone is quite unusual and appears to be a much darker version of the more often seen pale honey agate. Barely visible in the illustration is a very fine wide network of natural cracks within the matrix of the entire stone. Though they appear to be a natural fault, it is possible that the bottle survived a fire, which may have caused the stone to darken.

For an example of another 'Han tile' bottle in red overlay glass from the Carl F. Barron collection, see Moss, *The Barron Collection: Illustrated Handlist*, ICSBS Convention, Boston, 2008, p.23, no. 1625.

(CBL C 582)

71

Agate, one main face carved through a white inclusion on the otherwise grey-brown stone with an oval panel with a bird flying above plum (prunus) and rockwork, the other main face carved with another oval panel with a poetic seven-character relief inscription followed by an engraved seal, the neck cylindrical with a very wide mouth and quite well hollowed interior, the base cut flat and the centre scooped out to form a flat oval foot ring

1820-1900

Stopper: chalcedony agate (probably a conversion)

Height: 6.0 cm
Mouth: 0.95 cm
Neck: 1.7 cm

The inscription reads:

Yi zhi feng wu bian qing he followed by the seal *Pian yun*

This may be translated as:

'One branch scene (painting) immediately peaceful', followed by the seal, 'Piece of cloud'

The subject of plum blossoms (prunus) is a popular one. See Bartholomew, *Hidden Meanings in Chinese Art*, p. 35, nos. 1.8 and 1.8.1. The blossoms are emblematic of perseverance and purity. Blooming on withered old branches, the plum is not only a welcome sight in winter but also a symbol for vigor-

ous old age. There are five petals—an auspicious number as it represents the five blessings: old age, wealth, health, love of virtue, and a peaceful death. It is hard to distinguish what type of bird is incorporated in to the design on this bottle but we can probably assume that it depicts a magpie as the magpie, *xique*, and plum, *mei*, is a common theme that forms the rebus 'joyfully announcing the arrival of spring', *xibao chunxian*.

Unfortunately for the carver of this bottle, the white inclusion that was used to frame and form the scene did not sink as deep in to the stone as initially presumed. Therefore, he had to use the darker material of the base material to finish the oval border. This has the unfortunate effect of making it look as though the panel is chipped when it is not. The agate used is a semi-transparent material of slightly grey-brown colour that is livelier when held up to the light helping to silhouette the scene that is whiter at its deepest points.

The shape of the bottle is not the most satisfactory, nor is the degree of hollowing very fine. The stone is secondary in quality and the carving, whilst acceptable, is not remarkable. All such factors probably point to a late manufacture date, certainly not before 1800.

The stopper is actually drilled horizontally suggesting that it was almost certainly converted to a stopper for this bottle because it matched the bottle's material so well.

(CBL C 586)

72

Dendritic chalcedony, the bottle plain with rounded narrow sides, the variegated semi-translucent stone with rust-red inclusions to the upper third, creamy yellow-brown inclusions in the centre and green moss-like inclusions in the lower third, with some green encroaching up the bottle, the shoulders rounded, the neck very slightly waisted, the rim concave, a regular mouth but fairly well hollowed interior, a flat oval foot ring and shallowly cut base

1800-1900

Stopper: agate

Height: 6.3 cm
Mouth: 0.75 cm
Neck: 2.1 cm

The subject could just as easily be interpreted as terrestrial or celestial. It is certainly suggestive of a misty forest landscape below mountains with cloudy peaks but could also be read as a heavenly firmament with swirling clusters of expanding galaxies. Interestingly the shape and weight of the bottle encourage these two different possible readings. It is unusually horizontal in format, and its width helps to broaden the image, which sits very comfortably on a rather short foot that is given balance by having an edge that tapers outwards. The neck is very delicately pinched at its centre, which has the peculiar effect of making the bottle appear lighter. Additional to this the lapidary has done a very good job of hollowing the interior. Not only do these aspects lighten the actual weight of the bottle but it allows for a great deal of light to pass through the walls, enhancing the natural mossy inclusions held in suspension in the matrix of the material.

The practice of finding images within the matrix of a stone was popular and with a long history. Bringing out the natural designs that would otherwise languish in the stone was the perfect expression of a belief in the harmony between the natural world and humanity. The game of visual interpretation is akin to 'ink-play' paintings, as termed by Hugh Moss, see *JICSBS*, Autumn 1997, pp. 4.16, which is how the use of parti-coloured chalcedony bottles relates to the high art of painting. Ink-play in the painting tradition refers to the interpretation of random markings on absorbent papers or silks, made by mixtures of ink and water.

For bottles carved from a similarly-marked material, see Nicollier, *The Baur Collection*, pp. 300-301, nos. H 139-140.

(CBL C 595)

70

71

72

73

Jasper, the main faces plain and very slightly bulbous, the narrow sides rounded with very high quality large lion-mask handles with unusually small rings, the shoulders rounded below a cylindrical neck, a concave rim, a small mouth and very well hollowed interior, the extremely attractive stone of primarily dark green tone with inclusions of bright turquoise, rust-red and some yellow, a flat oval foot ring and regular cut base

1780-1860

Stopper: jadeite or glass imitating jadeite, metal collar

Height: 6.75 cm
Mouth: 0.6 cm
Neck: 2.35 cm

The lion-mask handles are of an unusually large size for the narrow side, and the mask is more than two-thirds the size of the ring which is carved as a horizontal oval rather than a vertical ring. The lion mask has a large bare forehead below small curls and thick brows over wide eyes and simple whiskers. Despite their massive appearance, when viewed from the main faces, they are remarkably low in profile and the rings are actually slightly concave which aids handling. The bottle has a satisfying formal integrity, which is enhanced by a great degree of internal hollowing. Whilst there is a good possibility that this bottle dates from the latter part of the eighteenth century, with no decoration other than the handles to guide us, it is advisable to leave the possibility open that the bottle might be of later manufacture.

The stone, which is opaque has rich turquoise-coloured veins and misty rust-red inclusions that generally run vertically through the stone, but with some paler blotches on the narrow sides and one yellowish streak that runs diagonally across the stone like a flash of lightning, which is apt as the inclusions on this bottle are reminiscent of a dark tempestuous stormy sky or a vicious squall at sea and positively throb with energy. According to Moss, Graham, and Tsang, *A Treasury of Chinese Snuff Bottles: The Mary and George Bloch Collection*, Vol. 2, Part 1, Quartz, pp. 67-69 no. 204, the various colours found in jasper which is a crypto-crystalline quartz are caused by various oxides. The red is due to ferric oxide, the green to ferrous oxide and hydroxide, yellow to hydrated ferric oxide and brown to manganese oxide. The authors suggest that Eastern Siberia may have been a Qing-dynasty source for the Chinese lapidary and it was almost certainly mined in Xinjiang province. The brilliant, variegated markings in jasper provide a wealth of potential for the viewer's imagination.

See also ibid, pp. 74-75 for a jasper bottle of similar material sometimes known as bloodstone.

(CBL C 598)

74

Quartz, possibly jasper, the main faces slightly bulbous and the narrow sides rounded, the attractive stone with an opaque upper portion on one side and a corresponding opaque lower portion on the other side with a matrix of fractured needle-like cells elsewhere, a more transparent orange-brown colour to the other parts with circular inclusions, the neck cylindrical, the rim very slightly concave, the mouth and interior hollowing are regular, a flat oval foot ring with the base regularly cut

1800-1900

Stopper: jadeite

Height: 6.5 cm
Mouth: 0.6 cm
Neck: 2.3 cm

Whilst the stone is definitely a form of quartz, it is difficult to be sure exactly which variety we are dealing with here. In colouration, opacity, and the fractured nature of the inclusions it appears to be a jasper, though it may also be an unusual agate.

The possible interpretations of the natural inclusions in this bottle are endless. The lighter almost transparent patch on the lower half of one main face might suggest a bug-eyed fish swimming down a steep underwater rock face, whilst the reverse side could be the sharp edge of a coral reef. Alternatively, it is easy to see this as a mountainous landscape receding to an endless sky, and the reverse as water passing under a sedimentary rock. To the twentieth century viewer the fractured needle-like structure of the matrix could appear almost cubist. The possibilities go on and it matters not. Merely the active participation of the viewer is required to bring the art to life.

There is a pleasant formal quality to this bottle enhanced by the soft rounded edges to the main faces, narrow sides and the shoulders. The large solid foot is neither too short nor too high, and despite the regular hollowing to the interior the bottle is quite light in weight. Once again a wide date range for production seems the inevitable choice with so little 'decoration' to help establish a definitive period of manufacture.

For two jasper bottles with similar colouration see Moss, Graham, and Tsang, *A Treasury of Chinese Snuff Bottles, The Mary and George Bloch Collection*, Vol. 2, Part 1, Quartz, pp. 70-71 and pp.76-78 nos. 205 and 208.

(CBL C 587)

73

74 (two views)

75

Jasper, carved through an orange-brown inclusion on one main face with a cricket atop a gourd cricket cage engraved with cash symbols, the other main face also carved through an orange-brown inclusion with a seated monkey and the remainder of the design comprising the rock it sits on and wispy plumes carved from the olive-green and rust-red ground, the stone fading to a rusty brown at the narrow edges with some creamy pink markings to one edge, the neck cylindrical, a slightly concave rim, a narrow mouth and regular hollowing to the interior, a flat oval foot ring and regularly cut base

Official School, 1780-1880

Height: 7.3 cm
Mouth: 0.7 cm
Neck: 2.5 cm

A large natural flaw in the stone that runs vertically through the bottle on one main face and halfway down the other face is cleverly 'hidden' within the scene. It is visible in the illustration starting at the foot and running up the left edge of the large rock behind the monkey and is then incorporated in to the swirling plume that rises to the shoulder and continues around the base of the neck of the bottle to appear on the other side where it runs to the right antennae of the cricket before disappearing back in to the stone.

The depiction of the cricket is masterful. Its body has been fully delineated and its large rear legs appear to be in process of rubbing against each other to begin its distinctive song. Note also the delightful touch of the cricket actively cleaning its left antennae with its front leg. The cash symbols are extremely well rendered and whilst there is no reason for the artist to carve out the negative space in the mouth of the gourd vessel, it is actually very effective in encouraging a feeling of an empty space within. The placid monkey on the other side of the bottle sits rather comfortably with its feet crossed and has its fur lightly incised throughout the body. The slight cock of the head takes the attention of the viewer to the wispy plume that rises behind him and leads the eye around the bottle.

According to Moss, Graham, and Tsang, *The Art of the Chinese Snuff Bottle, The J & J Collection*, p. 598, no. 359, the design of a cricket, or a cricket on its cage may be intended to exhort the recipient to maintain loyalty to the emperor. Whatever the possible reading, it does mirror the immense popularity of the cricket in Chinese society. They were enjoyed for both their singing but perhaps more importantly for their fighting prowess. The best crickets could make a fortune for their owners and thus the use of cash symbols on the cricket cage can add another layer of meaning.

The depiction of crickets became a very popular one on snuff bottles particularly during the first half of the nineteenth century and particularly so during the reign of the Daoguang emperor (1820-1850) at the porcelain factories at Jingdezhen, when numerous examples were made, presumably at the height of the craze. This same fascination with crickets was also mirrored in the vast production of gourd cricket cages during the late eighteenth and early nineteenth century.

Moss et al, ibid, p. 236, no. 145, illustrate a jasper bottle, with five layers of colour depicting a similar cricket also cleaning its antennae and standing on a gourd cricket cage, which they date 1780-1870.

The same authors also illustrate another jasper bottle, see Moss, Graham, and Tsang, *A Treasury of Chinese Snuff Bottles: The Mary and George Bloch Collection*, Vol. 2, Part 2, Quartz, pp. 346-347, no. 308, carved with a monkey seated on simple rocks that is almost an identical mirror image of our monkey down to the overlapping feet, the tucked tail, the short thick arms, the finely engraved fur, the facial expression with long nose and furrowed brow and the pose looking back over its shoulder; the striking material is also similar. The authors give a wider possible dating for that bottle which they date between 1740 and 1850.

According to Williams, *Outlines of Chinese Symbolism and Art Motives*, p. 277, the species of monkey most common in China are the yellow monkey, *macacus thibetanus*, of the Tibetan borderlands, and the golden brown monkey, *Rhinopethicus roxellanae*, of Szechuan and Gansu. This makes the choice of stone especially suitable. The monkey, whilst associated with trickery, is supposed to be able to bestow health, protection, and success by keeping away malicious spirits.

According to Bartholomew, in *Hidden Meanings in Chinese Art*, p. 118, no. 5.20.1, the monkey, *hou*, is a pun for a high ranking noble equivalent to a marquess, *hou* and is often depicted clambering amongst pine, or climbing on a bag, poking at a wasps' nest and carrying young, all of which relate to the same theme of ascending to high rank.

(CBL C 588)

75 (two views)

76

Jasper, the main faces plain and slightly bulbous, the narrow sides rounded, the neck cylindrical, the rim very slightly concave, the mouth and the hollowing regular, the very attractive stone predominately yellow brown on one main face with vertical swirling inclusions of rust-red and grey-black in a sweeping movement, the other face predominately olive-green in colour with diagonal inclusions of red, black, and yellow-brown, the entire stone with minute flakes of glinting gold, a flat oval base

1800-1900

Stopper: clear glass over a green stained metal to imitate jadeite

Height: 5.75 cm
Mouth: 0.7 cm
Neck: 1.9 cm

This most unusual stone is mesmerizing. The colour is quite rare in hard-stone production and very appealing. The brilliant variegated abstract markings provide multiple readings for the imaginative mind willing to linger over the natural stone. For the modern viewer familiar with the photos sent back from the depths of space by the two Spacecraft Voyagers1 and 2, one might be forgiven for seeing the rings of Saturn or the swirling clouds of Jupiter that appear to spin around the surface of the bottle. It certainly has the appearance of a celestial body, and perhaps when it was made it did indeed bring to mind much closer celestial bodies like the moon or perhaps even the sun. There is a haunting quality in the dark patch which though opaque appears almost transparent because of the effect of appearing through the 'skin' of yellow and rust red inclusions. One could also read it in a more down-to-earth manner as a yellow large bat with wings outstretched and enveloping the sides, its head centred on the black patch. The Chinese word for bat, *fu*, is the same as the words for blessings and riches, and when combined with clouds, *yun*, one can easily read in to the red inclusions on this bottle, it forms the rebus 'May you have good fortune or luck', *fuyun,* the word *yun* for cloud is homophonous with the word for fortune, *yun*.

The bottle has a very satisfying form and the lack of any surface decoration in the form of handles, engraved decoration or calligraphy, allows the capacious inclusions within the stone to realize their full potential. The bottle is quite well hollowed, of a light weight, and sits comfortably on its flat oval base, which happily does not truncate the vessel. Whilst possibly dating to the late eighteenth century, a nineteenth-century date is more likely.

(CBL C 605)

77

Jasper, one main face carved in low relief with a plum tree (prunus) rising from rocks and cleverly disguising a flaw line in the stone, the other face plain, both very slightly bulbous, the narrow sides rounded, the neck cylindrical, the rim very slightly concave, the mouth and hollowing regular, the stone of dark olive-green colour with attractive rust-red inclusions throughout and a solid rust-red area at the partially-rounded flat oval foot ring, a shallowly cut base

1800-1900

Stopper: disc of malachite in metal collar

Height: 5.6 cm
Mouth: 0.7 cm
Neck: 1.95 cm

This variety of jasper is sometimes been called bloodstone. See Stevens, *The Collector's Book of Snuff Bottles*, nos. 499 and 509-513. It appears that that term should really only apply to stones in the green and red range of the opaque jasper material. Initially our bottle appears to be black and red in colour but in fact the dark ground of the stone is on close inspection a very dark olive-green colour.

The carving of the rockwork and plum tree is most exquisite and of the finest quality. The handling of the rockwork with layers of low-relief rocks spreading out like a deck of cards, brings to mind that on bottle No. 83, in this collection and may suggest a link between the hard-stone workshops that produced them.

Certainly we again have master craftsmen at work. The juxtaposition of the red and dark green material forms an evocative backdrop to the plum, perhaps suggestive of a winter landscape with rising mountains or a nearby cliff face.

The subject of plum blossoms (prunus) is a popular one. See Bartholomew, *Hidden Meanings in Chinese Art*, p. 35, no. 1.8 and 1.8.1. The blossoms are emblematic of perseverance and purity. Blooming on withered old branches, the plum is not only a welcome sight in winter but also a symbol for vigorous old age. Five petals are an auspicious number and represent the five blessings: old age, wealth, health, love of virtue, and a peaceful death.

A nineteenth-century date would appear appropriate for this bottle, although the quality of the carving might suggest it is earlier.

(CBL C 606)

76

77

78

Agate, of bulbous form, the main faces rounded and bulbous, the narrow sides gently rounded, the extremely attractive stone of orange and reddish-orange-brown tone with a matrix of cell-like fractures in olive-green and black which is more dense on one side and almost web-like on the other, a tall very slightly tapering neck, a small mouth and well hollowed interior, a simple flat oval foot

1750-1850

Stopper: jadeite with metal collar

Height: 4.8 cm
Mouth: 0.55 cm
Neck: 1.7 cm

This is an intriguing bottle. The inclusions in this bottle are very much reminiscent of realgar, a toxic arsenic compound much valued in Daoist alchemical practice. Small amounts were mixed in elixirs as a hallucinogen to help enter a transcendent state. Its use as an actual material for snuff bottles proved impossible, as the material had a tendency to decompose upon prolonged exposure to sunlight, hence its fractured appearance in other works of art made from the material and, perhaps more importantly, because the material is very poisonous. For a rare ruyi sceptre in realgar, see Christie's, New York, 19 September 2007, lot 27. The surface of our bottle resembles very closely the fractured surface of the sceptre. Large quantities of glass bottles imitating realgar were made, see nos. 198-200 in this collection, but few stones come close to naturally resembling the material. This is one of the few exceptions and a true masterpiece.

The formal integrity of this bottle is unsurpassed. It is one of the most satisfying bottles both to see and to hold. The degree of hollowing is unnecessarily fine considering that is not visible, but this does add a certain attractive lightness in the hand, and allows at the end of the day for an extra pinch or two of snuff. The transition from foot to body is seamless, and the bulbous nature of the body has the effect of expanding the surface direction outwards towards the viewer. The gentle tapering of the neck quietly finishes off the vessel.

The resemblance to realgar would surely not have gone un-noticed.

According to Bartholomew, *Hidden Meanings in Chinese Art,* p. 283, no. 10.17.6, it was a common practice in ancient times, on the fifth day of the fifth month (the most inauspicious 'poisonous' day of the year) for adults to drink a realgar wine, *xionhuangjiu,* to ward off evil. The wine combined powdered realgar (one assumes minute amounts), and the sliced roots of sweet flag, *changpu,* also known as calamus, *acorus gramineus.* Therefore, it is highly likely that a stone that resembled realgar would be seen as serving the same purpose, to ward off evil.

Before an image even springs to mind when interpreting a reading of the matrix of the stone, the initial reaction, because of the actual fractured nature of the material is one of immense heat in its formation. This is amplified by the richness of the fiery yellow, orange, and red range of the stone. Volcanic lava flows, with bright glowing magma topped by dark hardening crusts and vented fissures come immediately to mind. But as in all things there is balance of opposites. On handling the extreme coldness of the stone becomes apparent and the imagery immediately changes to that of ice floes breaking up above dark deep bodies of water, or even the pebbles at the bottom of a lake or stream viewed through the prism of clear cool water.

(CBL C 607)

78 (two views)

79

Quartz, of fish form, the fan-tailed fish with high-arched back and finely carved scales, the underside softly rounded with two small fins indicated to the sides, a deep undercut or hollowed area between the body and the tail, a very small mouth neatly cut, the semi-transparent misty white stone with areas of yellowish-orange and pale rust inclusions

1800-1900

Length: 7.2 cm
Mouth: 0.3 cm
Neck: no neck

As mentioned in an earlier entry, the fish is an extremely popular subject in Chinese art. This example almost certainly depicts a goldfish, *jinyu*, which is homophonous with the term meaning 'gold and jade', i.e. wealth. The second sound, *yu*, also represents abundance or plenty and given as a gift, this meaning would certainly be well understood.

The lips of the fish have been very carefully delineated and form the mouth of the bottle itself. The mouth is exceedingly small and the degree of hollowing quite acceptable given the narrow opening. Clearly this carving was intended as a snuff bottle from its inception and was not, as some fish bottles are, a conversion from a fondling piece. The bottle sits very comfortably on its rounded belly, tipping slightly to one side but supported by the fan-like tail. The stone is unusual. It is a misty quartz material with turnip-like inclusions within the matrix and soft yellow-orange and pale rust inclusions that are reminiscent of carnelian agate.

For a jade fish of slightly less arched form but with a 'hollowed' fan-like tail, see *Masterpieces of Snuff Bottles in the Palace Museum*, p. 137, no. 130.

For other nephrite fish bottles see nos. 12, 24, 25, and 54 in this collection. An example in chalcedony and another in carnelian are illustrated by Moss, Graham, and Tsang, *A Treasury of Chinese Snuff Bottles: The Mary and George Bloch Collection*, Vol. 2, Part 1, Quartz, pp. 174-177, nos. 245 and 246.

(CBL C 759)

80

Agate, a raised chrysanthemum flower-head carved on each main face and simple elongated panel handles on the narrow sides, the neck cylindrical, the stone of semi-transparent grey colour with a few minor brown inclusions, a slightly concave oval base

1780-1880

Stopper: glass imitating jadeite

Height: 4.7 cm
Mouth: unknown (stopper not removable)
Neck: 1.5 cm

See Bartholomew, *Hidden Meanings in Chinese Art*, p. 175, 7.11 for a full discussion of the chrysanthemum, *juhua*. It is an important flower in Chinese symbolism, representing as it does autumn and longevity because of its hardiness; it blooms when most flowers wither under the onslaught of frost and icy winds. It also represents the flower of the ninth moon. During the Han dynasty people drank chrysanthemum wine on the ninth day of the ninth lunar month in order to prolong their lives. As the 'hermit' among flowers it is closely associated with the famous eastern Jin poet Tao Yuanming who wrote poetry in their honor. The first character of its name, *ju*, is a pun for 'dwell', *ju*,

As a shape, the chrysanthemum flowerhead was used widely in Imperial ceramics from the Song dynasty onwards, being a particular favorite of the southern kilns. Its use continued in the Ming and Qing periods, particularly during the eighteenth century when it was a favorite of the Yongzheng and Qianlong emperors, as attested to by the large number of exquisite fine porcelains, jades, lacquers, and paintings in the Imperial collections today.

The bottle is a simple small shape and perhaps the foot lacks the broadness necessary to support the weight of the body. However the simplicity has its merits and the delicate grooving of the petals counterbalances the plainness of the handles. The bottle has two small holes drilled on the foot edge, which serve no apparent purpose.

For another rare example of a clear crystal bottle carved with a flowerhead, possibly a chrysanthemum, see Hall, *Chinese Snuff Bottles II*, p. 56, no. 38. The same publication illustrates a range of monochrome and single overlay glass bottles that are similarly carved with single flowerhead designs and which may be the inspiration behind the much more rare quartz examples, pp. 106-103, no.s. 86-93.

(CBL C 635)

79

80

81

Chalcedony agate, of pebble shape, one main face carved through a creamy pink-white inclusion with two confronted moths or possibly butterflies, their markings clearly delineated, set against a large area of mostly transparent reddish-brown stone which pales in colour towards an amber at the narrow rounded sides and continues on the other face, the mouth quite large and well hollowed to the interior, a simple flat oval foot

1800-1880

Height: 6.0 cm
Mouth: 0.55 cm
Rim (no neck): 1.1-1.3 cm across (oval)

The first question to address is what classification of Lepidoptera, these delightful creatures belong to, butterfly, *rhopalocera*, or moths, *heterocera*. The differences between them are subtle, although in fact moths have existed for many millions of years longer than their relative newcomer, the butterfly. The fact that moths generally fly at night and butterflies mostly in the day is not really going to help us in identification unless, we consider the dark backdrop to indicate night-time or alternatively a burning sun.

The antenna is usually the best way to identify a butterfly from a moth. The butterfly normally has small knobs at the end whilst a moth's are either feather-like or thin and plain. Here we appear to have no knobs, which suggest a moth's antenna, though some butterfly species are plain. We can hardly expect the craftsmen to have felt this minute difference to have been important. Typically butterflies have brightly coloured wings and moths dull-coloured ones, though often with subtle markings. Here the degree of attention to patterning and shifts in gradation, suggest that these are the wings of butterflies but with a degree of stylization it is hard to be sure. Most butterflies have slender hairless bodies whilst moths have a fat abdomens and furry bodies. Here we have something in between, but perhaps the rings on the lower abdomen are meant to be indications of fur. So what decision do we arrive at? The more likely species is moths, with the caveat that they might be butterflies.

Historically the depiction of two facing butterflies, *hudie*, is a well known and popular one found in paintings and the decorative arts, and forms the rebus 'Joyful encounter', *xi xianfeng*. According to Bartholomew, *Hidden Meanings in Chinese Art*, p. 41, no. 2.5.1, two butterflies signify marital happiness but can also refer to unexpected meetings between friends.

For a very similar chalcedony pebble bottle with a darker ground material from the Man Lung and Floria Hung Collection, see Hui, Kwong and Sin, ed., *A Congregation of Snuff Bottle Connoisseurs*, pp. 160-161, no. 194. Another with the bottle lobed to form a melon, see Christie's Hong Kong, 1 November 1994, lot 1298. A white overlay glass example was illustrated in an advertisement for Asiantiques in the ICSBS *Journal*, Spring 1994, p. 33.

Moss, Graham, and Tsang, *A Treasury of Chinese Snuff Bottles: The Mary and George Bloch Collection*, Vol. 6, Part 2, Arts of the Fire, p. 524, no. 1234, mention that many catalogue descriptions (including one of my own in *The Blair Bequest: Chinese Snuff Bottles in the Princeton University Art Museum*, no. 295) confuse moths and butterflies, most often because of negative connotations associated with the moth in the West. Hence the overzealous attention to detail in this entry. The authors further point out that that in China the brows of lovely woman were called 'moth brows' and that coyly arched eyebrows were called 'moths rising up'.

As a miniature work of art, the use of the pink inclusions to form these dancing moths is masterful. The curves of the leading wing edges are wonderfully mirrored and form a beautiful sweeping S-shape that has the effect of pulling the moths together. The negative space between the moths can also be read as either a double-gourd shape or perhaps even a yin-yang symbol set within the confines of the perfectly-shaped ovoid bottle. It stands perfectly on its flat oval base and this horizontal truncation is mirrored in the handling of the horizontal rim of the mouth. The fine degree of hollowing also allows for a suitable amount of light to pass through the walls and further highlight the scene. This is a great example, where despite the bottle probably dating to the nineteenth century, the quality is equal, if not superior, to many pieces made a century earlier.

(CBL C 618)

82

Shadow agate, cleverly carved on one main face, using both white and dark inclusions with two horses, the other face plain with some inclusions, one resembling a running figure, the remaining stone of semi-transparent grey colour, the neck cylindrical, the rim slightly concave, a small mouth and well hollowed to the interior, a simple flat oval foot ring and regularly cut base

Official School, 1750-1850

Stopper: coral *chilong* on green-stained ivory or bone collar

Height: 6.5 cm
Mouth: 0.75 cm
Neck: 1.9 cm

The name 'Official School' was coined by Hugh Moss, to identify an extremely broad range of agate bottles. This large and loose-knit group was designated 'Group B' by Moss in *Chinese Snuff Bottles of the Silica or Quartz Group*. As Moss admits, this uninspiring name that covered such a diverse group never really gained common currency. Moss believes the group is strongly connected to the court, though not always specifically Imperial, and therefore chose the term 'Official School' as much of the subject matter is ideally suited to the official class, those scholars appointed by the Emperor to administer his state. Workshops catering to the hard-stone market were established in Beijing but the centres of Gaungzhou, Suzhou, and elsewhere must surely have also catered to these patrons. Plain and decorated bottles fall in to the group.

Of the decorated bottles, many are shadow agates that use dark inclusions in the stone to form 'silhouette' pictures, a lesser number use a creamy-white inclusion carved in cameo to form the scene. On rare occasions the two methods are used in combination. This is one such rare example. Two others are worthy of comparison. One depicts three goats and the sun (see Moss, Graham, and Tsang, *A Treasury of Chinese Snuff Bottles: The Mary and George Bloch Collection*, Vol. 2, Part 2, Quartz, pp. 312-313, no. 297) and the other depicts two horses and a tree (see Moss, Graham, and Tsang, *The Art of the Chinese Snuff Bottle: The J & J Collection*, Vol. 1, p. 222, no. 134). All three bottles must surely be linked at least by workshop, if not by individual craftsmen, and all are masterpieces of the genre. A fourth bottle depicting two horses cut in cameo from a white inclusion also bears comparison (see Moss, Graham, and Tsang, *The Art of the Chinese Snuff Bottle: The J & J Collection*, Vol. 1, p. 246, no.153).

The white horse of our example is carved in relief from the outermost inclusion. The mane and tail are formed by simple engraved strokes, as is the hair just above the hooves. The eyes are more deeply engraved using slightly geometric strokes. All three features can be found on the horses in both the J & J bottles cited, though admittedly difficult to see in the illustrations. However more obvious is the similarity in the treatment of the horses' legs. Moss notes that this might be no more than a general style for carving horses, but the fact that the leg positions, particularly the hind legs and the raising of the foreleg furthest from the viewer are perhaps more than coincidental. The tails also all fall straight down to hoof level on the outside rear leg. The carver here has also made good use of the darker inclusion that sits beneath the white inclusion. Rather than edit out, perhaps leaving an unsightly cavity behind the horse's head, it has been left and resembles the horse's warm breath on a cold morning. The darker and smaller horse below is lightly edited in silhouette from a two-colour dark inclusion. It is unfortunate that the placement of the inclusions dictated that the cameo depiction had to be cut above the darker one. The lighter material, coupled with the convex nature of cameo, has the effect of reading as foreground, whilst the darker patch, which is slightly concave due to editing, has the opposite effect. The corollary of this is that the larger horse appears to be floating above the darker horse rather than receding in to the background as perspective dictates. On the other hand the carver may actually have intended this difference of scale. According to Moss et al, op cit, p. 246, no. 153, the depiction of two horses, one well fed, and the other not (which might be implied by the scale of our horses) is a reference to Confucian duty. The fat horse represents the official who takes

advantage of his position and becomes wealthy at others expense, whilst the thin horse represents the honest official who strives to care for other people at his own cost.

The reverse side of the bottle has a few inclusions that could represent a cursory landscape but also has a darker patch at the neck, which might be interpreted as a running figure perhaps the groom chasing down his steeds.

For another Official School agate bottle depicting two white horses on a similar form bottle from the Carl F. Barron collection, see Moss, *The Barron Collection: Illustrated Handlist*, ICSBS Convention, Boston, 2008, p.5, no. 4005.

(CBL C 642)

82 (two views)

82 (detail)

83

Chalcedony, one main face carved in high relief through a deep, almost turquoise olive-green inclusion with a smiling large-mouthed Buddhist lion and a bushy-tailed cub playing with a ribboned-ball above rockwork, the other face and narrow sides plain, the stone of semi-transparent grey tone with some swirling whiter-grey inclusions visible on the reverse face, the shoulders sloping to a cylindrical neck, flat rim, regular mouth and hollowing, a flat oval foot ring and a regularly cut base

Official School, 1800-1880

Stopper: ice-green jadeite

Height: 6.6 cm
Mouth: 0.7 cm
Neck: 2.3 cm

Published: Chapman, 'The Chester Beatty Collection of Snuff Bottles', *Arts of Asia*, March-April, 1988, p. 61, fig 6.

The lion, *shi*, the 'king of beasts' was first introduced to China as tribute. As a result of the introduction of Buddhism, where it figures as the defender of the law and protector of sacred buildings, it became a popular and powerful symbol in the arts. Stone or bronze lions were regularly used as doorway guardians. The character for lion, *shi*, is a pun on the words for 'master' *shi*, and 'generations' *shi*. Williams, *Outlines of Chinese Symbolism and Art Motives*, p. 254, proposed that the subject of two lions playing with an embroidered ball might have the same significance as two dragons contesting the pearl of supremacy. According to Bartholomew, *Hidden Meanings in Chinese Art*, p. 116, no. 5.17.1 and 5 17.2, a large lion, *dashi*, and a small lion, *xiaoshi*, form the rebus 'May you and your descendants achieve high rank, *taishi shaoshi*.'

A large number of late Qianlong and Jiaqing porcelain bottles from Jingdezhen molded with designs of this subject are known. They were made for the Palace and bear the appropriate Imperial reign marks. See No. 245 in this publication.

Moss, Graham, and Tsang, *A Treasury of Chinese Snuff Bottles: The Mary and George Bloch Collection*, Vol. 2, Part 2, Quartz, p. 354, no. 311, note that a certain type of chalcedony that has planes of green running through it is used because of its colour for a range of subjects where the colour green was of significance, most often frogs, lotus, and crickets. The significance of green lions is uncertain but perhaps the colour was chosen simply to emulate jade. Whatever the reason, we are left with a fascinating image. The carver has had some trouble with a central flaw, which runs vertically between the lion and cub, causing a rather un-natural break between the two subjects. However this has been quite cleverly handled by turning the cub on its head, so to speak, so that its magnificent bushy tail forms an almost flame-like torch, distracting the viewer from the flaw. It is almost certain that the flaw did not come to light until the carving process began.

This is an unusually large bottle in overall breadth and depth, which gives it a massive feel in the hand, perhaps a little cumbersome, but in keeping with the majesty of the subject. Rather unusually the subject itself, cut from the green inclusion, continues to the base of the foot ring, rather than stopping above it. This may be a unique feature, singular to this bottle. Certainly it is not rare on bottles with flat bases where the decoration naturally ends at the base and sometimes even continues over it. Occasionally on bottles with a foot ring, the markings in the stone will continue naturally to the foot ring, but the carving always stops above. Perhaps the flaw line required this type of truncation. The reverse side of the bottle is plain but the stone does have some creamy-grey swirling inclusions that add some movement to the otherwise dull stone.

The ungainly size, slightly ponderous carving, uninspired shape, and regular degree of hollowing all point to a nineteenth-century production for this bottle.

(CBL C 639)

84

Agate, carved on one main face in high relief from orange-brown and white inclusions with a monkey seated on rockwork near a horse tethered to a post, all on a rocky promontory which is surrounded by a halo of semi-opaque creamy-white inclusion within the otherwise transparent grey stone, which is lightly engraved with further rocks or possibly a stylized tree, the other face plain and mostly transparent, the narrow sides rounded, the shoulders sloping below a cylindrical neck, the rim very slightly concave, the mouth regular and quite well hollowed, a large oval foot ring and regularly cut base

Official School, 1800-1880

Stopper: glass imitating coral, glass bead finial imitating a pearl

Height: 7.25 cm
Mouth: 0.75 cm
Neck: 2.4 cm

Whilst the use of two layers of contrasting relief (parti-coloured cameo relief) is not uncommon to this school, particularly with horses as the main subject, the use of orange-brown and white inclusions on a transparent grey stone is most unusual. It is also quite unusual in that the horse, albeit only slightly, is carved in a more three-dimensional pose, with the head turned outwards towards the viewer on a slightly different plane than the rest of the body, rather than as normally depicted, with a more two-dimensional aspect. Admittedly our horse is not as rounded or as three-dimensional as the examples illustrated by Moss, Graham, and Tsang, *A Treasury of Chinese Snuff Bottles: The Mary and George Bloch Collection*, Vol. 2, Part 2, Quartz, pp. 344-345, no. 307, but it is certainly an improvement on the somewhat static nature of the majority of the genre. Our horse is tied to a very typical horse post. The majority of images of horse posts depict a beehive-shaped brick structure supporting a cylindrical pole surmounted by a lotus-bud or ovoid finial. Occasionally, the rope or rein that ties them is looped under a loose-ring as in our example. The subject of a tethered horse suggests unrealized potential and expresses a wish for speedy promotion for a deserving candidate. As a gift to an official sitting ongoing examinations it is very fitting. The clever use of a minute portion of the orange-brown inclusion to depict the eye of the horse shows some mastery.

Having said that however, it is interesting to compare the monkey on this bottle with a monkey depicted on another 'Official School' jasper bottle in this collection, No. 75. It is carved with a monkey of similar colour seated on simple rocks also looking over its shoulder. The handling of this monkey however, whilst similar enough to draw conclusions of the same school at work— note the comparable pose, long nose, furrowed brow and awkward feet—does not allow us to suggest as early a date of production. This bottle is clearly of inferior craftsmanship than the jasper bottle, the stone is of a less superior type, and the overall concept is a little heavy-handed. A date somewhere in the nineteenth century seems most plausible.

According to Williams, *Outlines of Chinese Symbolism and Art Motives*, p. 278, the monkey, whilst associated with trickery, is supposed to be able to bestow health, protection, and success by keeping away malicious spirits. According to Bartholomew, *Hidden Meanings in Chinese Art*, p. 118, no. 5.21, the monkey, *hou*, is a pun for a high ranking noble equivalent to a marquess, *hou*.

It is often depicted in combination with a horse. She also notes that 'Early agricultural guidebooks, such as Han E's *Sishi zuanyao* (Essential Notes for the Four Seasons) and Li Shizhen's *Bencao gangmu* (Compendium of Materia Medica, 1578) advised breeders and herders to tether a monkey in the stable in order to keep their horses in good health and prevent skin diseases.' She continues that 'the gibbon (monkey) and horse were symbolic images used in early Tang-dynasty literature to represent the 'willfulness and wayward nature of human desires.'

(CBL C 645)

83

84

85

Agate, one main face carved through an opaque chalky cream inclusion with a mythical horse seated on jagged 'cog-like' waves, a plume of vapor rising from its mouth and supporting a moon with two bats flying nearby, the other face carved from a more yellowish-cream inclusion with a large cat, probably a tiger, clambering down a rock below a simple pine near a swirling patch of concentric oval rings lightly carved with a five-clawed dragon coiling around clouds, the narrow sides mostly plain and rounded below the cylindrical neck, the rim very slightly concave, the mouth small, the interior quite well hollowed, the stone of a semi-transparent brown and grey colour, a slightly rounded oval foot ring with regular cut base

Official School, 1750-1850

Stopper: jadeite

Height: 6.5 cm
Mouth: 0.6 cm
Neck: 2.3 cm

Here we have a bottle that uses at least two layers of contrasting relief; three if we include the pale grey silhouette that forms the clouds and parts of the waves, though this is really just a thinner part of the chalky white inclusion. The effect though is that of an additional colour. Once again we have a horse subject so beloved of the school but here we have something quite unique that is dramatically different from other common examples. The horse is definitely mythical, as expressed in its ability to float on water, the strange catfish-like whiskers on its cheeks and the plume of vapors that emanates from its mouth and supports the moon. The curious jagged 'cog-like' waves appear to be unique and may well be the 'finger-print' of this particular artist. The subject of bats, *fu*, hovering above waves or the sea, *hai,* form the rebus 'May your blessings be as deep as the Eastern Sea', *furu donghai*; bats in pairs, *shaung*, form the rebus 'May you have double blessings' and the combination of bats and clouds, *yun*, 'May you have good fortune or luck', *fuyun*. Generally the horse, *ma*, is considered an emblem of speed and perseverance, but here in its sedentary magical guise it may have alternative readings relating to Daoism or Buddhism. In Daoism shamans experimented with herbs and other medicinal substances that eventually became the basis for Chinese herbal medicine. One of the tonic formulas that the shamans experimented with used seahorse, *hai ma*. It is supposed to help vitality and promote brain activity and spiritual development. The seahorse is reportedly known as 'fallen baby dragon' in folklore, see McCann, *Herbal Training Formulas in the Taoist Tradition*, The Tao of Healing web page (Henry N. Mc Cann, III). There is a slim possibility that the depiction, whilst not literally a seahorse, *Hippocampus kelloggi*, may represent such an idea.

The other side depicts a tiger or possibly an over-fed cat. If this smiling feline with its Cheshire grin is indeed a cat, *mao*, then the rebus formed can be read as 'age eighty to ninety', *mao*, a symbol of longevity. This is normally depicted in combination with a butterfly, but here the small pine tree that rises from the very rock on which the cat sits, is just as fitting a longevity symbol. More likely, it depicts a tiger, *hu*, which is a much more appropriate animal in combination with the lightly carved Imperial five-clawed dragon that emerges from clouds carved in the oval patch of grey and white concentric rings nearby that the animal appears to be looking at in such a surprised manner. The dragon, *long*, and the tiger represent the *yin* and the *yang* protective guardians and each is one of the four divine animals, *siling*.

The carving technique, whilst in some respects singular (the 'cog-like' waves), is of the very finest quality in terms of design and execution. The use of the various colours of inclusion and the balanced spacing of the scene are masterful. The stone is of a good quality and the overall shape and size satisfactory. The degree of hollowing is regular and the foot well balanced. This bottle may well date to the eighteenth century but might also be a very fine example of the best that the nineteenth century carvers could produce.

(CBL C 646)

85 (two views)

86

Agate, of pebble shape, carved in a continuous scene with a seated young deer looking over its back at the moon amidst sparse pine on one main face and a crane amidst dense pine on the other, the mouth small and regular hollowing to the interior, the design cut primarily from a fine network of 'macaroni-like' white concentric circle patches below a green skin which has been cleverly carved to depict pine needles which cover the entire surface and surround the scenes, all on a semi-transparent grey ground, pine clusters carved on the irregular foot

Possibly Official School, 1750-1850

Height: 5.7 cm
Mouth: 0.55 cm
Neck: no neck

This bottle belongs to a small group of bottles, which are all carved from this distinctive material of a semi-transparent grey agate with swirling white and grey concentric bands and rings with a moss-green 'skin'. The subject matter appears to stay within a narrow range of deer, crane, a pine setting, and the moon. The quality of the workmanship within the group tends to vary from inspirational to adequate, this example falling somewhere in between. For other examples see Moss, Graham, and Tsang, *A Treasury of Chinese Snuff Bottles: The Mary and George Bloch Collection*, Vol. 2, Part 2, Quartz, pp. 408-411, no. 332 and the same authors, *The Art of the Chinese Snuff Bottle: The J & J Collection*, Vol. 1, p. 255, no. 159.

The 'skin' is not a true skin, as one would find on a jade pebble, but is an inclusion from the very edge of the geode from which the material is cut. In most bottles of this group, with the exception of the more sculptural deer-form bottles, all have the cleverly and imaginatively used moss-green 'skin' carved as a stylized pine motif of a disc engraved with a star-burst, which is all the more effective because of the mottled nature of the material. Similarly, the white areas of the various bands that run through the stone are generally used for the gnarled branches of the pine trees and rockwork, and where an animal or a bird is depicted. The circular concentric bands are clearly effective for moons, though in our example perhaps a little on the small side and unfortunately juxtaposed with other rings nearby. However our carver has managed to lesson this distraction by incorporating these in to the fur pattern of the young deer. The semi-transparent grey areas of the stone are used for the backdrop.

Unusually, the moss-green inclusions on our bottle are actually found on both main faces, something of a departure from the norm. This gives the false impression that 'pebble' was originally encased in a skin. This is most likely attributable to the angle at which the material was cut from the original geode. Our bottle probably came from a narrow nook and perhaps three-quarters of the stone was covered by the inclusion.

The crane, deer, and pine are all longevity symbols and this bottle would have made a most acceptable birthday gift. However, the subjects, either individually or in combinations can also form rebuses with alternative readings though similar sentiments. According to Bartholomew, *Hidden Meanings in Chinese Art*, p. 108, no. 5.7, the deer, *lu*, is a pun for 'emolument' or 'official salary', *lu*, and can represent Luxing, the God of Rank and Emolument. The deer and the crane, *he*, together can form the rebus 'The universe is enjoying springtime or longevity', *liuhe tongchun*. Princes once kept deer and cranes in their palace gardens in order to convey this sentiment. The crane and pine, *song*, together form the rebus 'May you, like the crane and pine, enjoy similar longevity', *songhe tongchun*. The subject would therefore be appropriate as a birthday or a wedding gift. The roundness of the moon, *yueliang*, is associated with the cohesion of the family.

Presently, for want of a better designation, this small group of bottles, based on the parti-coloured cameo relief carving with auspicious subjects, has been assigned to the 'Official School' grouping by Moss et al, and there seems no reason to argue that point of view. A fairly wide dating of between 1750-1850 also seems appropriate.

(CBL C 651)

86 (two views)

87

Dendritic chalcedony, one main face with a dark inclusion suggestive of a fat fan-tailed fish with two simply delineated eyes cleverly edited from the stone, a small bubble rises nearby, an inclusion above resembles the tail of a diving fish, the reverse face with abstract inclusions which resemble a sun rising from the foot with a landscape of sorts in the background, rounded shoulders, cylindrical neck, slightly concave rim, a regular mouth with regular hollowing to the interior, the semi-transparent pale-brown stone with various black and brown inclusions, a flat oval base engraved with a four-character inscription

Official School, 1750-1880

Stopper: glass imitating jadeite, metal collar

Height: 6.2 cm
Mouth: 0.7 cm
Neck: 2.2 cm

The four-character inscription on the base reads:
Hai tian xue ri

This can be translated as:
Sea, sky, early or rising sun

The inscription is not particularly neatly carved but seems adequate to be accepted as original and appears to describe the scene depicted on the bottle. The fish is obviously representative of the sea, a small disc-shaped inclusion behind the fishes' heads, might be representative of an early rising sun, but so might the larger disc inclusion on the reverse side. The sky forms the backdrop. It is nevertheless an unusual mark and may represent a private workshop name or perhaps the art name, *hao*, of a scholar collector, though this seems less likely.

As mentioned in earlier entries, Nos. 12 and 25 in this collection, the fish is an extremely popular subject in Chinese art. This example either depicts a goldfish, *jinyu*, which is homophonous with the term meaning 'gold and jade', representing wealth, or possibly a carp, *liyu*, which is homophonous with the word for 'profit', *liyu*. The second sound, *yu*, for fish, is also a pun on the word for 'abundance' or 'plenty', *yu*. The rising sun symbolizes a rise in rank or prosperity, *xuri gaosheng*.

The bubble that rises alongside our fish might actually represent the moon. There is a bottle illustrated by Moss, Graham, and Tsang, *A Treasury of Chinese Snuff Bottles: The Mary and George Bloch Collection*, Vol. 2, Part 2, Quartz, pp. 363-363, no. 315, with a similar subject depicted and an inscription on the reverse side that reads 'Carp watching the moon', *Liyu wangyue*. However the subject's meaning is not further discussed though it may be a reference to the fish leaping the rapids of the heavenly gate to transform in to a dragon, a metaphor for a poor scholar who by passing the civil services exams raises himself to the status of high official.

The natural inclusion of the two fish or really one and a half fish is quite remarkable. The only editing necessary to enhance the depiction was two simply drilled ring eyes and a little shaving around them. We are left with a free-spirited curling fish looking to the sky as a bubble (or moon) rises upwards nearby and the tail end of a fish diving in to the depths below. The reverse face with its abstract landscape and imperfect sun is less successful but certainly fulfills the needs of the inscription to the foot and has not been edited at all but left in its natural state.

Bottles of this school more often than not have a well-defined foot ring to support them. A much smaller number like this example, are simply truncated with a flat oval base, see Moss, Graham, and Tsang, *A Treasury of Chinese Snuff Bottles: The Mary and George Bloch Collection*, Vol. 2, Part 1, Quartz, p. 254, no. 274 and p. 265, no. 278 for two other examples. The form of a compressed rounded square without a protruding foot rim was a common one in the Suzhou School workshops, that almost certainly points to a link of sorts between the two schools. The overall shape with gently rounded shoulders and gently rounded base is extraordinarily satisfying both visually and in the hand. Though only a regular degree of hollowing was applied in this case, the bottle has a remarkable lightness of weight.

(CBL C 661)

87 (mark)

87 (two views)

88

Agate, one main face with grey and black-brown inclusions which have been partially 'edited' to depict two birds, a leafy tree, and a moon, the other face plain with minor inclusions, the narrow sides rounded, the neck cylindrical, the rim slightly concave, the mouth and hollowing regular, the remaining stone of semi-transparent grey tone with a slight brownish hue, the foot spreading slightly and with a flat oval foot ring and regular cut base

Official School, 1780-1880

Stopper: jadeite with metal collar

Height: 5.9 cm
Mouth: 0.7 cm
Neck: 2.0 cm

The subject on this bottle appears to be two eagles, one on rockwork, the other at the base of a tree, though conceivably meant to represent a *taihe* rock. A moon or possibly a sun completes the picture. An eagle, *ying*, is a pun on the word 'hero', *yingxiong*. When depicted on a solitary rock, it forms a pun on the words 'solitary hero' *yingxiong duli*. When depicted standing on one leg, as one of ours certainly is, it represents the independent spirit of the hero, see Bartholomew, *Hidden Meanings in Chinese Art*, p. 125, nos. 5.30 and 5.31.

The upper half of this bottle remains untouched in terms of editing, however the lower half has extensive editing, albeit in extremely low relief. Obviously the eyes of the birds are the most obvious case in point, but so is the raised (and in fact removed) lower right leg of the eagle standing separately to the left. This deliberate edit confirms that this bird is meant to represent an eagle.

The reverse side, but for a few abstract inclusions, is plain. The narrow sides are rounded but as is clearly visible on the right side of the bottle as illustrated, the lapidary had a problem resolving the need to edit and the desire to form a perfectly smooth arc of the profile. Unfortunately it remains unresolved. The foot of this bottle has a pronounced flair and the hollowing is good without being stellar. Whilst there is a chance the bottle might date to the last years of the eighteenth century, it is more likely to have been produced in the nineteenth century.

For a similar depiction on a Official School bottle from the Carl F. Barron collection, see Moss, *The Barron Collection: Illustrated Handlist*, ICSBS Convention, Boston, 2008, p.4, no. 2519.

(CBL C 654)

89

Dendritic agate, carved through a black inclusion on one main face with one of the laughing twins, *Hehe erxian*, seated on rockwork with his box by his side emitting a thin vapor with three flying bats, next to a four-character inscription, the reverse face plain but for a thin wavy horizontal inclusion, suggestive of two further bats, the narrow sides rounded, the neck cylindrical, the rim slightly concave, the mouth small and regular hollowing to the interior, the stone of semi-transparent grey colour, a rounded oval foot ring and regularly cut base

1780-1850

Stopper: jadeite with metal stopper

Height: 5.7 cm
Mouth: 0.65 cm
Neck: 1.8 cm

The inscription reads:
He qi sheng fu

This can be translated as:
Friendly, receive good luck

This is a typical auspicious wish given the nature of the subject. The use of the word *he* in the inscription confirms that this figure is one of the two laughing twins, *hehe erxian*, just in case a doubt still remained based on the iconography. These two immortals, who preside over harmonious marriages, are actually a manifestation of the two famous and mirthful Tang Dynasty poet-monks, Hanshan and Shide. Over time their images changed to that of two playful boys, one carrying a circular box, *he*, the other a lotus, *he*, which is a pun on harmony, *he* and unity, *he*. The Yonzheng emperor designated them as saints in 1733 and their popularity expanded greatly. The combination of a box and five bats, *wufu*, can be read as 'May you have an harmonious marriage filled with the five blessings', *wufu hehe*, the circular box represents harmony and togetherness and the five bats represent the Five Blessings, longevity, health, love of virtue and a peaceful death, see Bartholomew, *Hidden Meanings in Chinese Art*, p. 40, no. 2.3.3. Although only three bats are visible rising from the box alongside the immortal, the reverse side of the bottle has a needle-thin inclusion that at first appears to represent a large winged bird but which surely is meant to be read as the two remaining bats, flying wing-tip to wing tip.

The scene of the immortal is sadly not un-edited, but then it would be remarkable, even a miracle, if it were not. The pale areas such as the hand, foot, the open box cover, and the face of the figure are all lightly edited to reveal the paler stone beneath, whilst the bats and the inscription are deeply 'edited' as one would expect. The choice of position of the inclusion is masterful. The asymmetrical placement allows the bats to fly over the rounded shoulder, which adds a sweeping movement around the bottle rather than cutting the scene off at the neck. It also makes the reading of the bats to the other side more plausible.

Despite the exquisite handling of the scene, the standard shape, regular foot, and normal hollowing probably identify the bottle as a nineteenth-century workshop production.

For another chalcedony agate bottle similarly carved through a dark skin with the two twins and five bats from the Denis S.K.Low Collection see Kleiner, *Treasures from the Sanctum of Enlightened Respect*, p. 209, no. 180.

(CBL C 648)

88

89

90

Dendritic chalcedony, one main face carved through a primarily brown and creamy-blue inclusion with a 'bannerman' on horseback, the banner inscribed with the character *ling* (command), a paler brown patch at the neck, the reverse face plain but for a few small dark flecks, the neck cylindrical, the rim flat, the mouth quite large and regular hollowing to the interior, the stone of semi-transparent grey colour, a flat oval foot ring and regularly cut base

1760-1880

Stopper: coral with white glass collar

Height: 6.0 cm
Mouth: 0.6 cm
Neck: 2.1 cm

The subject of the bannerman was particularly popular with the chalcedony carvers and numerous examples are recorded. Glass examples also exist but appear to be fewer in number. For a full discussion of the background to the subject, see Moss, Graham, and Tsang, *The Art of the Chinese Snuff Bottle: The J & J Collection*, Vol. II, pp. 621-622, no. 375. To paraphrase, the Qianlong emperor claimed ten great victories in military campaigns during his 60-year rule, the crowning achievement in his eyes being the subjugation of what is now Xinjiang province, which included the jade producing region of Turkistan. The conquest took place between 1757 and 1759 and was commemorated by the commission of a series of prints based on paintings made at Court by the resident Jesuit artists, including Castiglione. The depiction of the battles includes Manchu bannermen. The celebrations that followed the victory, and the concomitant interest in all things military, no doubt fostered the depiction of a Manchu bannerman galloping at high speed to announce a great Qing military victory. No different really from the rash of Nelson and Wellington memorabilia that suddenly appeared in England after the great victories of Trafalgar and Waterloo.

A number of chalcedony and glass bottles bear inscriptions that appear to corroborate this theory, the most important perhaps being a chalcedony example in the Imperial Collections today and illustrated in *Snuff Bottles in the Collection of the National Palace Museum*, no. 335, which bears the title on the foot, which reads 'Picture of Victory', implying that the bannerman depicted is more than just any old bannerman out for a ride, but one specifically celebrating an important victory.

We cannot say definitively that this bottle dates to the immediate years following these victories but we can surmise that the subject probably was incorporated in to snuff bottle oeuvre sometime soon after, be it first in the glass or hard-stone workshops. The subject probably remained popular well in to the nineteenth century.

The depiction on our bottle has been 'edited' fairly extensively and the centre of the bottle has a definite concave depression as a result. Certain passages are quite magical like the 'natural' fleck inclusions to the right side of the reverse face, which appear as dirt thrown up by the rear hooves of the galloping horse and the 'natural' minute flecks in the background behind the horse which can also be interpreted as dust rising from under the speeding steed. The character, *ling* (order flag – command) is very precisely carved and appears calligraphic. The only real dissonance in the scene is the direction of the feather in the bannerman's cap, which according to the law of physics should be pointing in the other direction.

A wide date range is proposed, though we cannot rule out an eighteenth-century date of manufacture.

For three chalcedony examples carved in relief with the same subject, see see Nicollier, *The Baur Collection*, pp. 278-279, nos. H 119-121.

(CBL C 664)

91

Agate, carved in a continuous scene around the body, one main face carved from a large opaque white inclusion with the elderly Meng Haoran on his mule followed by his assistant carrying a plum blossom, the reverse face has a continuation of the low-relief rocky ground running above the foot and a small orange-red inclusion on the shoulder carved with a moon amidst clouds, the cylindrical neck with a slightly concave rim, the mouth and hollowing regular, the stone of semi-transparent grey-brown colour, a flat oval foot ring, a regularly cut base

Official School, 1800-1880

Stopper: glass imitating coral

Height: 5.4 cm
Mouth: 0.7 cm
Neck: 1.9 cm

The subject of this bottle is the Tang dynasty poet, Meng Haoran and his assistant plodding through the snow on a moonlit night, he on his mule brandishing a whip, his cold assistant breathing on his freezing hands covered by his long winter sleeves, whilst clutching the all important early plum blossom (prunus). The scene has been mistaken over the years as depicting a variety of historical or fictional characters. The many erroneous attributions include Zhuge Liang, Huang Chengyan, and Lin Bu. Zhuge Liang is a character from the epic *Sanguo yanyi* (Romance of the Three Kingdoms), apparently beardless and 37 years old and thus beyond doubt not the rider depicted. Huang Chengyan, who also appears in the same classic mentioned above, rides a donkey and wears a hood against the snowy winter elements but whose young page or assistant carries a double gourd of wine not a plum blossom, and Lin Bu (967-1028), a celebrated recluse who grew plum trees and wrote poetry about them. He also raised cranes for company in his lonely frugal existence. Depictions show him with an assistant carrying a plum blossom over his shoulder but he does not ride a donkey and is usually shown with a crane nearby. For a lengthy discussion of these figures and many more associated with this iconography, see Tsang, 'Who is the Rider on the Donkey? Some New Observations,' *JICSBS*, Summer 1994, pp. 4-16.

We can safely conclude that the scene does take place at night because Tang Yanquin, a Tang dynasty poet left a poem entitled 'Remembering Meng Haoran' in which the subject is pictured riding a donkey on a cold winter night in a setting of pear, rather than plum, blossoms but he is still clearly our subject.

The treatment of the rockwork on this bottle is remarkably close to the serrated type so indicative of the Suzhou School, with small deep strokes forming part of a shallower longer line. However, the remainder of the decoration does not equate with the more three-dimensional rounded-relief carving of the school, nor the handling of the available space. Again a link of sorts with the Suzhou School must be entertained. The formal integrity of the bottle is quite satisfactory though the degree of hollowing is just scarcely so. The stone is rather attractive and of good quality. The carving of the rockwork and the moon and clouds is exemplary whilst the figural scene is rather workaday with the exception of the masterly stroke of leaving a thin layer of the white inclusion beneath the hooves of the mule to replicate a covering of snow.

For a bottle of the same subject see Stevens, *The Collector's Book of Snuff Bottles*, pp. 142-143, no. 549.

(CBL C 671)

90 (two views)

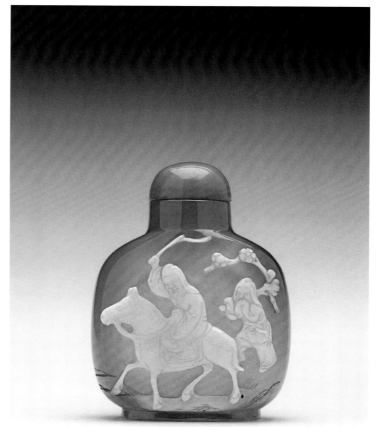

91 (two views)

92

Dendritic agate, one main face carved through a white and grey inclusion with an eagle standing on a rock looking over its shoulder at the sun on the opposite shoulder which is an inlaid disc of striated agate surrounded by engraved clouds, the other face with abstract markings, the neck cylindrical, the rim slightly concave, the mouth and hollowing regular, the brown and grey stone variegated with brown, grey and creamy white inclusions, a flat oval foot ring with regular cut base

1780-1870

Stopper: tourmaline or ruby, metal collar, spoon stamped

Height: 5.9 cm
Mouth: 0.7 cm
Neck: 2.0 cm

Bird subjects are exceedingly popular amongst the hard-stone carvers as the large number of published examples depicting hawks, ducks, geese, and cranes and even the mythical phoenix, attest. The natural world was of course a major source of inspiration for these artists and this fact should be hardly surprising.

The subject on this bottle, an eagle, *ying*, is a pun on the word 'hero', *yingxiong*. When depicted on a solitary rock, it forms a pun on the words 'solitary hero' *yingxiong duli*. In our example, waves have been lightly carved under the rock, adding to the solitary quality of the depiction. When shown standing on one leg, it represents the independent spirit of the hero, see Bartholomew, *Hidden Meanings in Chinese Art*, p. 125, nos. 5.30 and 5.31.

The question we need to try and answer is 'When was the sun disc added to the bottle?' Is it a later addition, added as a selling tool when the bottle went to market or was it an original embellishment? The strong likelihood, given that no other convincing bottle of this embellished type appears to exist, is that it was a cunning sales move by an unscrupulous dealer, who not only inserted a colourful orange disc, presumably to depict the sun, but then carved a cloud design on the surface of the bottle to give the appearance of cohesion. However, we cannot entirely rule out the very slight possibility that during the cutting of the bottle or the hollowing out process, the integrity of the surface was somehow compromised by an errant tool, and the result was a hole that needed to be repaired, not only for aesthetic reasons but for functional ones as well. Whatever the answer, it seems unfortunate that the lapidary choose to insert the disc with the bands of colour running at right angles to the main flow of the bottle's inclusions, when this course might have been less jarring. The concentric markings within the stone are suggestive of two cliff faces framing the bird. The other side of the bottle is plain and the various inclusions, which comprise concentric rings at the neck and upper body and a splattering of small moss-like inclusions, might be considered a continuation of the rock-face from the other side with the addition of lichen.

The eagle has been extremely well delineated for what otherwise appears to be a nineteenth-century bottle.

The stopper has two marks: *yi lai* which is probably a shop name and *Wen yin*, pure silver.

(CBL C 659)

93

Chalcedony, one main face with a mottled brown, orange, and white inclusion carefully edited to depict a swimming duck, with a beak and eye very simply incised, the neck cylindrical, the rim very slightly concave, the mouth large and the interior very well hollowed, the transparent honey-brown stone of even colour with some 'honey-comb' markings throughout, a flat oval foot cut with a shallow depression at its centre

Official School, 1740-1850

Stopper: buffalo horn

Height: 5.55 cm
Mouth: 0.9 cm
Neck: 2.2 cm

Without question this bottle can be linked to a group of cameo chalcedony bottles of very similar shape and material, an example of which is illustrated by Moss, Graham, and Tsang, *A Treasury of Chinese Snuff Bottles: The Mary and George Bloch Collection*, Vol. 2, Part 2, Quartz, pp. 322-325, no. 300, which has a tentative attribution to the palace workshops and which might date to as early as 1740. As with that bottle, the artist has stripped the subject of all unessential elements and left us with a powerful yet rudimentary characterization. The inclusion is only lightly edited and incised with the minimum effort of two short strokes and one circle to bring to life, by subtle suggestion, an otherwise abstract patch.

It is an extraordinarily potent image, which is superbly balanced on the broad honey-brown canvas of the fittingly formal bottle. The degree of internal hollowing is exceptional and mirrors the soft spherical profile. The choice of recessed foot, rather than a protruding one, must surely be an artistic one, rather than a technical one, reflecting the lapidary's desire to continue the smooth silhouette without interruption. The same desire seems to have guided the transition between the shoulder and the neck, which appear to melt together. The interior hollowing has left a matrix of honey-comb-like markings to the inside walls, a common feature on well-hollowed chalcedony bottles. For a full explanation of the causes of this feature due to the interlocking micro-crystals, see Moss, Graham, and Tsang, *A Treasury of Chinese Snuff Bottles: The Mary and George Bloch Collection*, Vol. 2, Part 1, Quartz, pp. 208-209, no. 258.

For another Official School bottle carved with a shadow duck from the Carl F. Barron collection, see Moss, *The Barron Collection: Illustrated Handlist*, ICSBS Convention, Boston, 2008, p.4, no. 2260.

Here we have a masterpiece that might easily date to the first half of the eighteenth century based on all the characteristics listed but which cannot be proven without a doubt and therefore has been assigned a wider dating range.

(CBL C 657)

92 (two views)

93 (two views)

94

Chalcedony, carved on one main face through yellow-brown, orange-red, and white inclusions with the *Hehe erxian* (laughing twins), two bats, two ribboned coins, the sun and wispy clouds, the other face carved through a pale orange-red inclusion with a small long-tailed bird amidst a large spray of fruiting pomegranate rising from rockwork, a bee or wasp nearby, the neck cylindrical, the rim very slightly concave, a small mouth and a very well hollowed interior, the stone of semi-transparent grey tone, a rounded large oval foot ring with regular cut base

Official School, 1750-1850

Stopper: jadeite

Height: 6.4 cm
Mouth: 0.6 cm
Neck: 2.5 cm

Published: Chapman, 'The Chester Beatty Collection of Snuff Bottles', *Arts of Asia*, March-April, 1988, p. 61, fig 5.

These two immortals, *Hehe erxian*, who preside over harmonious marriages, are actually a manifestation of the two famous and mirthful Tang dynasty poet-monks, Hanshan and Shide. Over time their images changed to that of two playful boys, one carrying a circular box, *he*, the other a lotus, *he* (though here depicted with a millet, rice or reed spray). Usually five bats are shown escaping from the box. In this instance we can glimpse at least one or two of the remaining three bats attempting to escape between the box and its cover. The combination of a box and five bats, *wufu*, can be read as 'May you have an harmonious marriage filled with the five blessings', *wufu hehe*. For further discussion of this subject see the entry for No. 89 in this collection. The double coins trailing ribbons, *shuangqian*, is one of the eight treasures, *baobao*, and is another auspicious reference. The sun, *taiyang*, represents the foremost male principle, *yang*. Though in this case it appears to be high in the sky; a rising sun brings a new day and good fortune.

The other side of the bottle depicts a large pomegranate spray with bursting fruit and a bird flying headlong downwards. The pomegranate blossom was much appreciated and even worn on certain days to ward off evil. The bursting fruit with its numerous seeds make it a fertile subject for progeny. The bee or wasp, *feng*, carved from a pale inclusion near the narrow side of the bottle, whilst being a pun for 'confer' *feng*, as well as for 'harvest', *fengdeng*, may simply be an artistic tool to utilize the inclusion.

This is a magnificent bottle of the very highest quality. It uses a multi-coloured stone to brilliant effect and the carving is confident and dynamic. It is a complex composition that has been handled imaginatively. The bottle has a superb degree of hollowing for a bottle of this large size and the shape is a satisfactory one.

(CBL C 667)

94 (two views)

95

Dendritic chalcedony, carved with a continuous landscape scene, one main face with the bending figure playing a flute near rocks as a large phoenix swoops down behind him, the other face with a bending gnarled pine tree rising from further rocks, up the neck and over the slightly concave rim, the interior with regular hollowing, the grey and pale brown stone with black, brown and misty cream inclusions, a flat oval foot ring with regular cut base

Suzhou, School of Zhiting, 1750-1850

Stopper: jadeite metal collar (oxidized silver)

Height: 5.5 cm
Mouth: 0.65 cm
Neck: 1.8 cm

The 'School of Zhiting' is a recent designation coined by Moss, Graham, and Tsang, *A Treasury of Chinese Snuff Bottles: The Mary and George Bloch Collection*, Vol. 2, Part 2, Quartz, pp. 504-507, no. 366. The term is an attempt to clear up a long-held misconception, that the well-known group of bottles classified as 'Suzhou School' and identified by distinctive features that include 'serrated rockwork' formed by serrated ridges with small indentations, represented Suzhou style as a whole. As pointed out by the authors, this assumption is unsustainable, given the substantial number of jade and other hard-stone objects, other than snuff bottles and pendants, produced in Suzhou, which lack this feature entirely.

Whilst it is agreed that Suzhou is the centre where these bottles and pendants were produced, a new designation, pertinent to bottles alone, was appropriate. The term 'School of Zhiting' was chosen for very good reasons. The use of distinctive 'serrated rockwork' appears to be typical, if not unique, to the miniature craft of bottles and pendants and possibly exclusive to one workshop. Although the precise dates of the artist Zhiting's career are unknown, six bottles and countless pendants in jade bearing his name are recorded and all are carved with this distinctive feature. These can be linked to unsigned works in chalcedony similarly carved. It is generally accepted that he worked in the eighteenth century and was one of the earliest proponents of this style. Whilst bottles signed by others are known, in both jade and chalcedony, suggesting that a school or workshop existed that employed more than one carver working over a long period of time, the term 'School of Zhiting' is extremely helpful and in terms of style more precise than other alternative designations.

The subject on this bottle is not entirely clear. The bending figure on one side appears to be playing a flute held in his over-size hands. If this is the case, he may depict the Daoist immortal Han Xiangzi. This would explain the appearance of the mythical phoenix overhead. The phoenix is one of the symbols of Xiwangmu, the Queen Mother of the West, who held a famous 'Peach Banquet' to which the eight immortals, including Han Xiangzi, were invited. She is also considered a goddess of longevity, which might account for the depiction of pine and rockwork, both longevity symbols that are carved on the bottle. According to Williams, *Outlines of Chinese Symbolism and Art Motives*, p. 324, in describing the phoenix, 'the tail is graduated like Pandean pipes, and its song resembles the music of that instrument, having five modulations'. Thus, perhaps the appearance of the phoenix is connected to the playing of the flute by the immortal. The flute is usually made of bamboo and has joints, *jie*, and is considered a rebus for 'rising high', *jiejie gaoxing*, which could also be a reference to the phoenix. The phoenix, *feng*, is also associated with rank and prosperity, which further cements this interpretation of the bottle's symbolism; see Bartholomew, *Hidden Meanings in Chinese Art*, p. 186, no. 7.22.

The serrated rockwork on this bottle is visible primarily on the reverse side of this bottle on the rounded rocks that support the pine tree. Another distinctly convoluted pierced rock, *taihu*, that runs horizontally underneath the figure and cleverly uses dark black-brown inclusions in the stone, is yet another method, other than 'serrated', of depicting rocks that we find utilized by the school. It involves carving an irregular three-dimensional surface and boring circular holes with a countersunk drill-head, some of the holes are large, some small, and some run one in to the other to produce a short worm-like cavity.

The overall effect is surprisingly effective for depicting this peculiar type of weathered rock, *taihu*, characterized by its large cavities and so justly famous in China. Interestingly the rock, *taihu*, when combined with the pine, *song*, represent the famous Mount Song, *Song Shan*, in Henan province. Mount Song, the central peak among the five sacred mountains of China, is believed to be an abode of the immortals, see Bartholomew, op cit, p. 212, no. 7.47.9.

The overall carving is actually very fine and in quite low relief despite its three-dimensional quality that is no doubt enhanced by the depth of the inclusions. On this bottle the design, albeit only slightly, continues over the narrow edges. This is against the general trend for the school where according to Moss et al, op cit, p. 509, sufficient examples exist with plain narrow edges and a truncation of the 'continuous' scenes to suggest a trend. On the occasions when there is decoration to the narrow sides it appears, as in this case, that it is dictated by inclusions in the stone. In this case the inclusions continue at the neck and rim and these have been engraved with pine decoration.

The spoon bears a stamped seal that is difficult to read but possibly reads *Tian fu yang* , 'heaven good fortune forever' that may be the fanciful name of a silver workshop.

(CBL C 666)

95 (two views)

Dendritic chalcedony, one narrow side carved through a mixed inclusion with two immortals supported on a massive gourd vessel floating on waves, one standing holding a peach, the other lying out-stretched, a rock face behind them continuing on to one of the main faces of the bottle and engraved with a seven-character inscription and two-character signature above stylized pine, the other main face carved with a wide expanse of sea with a fish breaking the surface, the immortals just visible at the right edge, and a monkey on a rocky promontory carved from a small white inclusion on the left edge, the sky above carved in high relief with another seven-character inscription followed by a seal, the neck slightly waisted and beveled at the edge, the rim very slightly concave, the mouth regular and the interior well hollowed, the stone of semi-transparent brownish-grey tone with darker brown, black and creamy inclusions, a short foot edge but the oval base cut flat and incised with rocks

Suzhou, School of Zhiting, signed Xigang, 1750-1850

Stopper: jadeite with metal collar (oxidized silver)

Height: 7.5 cm
Mouth: 0.8 cm
Neck: 2.35 cm

The relief inscription above the sea on one side reads:
Xiao yao hei shang fu pan tao followed by the seal *Wenwan*

This can be translated as:
'Flying freely and relaxed on a sea going to a birthday celebration', followed by the seal 'plaything'

The incised inscription on the sweeping rockwork reads:
Fu ru dong hai shou ru (?) shan followed by the signature *Xigang*

This can be translated as:
'Good luck as big as the East Sea, longevity as high as a mountain', followed by the signature Xigang

The subject is again rather problematic. According to the inscriptions, which almost always refer to the scenes depicted on a bottle, one mentions a journey by sea for a birthday celebration; the other mentions the East Sea. In our depiction we have two immortals traveling on a gourd on waves. So far, so good, but which immortals are they? One stands holding a peach suggesting this is Shoulao, the immortal of longevity, who brings birthday greetings, but he is usually depicted with a high cranium and long staff. The other, as he is in a prone position may represent Li Tieguai, the lame beggar, who is never without his gourd but who is usually depicted as a hideous old man. Or possibly, though less likely, it is Zhonglai Quan, considered the leader of the eight immortals who is also occasionally depicted with a gourd. On the opposite rock across the sea, sits a mischievous monkey. The story that immediately springs to mind therefore, is that of the 'Peach Banquet' *pantao hui*, held by Xiwangmu, the Queen Mother of the West, also a goddess of longevity, see Little, *Taoism and the Arts of China*, pp. 319-321, no. 118. She lives at the Turquoise Pool high in the Kunlin Mountains to the West of China. She has a peach orchid whose trees bloom every three thousand years. On this auspicious occasion she invites all the immortals to attend a large banquet. The monkey god, Sun Wukong, peeved at not being invited, crashes the party, eats most of the peaches, and ruins the celebration. The problem with this reading is the inscribed reference to the East Sea and a birthday celebration. The East Sea is in the opposite direction and Xiwangmu's banquet was not a birthday celebration. It is possible, that the carver took some artistic license in his portrayal of the story, but more likely the subject depicts some other aspect of the tale.

This is one of those bottles with complicated imagery that utilizes inclusions that are not always 'front and center,' so to speak, and makes for quite difficult reading when photographed, in the usual manner, directly on each 'main' face. When held in the hand and turned, which was the original intention, it is more successful.

For a 'School of Zhiting' bottle, it does live up to the exacting quality of workmanship normally associated with the workshop. The material, however, almost certainly proved troublesome, with odd juxtaposition of inclusions that often cropped up on the narrow sides of the bottle, and an overall mistiness within the matrix of the stone that dulls the overall impression despite the very fine surface polish. The handling of the 'difficult' inclusions within the stone is quite a virtuoso performance however and presumably why the artist chose to include his signature. The immortals are cleverly carved using an awkwardly-shaped inclusion, whilst the gourd under them is cut from the pure transparent stone; the fish jumping above the waves has a small crescent shaped dark inclusion for its tail fin, and a smaller paler inclusion for its eye; the monkey uses three colours, primarily white for the body and limbs, a honey hue for the upper body and head, and a small dark patch for the eyes; further inclusions are cleverly integrated with carving of rockwork and pine trees.

The depiction of waves lapping up against a rock of longevity, usually shown with *lingzhi* growths but here with another long-life symbol, the pine, is typical of depictions of the Eastern Sea.

The signature Xigang is unknown and has no connection with the famous jade carver Zigang. Xigang, we presume, was on of the lesser-known carvers of the school.

(CBL C 668)

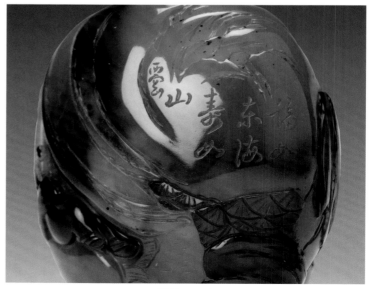

96 (signature)

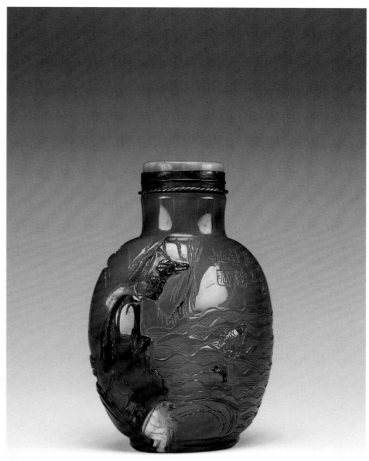

96 (four views)

97

Dendritic chalcedony, carved with a continuous scene, one slightly bulbous main face with a group of five boy musicians amidst rockwork below an engraved ten-character inscription, the other face with a sweeping pine tree rising from rocks with *lingzhi*, one narrow side partially carved with one of the five boys, the other narrow side with rocks, the neck very slightly waisted, the rim very slightly concave, a regular mouth and well hollowed interior, the stone of semi-transparent grey colour with honey-brown and black inclusions, a rounded oval foot ring with regular cut base

Suzhou, School of Zhiting, 1750-1850

Stopper: glass imitating jadeite with gilt-metal collar

Height: 6.0 cm
Mouth: 0.7 cm
Neck: 2.3 cm

Published: Chapman, 'The Chester Beatty Collection of Snuff Bottles', *Arts of Asia*, March-April, 1988, p. 61, fig 5.

The inscription comprising two sentences of five characters each reads:
Yuan xiao feng jing hao
Gong le tai ping chung

This can be translated as:
Beautiful scenery in Yuan Xiao (January 15th Festival)
Everyone happy and peaceful Spring

Yuan Xiao is celebrated on the fifteenth day of the New Year. In this depiction we have a group of five boy musicians, one blowing a horn, three playing different forms of drums, and one with cymbals. The motif of five boys is a popular one. According to Bartholomew, *Hidden Meanings in Chinese Art*, p. 68, no. 3.11, these boys represent the sons of the scholar Dou Yujun, who lived at Yanshan during the Five Dynasties period (907-960 CE). He had five sons, all whom enjoyed exceptional success at the civil service examinations and became high officials. As the epitome of the ideal parent Dou Yujun was included in the Trimetrical Classic, *Sanzijing*, the primer from the Song dynasty that was read until well into the twentieth century. The children are sometimes depicted as the Five Osmanthus Flowers, *Wugui*.

Five is also an auspicious number. Many depictions come in groups of five such as five bats, five blessings, five pillars, five coins, and five elements.

It seems quite likely that this is indeed the reference here depicted, although it may simple be a small troupe of boys, who happen to number five, bashing out a great tune during the festival.

Once again, we do have a magical use of the inclusions within the stone. For the most part the more orange brown markings on one side have been used to represent the clothing that the boys are wearing, whilst smaller black inclusions have been used to highlight either the hair or buns of some of the children, as well a support for the figure in the foreground, unnecessary but effective. The other side uses a pale honey inclusion to highlight a *lingzhi* spray, and a large crescent-shaped group of dark moss-like speckles to highlight pine needles that rise to the top of the neck.

As usual we have the classic 'serrated' rockwork common to the school, carved primarily to the reverse face. This is another reference to longevity. The three subjects—pine, rock, and *lingzhi*—all being symbols of longevity. The subject of 'New Year' must also be seen in the same context.

The shape of the bottle has a wonderful formal integrity. The slightly bulbous sides are well rounded and balance extremely well with the exterior rim of the foot and the gently waisted neck that has the effect of opening up the bottle. We have a surprisingly well-hollowed bottle especially given that the mouth is relatively small.

A date in the eighteenth century is certainly not out of the question although we must not forget that quality alone is not the only criteria for judgement, as many high quality bottles probably dating from the school's later period of production are known.

For another Suzhou chalcedony bottle utilising a stone with slightly darker inclusions but carved with an immortal and boys at play, see Nicollier, *The Baur Collection*, pp. 274-275, no. H 117 and also pp. 280-281, no. H 122, for another carved from a similar coloured stone depicting an immortal and a poetic inscription.

(CBL C 673)

97 (two views)

98

Smoky quartz, one almost flat main face carved through a grey and beige inclusions with an old man and a buffalo under a gnarled pine, the other face and both of the rounded narrow sides carved in very low relief with a winter lake scene of three boats approaching a small hut near a leafless tree and bamboo on a promontory with mountains in the background, the neck circular, the rim slightly concave, a regular mouth and hollowing, the smoky dark-brown crystal appearing almost jet black, a flat oval foot ring with regular cut base

School of the Rustic Crystal Master, 1750-1870

Stopper: rose quartz with ivory collar

Height: 7.7 cm
Mouth: 0.8 cm
Neck: 2.7 cm

The subject matter and the sparse low-relief carving on the lakeside face of this bottle is indicative of that found on a wide-ranging group of quartz bottles that have been assigned to the School of 'The Rustic Crystal Master' by Moss, Graham, and Tsang, *A Treasury of Chinese Snuff Bottles: The Mary and George Bloch Collection*, Vol. 2, Part 1, Quartz, pp. 194-196, no. 254. The school is discussed in the entry to No. 109 in this publication. The subjects most closely associated with this school are primarily painterly low-relief landscape scenes, influenced by the literati painting tradition and made up of a series of standard elements which seem to include wintry scenes with bare trees and humble dwellings, and pine and rocks, all present in this example. The school is also known for the clever use of the grey and beige inclusions often associated with the dark smoky quartz material.

The carving on one side of a black crystal bottle illustrated by Moss et al, op cit, pp. 204-205, no. 257, is so similar to the treatment on the lake scene of ours that it is nearly impossible not to believe that they were produced in the same workshop at the same time by the same hand. The mountain formation, leaning acutely to one side, is almost identical. The author's note that it is difficult to imagine a crystal any blacker, and ours is certainly equal in blackness. Like the J & J bottle, ours is of very large size, has an identical mouth size and by stint of a straight rather than a tapering neck, has a slightly wider neck. They suggest a mid to late Qing date for their bottle.

A bottle bearing the signature of Youqin and dated to 1805 (or possibly 1865) and made of a brown crystal with a pale skin to one side makes for an interesting comparison, see Moss, Graham, and Tsang, *The Art of the Chinese Snuff Bottle: The J & J Collection*, pp. 186-187, no. 104. Forgetting the shape, it would be very easy to imagine the main face of our bottle, prior to carving, resembling the un-cut skin of the J & J example. Even the slightly mottled grey and beige colour is very similar. The buffalo on our bottle is cleverly cut from the grey 'outer skin' of our inclusion, whilst the rather nonchalant or resting figure and the pine tree use the paler beige inclusion beneath it. We also have a quite idiosyncratic v-shaped marking to depict the pine bark. This is one of the few examples of the school where we have a large area of inclusion carved in relief and it gives us a fascinating glimpse at a style of carving that we can now associate with the school.

The subject on our bottle may simply be a bucolic one, though this is unlikely given the Chinese penchant for visual puns and double meanings. The scholar class certainly paid homage to farmers considering their work as one of the four honorable occupations or professions, which also included fishing, wood gathering, and scholarship. They certainly admired the simple way of life as depicted on this bottle and which is reflected in the 'crude' or 'rustic' simplicity of the depiction here and in the school in general.

For a similar scene of Shoulao and his deer standing under a pine tree also from the school of the Rustic Crystal Master but carved on a monochrome dark quartz bottle, see Low, *More Treasures from the Sanctum of Enlightened Respect*, p. 236, no. 219.

For a golden-coloured crystal bottle with an almost identical handling of the curious wave-like mountains found on the reverse side of our bottle, see Kleiner, *Precious Playthings: Important Chinese Snuff Bottles*, p. 73, no. 49.

(CBL C 830)

98 (two views)

99

Amethyst or smoky crystal, of cicada form, delicately carved with veined and dotted wings, with s-scrolls on the head and c-scrolls between the wings, the eyes bulbous, the underside of the ribbed body with six legs, slender rectangular hollowing to the interior, the translucent brown-black stone of very pale purple-pink tone

Possibly Imperial, 1750-1880

Height: 5.8 cm
Mouth: 0.5 cm
Neck: no neck

The quartz material initially appears to be a dark smoky crystal but when held to a strong light has a pale purple-pink tone suggestive of amethyst. We may have a combination of the two materials here, which according to Moss, Graham, and Tsang, *A Treasury of Chinese Snuff Bottles, The Mary and George Bloch Collection*, Vol. 2, Part 1, Quartz, pp. 178-179, no. 247, is quite rare in the snuff bottle oeuvre. Interestingly the cicada bottle they illustrate is made from a mixture of amethyst and crystal. They also illustrate a second cicada bottle, Vol. 2, Part 2, Quartz, pp. 442-443, no. 343 made only of smoky crystal, which bears close resemblance to it, certainly in the treatment of the eyes, whilst not being identical. However, there are enough differences in the details between the two Bloch examples and ours, to make the assumption, that whilst all may come from the same workshop, we are probably not looking at works by the same artist. The most obvious difference is the treatment of the eyes. In ours they are only visible on one main side, quite unlike the Bloch bottles which have high protruding eyeballs visible from one side and the skin-folds, or bags under the eyes, prominently featured when viewed from the other side. The eye skin-folds on our bottle are cleverly incised between the protruding eyes on one side only. Another divergence of technique is the depiction of the transparent wings. On the Bloch cicadas the veins are incised with a single line and the surface of the membrane cut with a series of vertical gouges. On our cicada the veins are incised with double lines, which is in fact more naturalistic, and the surface of the membrane cut with a series of horizontal gouges. On the underside of our cicada, the abdomen is also treated with more naturalism having more delicate rounded v-shaped folds (bracket-form) unlike the plain curved folds of the Bloch examples.

These may seem like minor differences but in a workshop with an apprenticeship system, only the master could initiate such changes, so the likelihood is that these differences probably indicate a different date of production. It seems that the Beatty bottle whilst still stylized, is an improvement on the Bloch examples in terms of naturalism, and it would seem unlikely that the workshop would make changes to work towards a less naturalistic style. This would indicate that our bottle is slightly later in date than the Bloch examples.

The cicada, *chan*, is a symbol of rebirth because of its emergence from a lengthy larvae stage, sometimes counting many years. It was a popular motif on ancient bronzes and jade and was used in jade form as an amulet for the dead. The cicada is also loved for its chirping song, which is only performed by the male. In the classic story 'Journey to the West', *Xi You Ji*, the lead character Prince of Tang was named the 'Golden Cicada' due to his ability to transform by shedding illusions and reaching enlightenment.

For a white nephrite example similarly decorated see Lawrence, *Miniature Masterpieces from the Middle Kingdom: The Monimar Collection of Chinese Snuff Bottles*, pp. 158-159, no. 73.

(CBL C 837)

100

Amethyst and smoky crystal, twin bottles, each bottle of slender ovoid shape carved from a single piece of two-coloured quartz, the larger is a smoky crystal and is carved on the outside face with an elderly bearded gentleman beneath pine and near bamboo which continues to the other side, the smaller bottle appears to be a very pale amethyst enhanced by the addition of a strong amethyst pigment painted to the interior, the outside face is carved with a raised seven-character inscription followed by a seal, both with spreading beveled necks, slightly concave rims, small mouths and both quite well hollowed and 'frosted', the bases shallowly cut

1800-1880

Height: 7.4 cm and 6.2 cm
Mouths: 0.5 cm
Neck: larger bottle 1.9 cm, smaller bottle 1.5 cm

The seven-character inscription reads:
Jun zi zhi geng xiao han je followed by the seal *Da ji*

This describes the scene on the remainder of the bottle and can be translated as:
'Gentleman like bamboo (and pine), very tall and reaching the heavens with the bamboo nodes', followed by the seal 'good fortune'.

Twin bottles conjoined at their mid-section seem to be something of a specialty in the quartz arena. Quite a large number exist suggesting that perhaps there was indeed one centre of production for such bottles. For other examples, see no. 110 in this collection and also Hughes, *The Blair Bequest: Chinese Snuff Bottles from the Princeton University Art Museum*, p. 57, no. 30, and p. 63, no. 41; Moss, Graham, and Tsang, *A Treasury of Chinese Snuff Bottles: The Mary and George Bloch Collection*, Vol. 2, Part 1, Quartz, pp. 183-191, nos. 249-252; and Bob C. Stevens, *The Collector's Book of Snuff Bottles*, no. 469.

The subject of the smoky crystal bottle depicting pine, bamboo, and an elderly gentleman is related to longevity (evergreen) and integrity (unbending in the wind). The scene itself is not dissimilar from many painted or engraved by scholar-artisans wishing to evoke the high-minded philosopher lost in a world of introspection, alone in his cerebral reveries away from the never-ending woes of the 'real' world. The natural pine backdrop and simple lone figures communicate the metaphor.

The treatment of the tree bark on this bottle is amongst the most naturalistic to be found in hard-stone carving. The scaly plates are very close to the actual texture of pine bark. The treatment of the pine needle clumps in the upper branches and the bamboo that wraps around the bottles narrow edge are in keeping with the standard stylized format normally associated with them.

The material that the smaller bottle is carved from does appear to be a very faint pink amethyst. However there is no question that the interior of the bottle has been enhanced with a purple stain, to enhance the colour of the stone. Whether this was done at the time of production to simply bring attention to the rare combination of stones or added later as a selling tool by an unscrupulous dealer is uncertain.

(CBL C 838)

99 (two views)

100 (two views)

101

Hair crystal, with a grouping of densely-packed black and silver tourmaline needles primarily to one main face and partially covering the two narrow sides, the needles give a faintly green appearance to the main face and where the needles break the surface at the narrow edges the exterior of the bottle is heavily pitted in contrast to the high polish of the two main faces, one of which is entirely clear and transparent, a tall cylindrical neck, a large mouth and regular hollowed interior, a flat oval foot ring and shallowly cut base

1750-1880

Stopper: rose quartz with metal collar

Height: 7.2 cm
Mouth: 0.7 cm
Neck: 1.95 cm

Moss, Graham, and Tsang, *A Treasury of Chinese Snuff Bottles: The Mary and George Bloch Collection*, Vol. 2, Part 1, Quartz, pp. 35, no. 193, note that some forty different minerals have been found as inclusions in quartz but that only three of these need concern the snuff bottle collector. The most common come under the heading 'hair crystal' and include needle-like crystals of tourmaline (black range of material), rutile (coppery-red or golden colour), and actinolite (green needle crystals).

Our example clearly falls in to the first category, and what an exceptional example it is. Not only has the lapidary carefully cut the bottle so that the needles bisect the centre line of the vertical axis on the narrow sides of the bottle (see side view illustration alongside) but he has also very subtly 'thinned-out' the rutile needles to the upper mid-section of the bottle by judicious interior hollowing to suggest a rising or setting moon appearing or disappearing, depending on your mood, behind a dense woody thicket. Admittedly this 'thinning-out' is partly dictated by the rectangular shape of the bottle and the difficulty of fully polishing out the interior shoulders and foot which leads to a certain density of stone in these areas, but nevertheless it has been remarkably well conceived and achieved.

With a bottle that has little or no decoration to speak of, dating is quite difficult. Here form is the primary indicator, with hollowing and degrees of polish a further guide, and finally the ability of the lapidary to utilize inclusions within the stone to suggest a satisfactory design as the final clue. The form here is a fairly standard mid-Qing one of rounded rectangular shape which might conceivably date anywhere from the mid-eighteenth century to late-nineteenth century. It does however have some subtle variations on shape from the core group in that the upper portion of the bottle has the widest dimensions when viewed face on (it tapers from shoulder to foot), whilst the main faces when viewed from the narrow side of the bottle have a slightly convex outline that is almost flat. These variations whilst qualitative are not indicative of a date of production. The hollowing, while satisfactory, may also be partially attributable to the need to leave darker clusters of needles to highlight the suggested 'moon' design. The polish on the exterior of the main faces is superb. However where the needles break the surface of the crystal on the narrow sides the stone is inevitably covered in pitting.

We must choose a wide dating range of between 1750 and 1880, for a bottle of this type, until such time as further information is available.

For another example formerly in the Edmond Dwyer Collection see the exhibition catalogue, *Chinese Snuff Bottles: Documentation of World Trade West to East*, The Oakland Museum, 1977, p. 17, no. 485 and another of similar shape is illustrated by Nicollier, *The Baur Collection*, pp. 236-237, no. H 95.

(CBL C 842)

101 (three views)

102

Crystal, each main face carved with a large raised rectangular panel from the ground crystal, and one main face carved through a mottled grey-green 'skin' with bamboo and rockwork and a small rectangular uncut seal alongside, the reverse side plain and transparent, the neck cylindrical, good hollowing to the interior, a flat foot ring of rounded rectangular shape and regularly cut base

1800-1880

Height: 7.2 cm
Mouth: 0.8 cm
Neck: 1.8 cm

If it were not for the enchanting depiction of bamboo and rockwork so neatly cut from a darker grey-green patch of stone that once ran through the clear crystal matrix, this bottle would be assigned to the 'also-ran' pile. Here we have a fairly standard mid-late Qing form, one of rounded rectangular shape that almost certainly dates to the mid-to late-nineteenth century. The overall form is unmemorable and the degree of hollowing is sufficient but not noteworthy. However what raises this bottle to a level well above the pedestrian and is indeed its redeeming quality is the notable use of the dark 'inclusion'. Not only is the design itself beautifully balanced with the three sprays of bamboo leaves nicely balanced by the juxtaposition of its seal and the two pierced sections of the rocks, the actual material that makes up the inclusion has the appearance of a classic ink rubbing. The gradations of tone, which give an almost graphite quality to the inclusion, resemble the inky gradations of tone produced when paper is dampened, placed on a stele or stone panel, and then traced. A scholar collector would not have overlooked this similarity. In all likelihood this reference was entirely understood by Chester Beatty when he purchased the bottle. Chinese ink rubbings make up part of the library's holdings though these are not published. For an example of an ink rubbing displaying the lightly-inked mottled-grey background see, *The Chinese Scholar's Studio: Artistic Life in the Late Ming Period*, An Exhibition from the Shanghai Museum at the Asia Society Galleries, New York, 1987, p. 101, no. 30.

For another bottle with a green-grey skin carved with two square seals below orchids, see Sotheby's London, 7 June 1990, lot 34.

(CBL C 874)

103

Crystal, the clear stone carved in relief on each main face with a large raised panel conforming to the shape of the bottle, one panel plain and carved from the clear ground crystal, the other carved through a cream and pale beige 'inclusion', to depict cymbidium (orchid) rising from an earth mound, the rounded narrow sides with simple lion-mask elongated ring handles, the neck cylindrical and with regular hollowing to the interior, a flat foot ring of rounded rectangular shape and a regularly cut base

1750-1860

Stopper: glass imitating coral on metal collar (oxidized silver)

Height: 7.0 cm
Mouth: 0.8 cm
Neck: 2.0 cm

This is an altogether more satisfying form than the previous bottle and even if undecorated, it would still have place in this publication. It has a formal integrity that raises it above the norm. For want of a better description the bottle appears to be taking a breath, the sides seem to be in the process of expanding outwards but are held in check by the very satisfying and carefully carved lion-mask handles which run over two-thirds of the way down the narrow sides of the bottle but which because of their extreme low relief barely impinge on the integrity of the profile. The degree of hollowing is perfectly satisfactory though not paper-thin.

It is tempting to call the 'inclusion' on this bottle, the 'skin' as one would do with a jade pebble, as it does have the appearance of such, sitting as it does on the surface of the stone. However this would be a misnomer as crystal is found in deposits mixed with other minerals that run through the matrix of the stone rather than surrounding it as in the case of the skin around a jade pebble.

The depiction here is of a type of orchid called cymbidium, *lanhua*, which is one of China's most ancient and best-known ornamental flowering plants. It is considered a symbol of spring. See Bartholomew, *Hidden Meanings in Chinese Art*, pp. 68-69, no. 3.8 and 3.8.1. It is always depicted with graceful grass-like foliage and with the flower petals surrounded by four or more usually five larger ovate sepals (calyx). It is often mistaken for narcissus. According to Bartholomew, Confucius found the fragrance so enchanting that he called it 'the scent of kings'. When grouped with plum, bamboo, and chrysanthemum they are known as 'four gentlemen among flowers'. One type of cymbidium, *sun*, bearing white and purple flowers is a pun for grandson, *sun*, and so the flower is associated with the wish for progeny. She also mentions how perfectly suited the rhythmic quality and simple outline of this dainty plant was to brush painting. Our example could almost be a brush painting. The fortuitous gradation of tone between the differing depths of the beige and cream inclusion appear as though intentional and the grass-like foliage is light-weight, lyrical, and appears almost alive.

Interestingly Bartholomew also mentions that the theme of cymbidium was among the wood carvings commissioned in 1818 by the Jiaqing emperor for his summer palace, the Yuanmingyuan. This date would fit perfectly in to the mid range of our dating attribution, and whilst of course the theme enjoyed widespread use over the course of many centuries, it is tempting to leap to the conclusion that this may have been an imperial commission.

For another example with a green-grey skin carved with cymbidium and two square seals, see Sotheby's London, 7 June 1990, lot 34.

(CBL C 877)

102

103

104

Crystal, carved in low relief from a pale creamy-white 'inclusion' on one main face with a bird on the branch of a plum tree (prunus) on a raised octagonal panel, the other main face with an octagonal panel cut from the ground crystal and carved in intaglio with a web-like design, actually composed of eight stylized trigrams centered by a yin-yang symbol, the narrow sides are beveled with three edges, the cylindrical neck with a flat rim and a quite well-hollowed interior, a flat foot ring of rounded rectangular shape and regularly cut base, the clear stone with some ice-like misty areas and a few brown inclusions

1800-1880

Height: 6.7 cm
Mouth: 0.8 cm
Neck: 1.95 cm

The subject of the origins of the octagonal facetted bottle has been covered extensively in many snuff bottle publications, but more recently the assumptions that the unusual octagonal form was introduced to the Imperial Court in Beijing from the West in the form of European pocket watches that were the rage at Court from the late seventeenth century onwards, and which was generally accepted, may in fact not necessarily be the case. See Moss, Graham, and Tsang, *A Treasury of Chinese Snuff Bottles: The Mary and George Bloch Collection*, Vol. 5, Part 2, Glass, pp. 296-297, no. 801, where it is now suggested that it is equally as likely that such forms evolved independently as a result of experiments in faceting techniques and glass production, admittedly initially with European input.

The somewhat mechanical carving of our bottle, both in its form and decoration, coupled with the use of a stone of secondary quality suggests that it is probably a product of the nineteenth century and conceivably quite late in the century at that. The eight panels that make up the narrow sides of the bottle are further facetted to form three bevels on each panel but the workmanship is a little untidy. The foot that supports the bottle is also wider than the width of the lower facet giving the bottle a slightly bottom-heavy appearance. The carving of the 'inclusion' however is very attractive, depicting a songbird seated in the branches of a plum tree (prunus). The bird may well represent a magpie as the rebus formed when a magpie, *xique*, sings in the branches of a blossoming plum tree, *mei*, can read 'joyfully announcing the arrival of spring' *xibao chunxian*, see Bartholomew, *Hidden Meanings in Chinese Art*, p. 52, 2.17.9.

The reverse side is in many ways rather more interesting. At a quick glance the eight fan-shaped panels look like a spider's web. However none of the panels is identical and they are centred by a yin-yang symbol. They are in fact a stylized form of the Eight Trigrams, *bagua*, favoured in Daoist imagery. The three-line elements, carved in intaglio and 'frosted' for clarity, represent the eight elemental forces in nature and they in turn are related to the yin-yang symbol carved at the center, since the broken lines correspond to the yin, the negative or passive principle, whilst the unbroken lines correspond to the yang, the positive or active principle.

For a nephrite bottle using similar trigram imagery within an octagonal panel and centered by a yin-yang symbol as its primary decoration see Moss, Graham, and Tsang, *A Treasury of Chinese Snuff Bottles: The Mary and George Bloch Collection*, Vol. 1, Jade, pp. 62-65, no. 20; for another in boxwood using the trigram imagery as a subordinate part of its decoration, see Moss, Graham, and Tsang, *The Art of the Chinese Snuff Bottle: The J & J Collection*, Vol. II, pp. 468-469, no. 280.

(CBL C 894)

104 (two views)

105

Crystal, the main faces and the narrow sides each carved with a slightly tapering raised rectangular panel that conforms to the shape of the bottle, one main face carved through a white and russet 'inclusion' with a phoenix, bamboo, and rockwork, the other main face carved in relief with an eight-character archaic 'bronze' inscription, followed by commentary, the two narrow sides each with an engraved inscription, one of six characters, the other of three characters followed by a seal, the shoulders flat and canted at the edges, the neck cylindrical, the rim flat, regular hollowing to the interior, a flat foot ring of rounded rectangular shape and a regularly cut base

Signed Lin Cai Nan, 1800-1880

Stopper: agate on metal collar (oxidized silver)

Height: 6.0 cm
Mouth: 0.6 cm
Neck: 1.6 cm

The eight-character archaic script that forms the first part of the inscription on one main face is copied from an archaic bronze vessel that bears the name 'Bo Shi Fu (Ding)'. The remaining seven-character inscription mentions this followed by wen dan lin, which can be read as 'vessel text copied by Dan Lin'.

The six-character inscription on one narrow side reads:
Dan lin shan xiang yu wan

This can be translated as:
For the elegant enjoyment of the third elder brother, Dan Lin

The three-character inscription followed by an incised seal of gourd shape on the other narrow side can be read as:
Lin Cai Nan, followed by the incised seal Cai Nan

Lin Cai Nan is the artist and he gave the bottle to Dan Lin who had originally copied the bronze text. They do not appear to be related.

The depiction of a phoenix, feng, and bamboo, zhu, was a popular one. The mythical phoenix appears during times of peace and bamboo can also represent peace. The subject makes perfect sense in the context of the family bronze vessel, Bo shi fu, mentioned in the calligraphy, as the revered archaic vessel harked back to a time of great prosperity and peace.

The unfortunate part of 'frosting' the interior in order to highlight the numerous calligraphic panels is that it also highlights the degree and quality of the hollowing. Sadly the uneven edges caused by the cutting tools are magnified in this environment and the result has the appearance of an inflated air bag. The carving of the phoenix standing on a rock shaking its wings and looking over its back to a short bamboo spray is adequate though cursory whilst the faint black and brown specks that dot the surface do not appear to serve any purpose. The calligraphy however is of a much higher standard altogether and should be commended, as should the stone itself that does indeed have an extraordinary clarity. Considering all the aspects of this bottle, it can be safely dated to between 1800-1880.

For another example from the Edmund F. Dwyer Collection of identical shape and carved with a bamboo panel panel on one face and an unspecified inscription (not illustrated) on the other, see Christie's London, 12 October 1987, lot 132.

(CBL C 895)

105 (four views)

106

Hair crystal, the clear stone with black tourmaline needles sparsely scattered throughout in a vaguely diagonal direction and with some density to one main face and one narrow edge, and a clear patch over much of the other main face, a short cylindrical neck with a flat rim, a small mouth and an extremely well hollowed interior, a rounded foot ring and regularly cut base

1750-1850

Stopper: Champleve enamel on metal collar (oxidized silver)

Height: 6.3 cm
Mouth: 0.7 cm
Neck: 2.2 cm

The basic outline of this bottle is a fairly standard Qing form of rounded rectangular shape which might date anywhere from the mid-eighteenth to the mid-nineteenth century. However the degree of hollowing in this bottle is extraordinary. When held, the bottle barely registers in the hand. So light is its weight, that one can imagine holding a small air-filled balloon. Quite how such a gossamer-thin body was achieved without damage or fault is remarkable. These qualitative judgements must be taken in to account when dating the bottle. Late production bottles simply do not demonstrate this level of skill in their execution. The polish on the exterior and interior of this bottle is superb, and there is no pitting where the needles break the surface of the crystal. This bottle could easily be a production of the mid-eighteenth century and probably is. It surely cannot date beyond the mid-nineteenth century when lapidary work was for the most part on the wane.

For another example of slightly more ovoid shape but with a similar light dispersement of tourmaline inclusions from the Carl F. Barron collection, see Moss, *The Barron Collection: Illustrated Handlist*, ICSBS Convention, Boston, 2008, p. 9, no. 2607, another is illustrated by Lawrence, *Miniature Masterpieces from the Middle Kingdom: The Monimar Collection of Chinese Snuff Bottles*, pp. 102-103, no. 45 and a third is illustrated by Brody, *Old Wine into Old Bottles: A Collector's Commonplace Book*, pp. 36-37, no. 36.

(CBL C 847)

107

Hair crystal, of bulbous form, carved in relief with a crab grabbing a leafy frond or reed and another crab nearby, both crabs 'hidden' by the two areas of tourmaline needle clusters primarily on one main face and extending to the narrow sides, a cylindrical neck, flat rim, regular mouth and very well hollowed interior, a flat oval foot ring and regularly cut base

1780-1880

Stopper: amethyst on metal collar (oxidized silver)

Height: 7.0 cm
Mouth: 0.85 cm
Neck: 2.5 cm

The tourmaline needles, whilst predominately black, also include some of silver colour and others of a yellowish-green tone. The crystal itself has a slightly misty quality not attributable to interior 'frosting' sometimes seen in such bottles.

The subject of crabs holding grass sprays (or millet, rice, or reeds) is a popular one, but because of the confusion of which particular grass variety is depicted, these subects can be interpreted in a variety of ways. For example Bartholomew, in *Hidden Meanings in Chinese Art*, lists at least five interpretations of the theme, plus an additional theme of crabs holding cockscombs. In this case the depiction of two crabs, *xie*, clutching at a reed, *lu*, forms the rebus 'May you pass high on the civil service examination', *erjia chuanlu*. This derives from the word for the armour-like shells of the crab, *jia*, combined with the word for two, *er*. *Erjia* stands for the second class of successful candidates in the final (palace) civil service exam. Whilst the reed, *lu*, is a pun for *chuanlu*, 'the announcement of the candidates', see Bartholomew, *ibid*, p. 98, 4.21.2. The crabs in our bottle are almost invisible at a first glance, melding in as they do with the darker patches of tourmaline needles. This may well have been the carver's intention, just as a crab might disappear behind aquatic fronds.

The teardrop shape of this bottle is extremely satisfying, even the more so with the interior hollowing matching the profile perfectly.

The foot is on the short side but it does cause the appearance of the bottle 'settling down' in to it and anchoring the bottle. A late-eighteenth-century date should not be ruled out but a nineteenth-century one is more likely.

(CBL C 849)

106

107

107 (detail)

108

Smoky crystal, carved in the form of a rolled hand scroll, a spiral edge leads down from the neck and around the body ending in the fold-over end of the scroll, a figure of a wine immortal resting against a stack of tied books and two gourd-shaped wine vessels, each with ladles and engraved with ice-pattern, all below a low-relief five-character title slip, the neck cylindrical, the rim concave, the mouth quite large and the interior well hollowed, the base with asymmetric flat foot shallowly cut, the clear stone slightly yellow-toned

1800-1880

Height: 6.2 cm
Mouth: 0.7 cm
Neck: 1.35 cm (notched at one edge)

The five- character title slip can be read as:
Chen shi jiu zhong xian

This can be translated as:
I am the wine drinking immortal (Li Taibai)

Li Taibai (701-762) or Lipo as he is sometimes called was a Tang dynasty poet famous for his fondness for wine. He is said to have died when drunkenly attempting to embrace the moon's reflection in a river. The bearded figure sits casually enough against his stack of books, unopened and serving merely as an armrest. His body tilts very slightly forward and his face bears a tired countenance suggestive of perhaps one cup of wine too many. His right arm rests languorously against his right leg. Even the handle of the ladle, which tips towards the figure, echoes the mood of drunkenness. The scene of one of the eight immortals of the wine cup drinking the elixir of immortality from gourds is an analogy of transformation from one realm to another, which is particularly appropriate as this bottle is itself a transformation from a hand scroll. Because of the down-twisting sloping edge of the scroll, a ziggurat-like structure has been formed which besides being a most appealing form forces the viewer to turn the bottle in the hand and to view the scene just as one would do if one were un-rolling a scroll to study the painting.

Dating of this bottle is slightly problematic due to its unique shape and subject matter. The bottle is admittedly well hollowed but the stone is not of the clearest quality. It has definite yellow tinges to the colour. The style of carving could date to the eighteenth century and the playful conceit of a scroll painting transforming to a bottle is certainly one that would have appealed to the scholar class but which we cannot say with any certainty might have been made for the court. It is probably best to suggest a nineteenth-century date for production but with the possibility of being crafted earlier.

(CBL C 898)

108 (two views)

109

Crystal, the clear stone carved in high relief on one main face with three goats or sheep on a rocky ground beneath the sun rising from a cloud cleverly carved from the only yellow inclusion in the stone, the other main face carved in exceedingly low relief with a large pine tree, very cleverly using two natural misty fissures concealed under pine branches and continuing into the cloud design on the shoulder, one narrow side carved with a small hut nestled under the pine near bamboo and a leafless tree, the neck cylindrical, the rim flat, well hollowed to the interior, a rounded oval foot ring and deeply cut base

Possibly the School of the Rustic Crystal Master, 1750-1880

Stopper: jadeite on metal collar (oxidized silver) with stamped swastika design

Height: 7.0 cm
Mouth: 0.7 cm
Neck: 1.8 cm-2.0 cm (oval)

Provenance: S. H. Kuhn, Peking, 1917

Here we have a bottle that was known to have been purchased from the Peking dealer, S. H. Kuhn, in 1917. This is one of the very few in the collection where we can be certain of a purchase date.

The stone has a wonderful ice cold clarity but for the yellow inclusion which has been used to great advantage as the cloud base for the rising sun and two very narrow misty fissures that are also 'concealed' within the branches of the pine that stretch across the design. The subject of three goats (or sheep) and a rising sun was employed in the decorative arts of the Ming but according to Bartholomew, *Hidden Meanings in Chinese Art*, p. 146, 6.16.1, did not gain prominence until the Qianlong period particularly in jade carving. The Xuande Emperor (1426-1435) is known to have executed a painting of this subject showing an ewe and two lambs under a rock and a flowering bush. No distinction is made in Chinese between sheep and goats, *yang*, the collective name for sheep, rams, lambs, ewes, and goats is homophone of *yang*, the male principle or positive force. Therefore, the depiction of three goats or sheep, *sanyang*, along with a rising sun, *taiyang*, form the rebus 'the new year brings a change of fortune', *sanyang kaitai*.

The carving of the pine branches on one side of this bottle appears to match the carving to be found on a wide-ranging group of quartz bottles that have been assigned to a school called 'The Rustic Crystal Master' by Moss, Graham, and Tsang, *A Treasury of Chinese Snuff Bottles: The Mary and George Bloch Collection*, Vol. 2, Part 1, Quartz, pp. 194-196, no. 254. The school appears to be the production of a large hardstone carving center, as yet un-identified, but possibly centered near Lake Tai at Huzhou or Wuxing (see Nos. 64 and 69 in this publication) which specialized in crystal and quartzite, but occasionally used other materials. A tentative attribution to Zhangzhou and Zhangbu in Fujian Provence has also been put forward by the authors, but it remains only a possibility. The style of the wares associated with this school are primarily painterly low-relief landscape scenes (influenced by the literati painting tradition) made up of a series of standard elements which seem to include wintery scenes with bare trees and humble dwellings (as in our example), pine and rocks, these are often further enhanced by 'frosting' the interior of the bottles or simply by utilizing a misty crystal.

It is quite interesting to note how often this subject is depicted in quartz materials. Obviously the school or their patrons favoured the subject. For other crystal bottles depicting the same subject, see Hughes, *The Blair Bequest: Chinese Snuff Bottles from the Princeton University Art Museum*, p. 60, no. 36; Holden, *Rivers and Mountains Far from the World*, pp. 146-147, no. 60, *Zhongguo Biyanhu Zhenshang*, (Gems of Chinese Snuff Bottles), no. 287; Moss, *Chinese Snuff Bottles of the Silica and Quartz Group*, no. 113; and Kliener, *Chinese Snuff Bottles: A Miniature Art from the Collection Mary and George Bloch*, no. 236.

(CBL C 892)

110

Crystal, twin bottles, the smaller of the two bottles of spade shape and carved in high relief at its base from an aquamarine coloured inclusion, with a three-legged mythical toad rising upwards from breaking waves and rockwork, which continue on to the reverse side, the taller bottle of narrow ovoid shape rides 'piggy-back' on the smaller bottle, its flat oval base not touching the ground, the main face carved in low relief with a *lingzhi* rising from a tripod vessel, *ding*, and stand, a book and a ribboned sword nearby, the rims flat, the mouths small and well hollowed and 'frosted' to both interiors

1780-1880

Stoppers: small bottle, jadeite with rose quartz finial; large bottle: glass imitating jadeite with glass imitating rose quartz finial

Height: 8.0 cm overall
Mouth: small bottle 0.45 cm-1.3 cm (oval); large bottle 1.3 cm (slightly oval)
Neck: small bottle 1.3 cm-1.8 cm (oval); large bottle 1.7 cm (slightly oval)

The well-hollowed interiors of both bottles have been 'frosted' (polished) to give an appearance of semi-opacity, when the stone is actually of extreme clarity. No doubt this helps to both highlight the decoration on the exterior whilst subtly obscuring the contents.

Unfortunately the bottle does not stand unaided. The three-legged toad that forms part of the foot to the smaller bottle has a rounded surface rather than a flat bottom, which combined with the weight of the bottle attached on one side forces the bottle to fall to one side.

Interestingly, a clever use has been made of the differing parts of the stone that the bottle was carved from. The squatter bottle, which is carved with the toad emitting a vapor stream from its mouth and cleverly utilizing small dark green inclusions that run up the bottle, is actually of a slightly more 'muddy' overall tone. The slightly clearer material of the more elongated tall bottle that does seem to rise above it, both metaphorically and literally, wonderfully balances this.

Twin bottles conjoined at their mid-section seem to be something of a specialty in the quartz arena. Quite a large number exist suggesting that perhaps there was indeed one centre of production for such bottles. For other examples, see Hughes, *The Blair Bequest: Chinese Snuff Bottles from the Princeton University Art Museum*, p. 57, no. 30 and p. 63, no. 41; Moss, Graham, and Tsang, *A Treasury of Chinese Snuff Bottles: The Mary and George Bloch Collection*, Vol. 2, Quartz, pp. 183-191, nos. 249-252; and Bob C. Stevens, *The Collector's Book of Snuff Bottles*, no. 469.

The subject of the smaller bottle appears to be that of the immortal Liu Hai's mythical toad. Both are associated with wealth. The three-legged toad is normally shown accompanying the immortal on his travels but occasionally the toad is depicted as a symbol by itself with the same wealth connotations. The subject of the more slender bottle relates to longevity (*lingzhi*), strength (sword), learning (book), and male descendants (*ding*).

(CBL C 890)

109 (two views)

110 (two views)

111

Smoky crystal, of cylindrical shape with short sloping shoulders and short neck with slightly beveled flat rim and mouth edge, the foot slightly spreading and the edge beveled, a flat circular foot ring, the base very slightly convex in shape, the clear stone with an even pale yellow-tinged tone, the bottle heavy and thick-walled

1730-1870

Height: 5.8 cm
Mouth: 1.3 cm
Neck: 2.9 cm

If one bottle could illustrate formal integrity, this is it: simple and satisfying. We have an uncomplicated basic cylinder that has been cut with short sloping shoulders and very slightly everted neck, which is mirrored in the lower half of the bottle by the slightly spreading foot, which like the rim is beveled. Despite the fact that the walls of the vessel are quite thick, it is well hollowed and polished to perfection. The thickness of the walls adds a solemnity to the bottle very much in keeping with the simplicity of the design. As this was more likely a table bottle than one to be carried, the additional weight that the walls provide anchors the bottle nicely.

It is interesting to compare this bottle with another more slender crystal example illustrated by Moss, Graham, and Tsang, *A Treasury of Chinese Snuff Bottles: The Mary and George Bloch Collection*, Vol. 2, Quartz, pp. 134-136, no. 230. Where the authors discuss the crystal cylindrical form as it relates to blue and white porcelain snuff bottles, a media in which the form is commonest, and suggest that there must be a link of sorts between them. The shape was popular in the Yongzheng reign (1723-35) and came back in to favour during the Daoguang reign (1820-1850).

(CBL C 853)

112

Smoky crystal, the very pale-yellow-toned clear stone, buff polished to the interior to give a slight impression of opacity, well rounded shoulders and slightly spreading short foot, a circular flat foot ring and slightly convex base

1750-1850

Height: 6.4 cm
Mouth: 0.7 cm- 0.8 cm, slightly beveled
Neck: 1.3 cm

The *meiping* shape is a most elegant form that has a long tradition in Chinese art. It was extremely popular during Song dynasty ceramic output, appearing in a wide variety of kiln production from the north and south. Its popularity continued during the early part of the Ming dynasty, particularly during the Yongle (1403-25) and Xuande (1426-35) periods of early blue-and-white production from Jingdezhen, which in turn were revived during the reigns of the Yonzheng and Qianlong emperors during the eighteenth century. In fact the Yongzheng emperor is known to have frequently sent actual antiques from the palace collection to the imperial ceramic factories in Jingdezhen, for copying and inspiration. Our form is loosely based on the more high-shouldered form. The quality of the cutting, the degree of fine hollowing, the sheer elegance of the form with its small but slightly spreading foot springing from the otherwise top-heavy form, are suggestive of mid-Qing production, possibly even as early as the mid-eighteenth century.

The word *meiping* describes a vase made to hold a single spray of plum blossom.

(CBL C 855)

113

Smoky crystal, carved as a mallow flower head with a stigma with spiraling filaments at its centre and surrounded by five petals, a short cylindrical neck, flat rim, and small mouth, the foot formed by one of the five petals, the clear stone with a very slight pale yellow tinge, buff polished to the interior to give a slight impression of opacity

1800-1880

Stopper: jadeite with metal collar (oxidized silver)

Height: 6.0 cm
Mouth: 0.7 cm
Neck: 1.6 cm

The mallow belongs to the *malvaceae* family and comes in many different forms but with flower heads that almost always have five or six petals. Historically this particular design of flower head has been termed a mallow, though in fact it really only bears a passing formalized resemblance to the blossoms. The mallow, like the sunflower, rotates to follow the path of the sun and so according to Moss, Graham, and Tsang, *A Treasury of Chinese Snuff Bottles: The Mary and George Bloch Collection*, Vol. 5, Part 2, Glass, pp.321-322, no. 816, the mallow is a symbol of obedience, the sun being emblematic of the ruler. As such it would have been an appropriate gift to officials serving the emperor at Court.

Two different types of bottle design appear to use this flower head as a primary subject. In one the flower head dictates the shape of the bottle, as in our example, and in the other it is superimposed as a panel at the centre of the design. Both are found primarily in glass bottles but a few examples exist in other materials. As a rule the quality of the mallow-form bottles varies greatly, suggesting that this type was made over a considerable time span. It seems unlikely that the bottle was made prior to the early-nineteenth century.

(CBL C 865)

114

Amethyst, carved in extremely low relief with a continuous landscape scene with pine and other bare trees to one main face and further pine, a small thatched building, and mountains in the distance on the other, the cylindrical neck with very slightly concave rim and small rather unevenly cut mouth, neatly hollowed but with quite thick walls, an oval flat foot ring and shallowly cut base, the stone with a soft violet tone and misty inclusions

School of the Rustic Crystal Master, 1780-1850

Height: 6.3 cm
Mouth: 0.7 cm
Neck: 2.15 cm

This bottle is remarkably heavy in the hand. The neatly finished interior has not been entirely hollowed, presumably to retain a certain depth of colour that might be lost if the walls were not as thick as they are. The matrix of the stone has quite a fine network of 'sea-spray' inclusions that actually appears like mist floating through the trees and mountains. The coldness of the stone further adds to the bleakness of the harsh winter landscape.

The subject matter and the sparse low-relief carving is indicative of that found on a wide-ranging group of quartz bottles that have been assigned to the School of 'The Rustic Crystal Master' by Moss, Graham, and Tsang, *A Treasury of Chinese Snuff Bottles: The Mary and George Bloch Collection*, Vol. 2, Part 1, Quartz, pp. 194-196, no. 254. The school is discussed in the entry to No. 109 in this publication. Whilst misty crystal seems to have been the most popular material for the school, they occasionally used other materials such as the misty amethyst of this example. Here the leafless tree branches are evoked by the simplest of cutting strokes at acute angles to the trunks and the thick and scaly and often-flaking bark of the pine is suggested by simple short strokes within a wavering line. The pines needles are suggested by over-sized rudimentary clumps. The various elements come together to form an evocative winter landscape.

(CBL C 870)

111

112

113

114

115

Crystal, the main faces of the clear stone plain and slightly convex, the narrow sides carved with high-relief stylized lion-mask ring handles below sloping shoulders, the rim concave, a regular mouth and exceedingly well hollowed interior, a rounded oval foot ring and regularly cut base

1770-1870

Height: 7.4 cm
Mouth: 0.8 cm
Neck: 2.15 cm

If it were not for the clear coldness of the material and the occasional, though barely visible, misty inclusions one might assume this bottle is made of glass. It is however an almost flawless crystal of the clearest colourless type. One of the earlier recorded Imperial gifts of a snuff bottle was of crystal, given to an envoy of the pope in Rome by the Kangxi Emperor late in his reign, see *Masterpieces of Snuff Bottles in the Palace Museum*, p. 29. The exact year of the gift is not mentioned but the pope in question was most likely Clement XI (1700-21), but possibly Innocent XIII (1721-24). Crystal had been carved in China in the form of amulets and pendants since the Zhou dynasty (c. 1100-256 BCE) and so had a long history. The Palace collections have many large crystal vases of differing forms most of which can be safely dated to the mid-Qing period. Knowing that crystal bottles existed in the 1720s one must assume that their production continued uninterrupted through the eighteenth and in to the nineteenth century. Once again, given the scant number of datable crystal bottles, we have to choose a quite wide date range for this bottle. The hollowing is exceptional, with paper-thin walls and superb polishing through a relatively small mouth. Interestingly, from a side profile the stylized mask handles are carved in exceedingly high relief, which gives a slightly bulky appearance as though seemingly 'applied' to the surface. However, when held in the hand, a probable explanation for this design decision becomes clear. The handles simply serve their intended purpose. They allow the fingers to grip tightly the otherwise shiny and slippery surface of the bottle. The handles are quite unusual and rather special. Whilst ostensibly appearing like common, typical handles, closer inspection reveals some anomalies from the norm, which due to our limited knowledge at this time, can not be explained. The eight curls or coils that form the stylized mane of the lion are far more elongated or vertical than is typical, whilst the area between the eyebrows and the jaw is overtly compressed and abbreviated. The ring itself is drawn out to form a slender oval, which perfectly balances the mane above. Overall it has an appearance akin to an open-mouthed Greek tragedy mask.

The overall integrity of the bottle is unquestionable. Moss, Graham and Tsang, *A Treasury of Chinese Snuff Bottle: The Mary and George Bloch Collection*, Vol. 2, Part 1, Quartz, pp. 22-24 no. 23, also remark on a surprisingly often overlooked fact regarding snuff bottles—they were intended for snuff users. 'Connoisseurship of the snuff itself was highly refined amongst the snuff-taking elite. Steeped in a culture where connoisseurship was an ingrained aspect of education and a natural hobby among the influential minority, there evolved an esoteric connoisseurship of snuff. Different colours and qualities of snuff were exquisitely graded and evaluated as fine vintages of wine are in the West. With a flawless, clear bottle, some of these qualities could be perceived: colour certainly, probably grade. The knowing eye would recognize a rare and expensive snuff through the walls of the bottle and rejoice in the companionship of arcane souls in which connoisseurship revels.'

For another rock crystal bottle (citrine) of slightly more truncated form than our bottle but similarly carved with large mask and ring handles, see Low, *More Treasures from the Sanctum of Enlightened Respect*, p. 243, no. 226.

(CBL C 860)

116

Crystal, the main faces slightly bulbous and plain, the narrow sides rounded and carved in low relief with unusual handles in the form of a bat suspending a ring attached to a tasseled musical stone, all below rounded shoulders and a cylindrical neck, the rim flat, a regular mouth but extremely well hollowed interior, the narrow oval flat foot ring very slightly beveled at its edge, the base shallowly cut

1750-1850

Stopper: jadeite with metal collar

Height: 5.8 cm
Mouth: 0.8 cm
Neck: 1.8 cm

The bat, *fu*, is the foremost motif for 'blessings' and 'riches'. The characters for both words are pronounced *fu* though they are written differently. When the bat is shown upside down, *dao*, as in our example, it is a pun on the word 'arrived', *dao*, and when depicted as such they can mean 'blessings have arrived'. The stone chime or musical stone, *qing*, is a pun for 'celebration' or 'joy'. The two combined can mean 'to celebrate or enjoy the newly arrived blessings'. The stone chime is also one of the eight treasures of Daoism, *babao*. See Bartholomew, *Hidden Meanings in Chinese Art*, pp. 20-30, 1.1 and 1.1.27.

The carving of the handles on our bottle is masterful. To produce such a fluid line from so unforgiving a stone shows extraordinary skill on the part of the lapidary. There is nothing jarring between the various elements and each gracefully flows in a steady progression from the shoulder down. The wings of the bats have been tucked in to the chubby bodies to almost inscribe a sphere and the oval ring that they hold in their mouths very cleverly bisect the smaller ring-attachments of the stone chime (or musical stone) at a point off centre. The chimes are very neatly engraved with four small stars that echo four engraved on the backs of the bats above forcing the viewer to pull the elements together. The chimes are neatly finished with a slightly asymmetric ribbon. More importantly the convex bulbous main faces of the bottle mirror very closely the same curvature of the bats' wings and the chimes profile to form an incredible homogenous whole, nicely framed by the simple short foot and taller cylindrical neck. Looking at quality alone there is certainly a good chance that this bottle may date to as early as the mid-eighteenth century.

(CBL C 862)

115 (two views)

116 (two views)

117

Crystal, one main face carved in low relief with a pine tree with bamboo and rockwork below, and a four-character inscription alongside, the other main face and the narrow sides plain, a short cylindrical neck with flat rim and a small mouth and well hollowed interior, a rounded oval foot ring and regular cut base, the clear stone of very slightly yellowish tone

1780-1850

Stopper: jadeite with metal collar (oxidized silver)

Height: 6.8 cm
Mouth: 0.7 cm
Neck: 1.5 cm

The four-character inscription reads:
Song qing zhu chiu

This can be translated as:
Pine clean and pure, bamboo very green

See Bartholomew, *Hidden Meanings in Chinese Art*, p. 60, 3.1 and 3.1.1 where the author notes that the combination of bamboo, *zhu*, and pine, *song*, form the rebus 'May the family unite and flourish', *zhubao songmao*. The motif is often used on gifts to celebrate a family moving in to a new residence. The phrase originated in the Western Zhou (1050-771 BCE) *Book of Odes*, according to which King Xuan was building a palace and recited a poem about the roots of the bamboo being firmly bound together and the pines flourishing.

The pine and the bamboo are also individually representative of longevity symbols because of their resistance to the elements and are also viewed models of fortitude and uprightness. They are also both evergreens, which further enhance the multiple levels of meaning.

The rock, which sits rather unobtrusively below the pine on our bottle, is yet another symbol of longevity.

This bottle may have been given as a birthday gift or as a house-warming gift, perhaps it was even intended to celebrate both occasions.

Interestingly there may have been an added twist to the meaning of this bottle, by the use of the *meiping* form, which was a vase shape designated for the plum blossom, *mei*. The combination of pine, bamboo, and plum, is of course, one of the most popular subjects in the decorative arts, the so-called 'Three Friends of Winter', *suihan sanyou*.

Whilst the calligraphy is certainly of a satisfactory standard on the bottle, the carved and engraved subject of the pine, bamboo, and rocks is arguably not. There is little that is laudable about the poorly constructed pine trunk and cartoon-like branches, nor in the cursorily 'scratched' pine needles. In defense perhaps this 'rustic' approach was meant to convey a certain other-worldliness, a simplistic ideal achieved by reducing elements to their essentials.

(CBL C 871)

118

Crystal, one main face carved in low relief with a seven-character inscription and two seals, the other main face with a chrysanthemum spray and simply delineated soil, the rounded narrow sides with stylized lion-mask handles, the shoulders nicely rounded below a cylindrical neck with a flat rim and a wide mouth, the interior well hollowed, a wide flat oval foot ring and regular cut base, the clear stone with a faint slightly yellowish tinge

1750-1850

Height: 6.1 cm
Mouth: 0.8 cm
Neck: 1.5 cm

The seven-character inscription reads:
Yuan ming qu hou wu zhi yi followed by two seals *Hua Yun*

This can be translated as:
'After Yuanming left (or died) I know everything,' followed by the artist's name, Hua Yun, in seal form.

Tao Yuanming was the art-name for the Eastern Jin dynasty scholar, poet, and recluse, Tao Qian, who died in 427 CE. Not only did he compose many enthralling poems on the subject of chrysanthemums but after his retirement was famous for lovingly planting them in profusion in his garden retreat, particularly at its East Fence, *Dong li*, where presumably the vagaries of the elements where less invasive. The East Fence is warmly mentioned in much of his poetry.

The chrysanthemum, *juhua*, is also an important flower. It is a symbol of autumn and the flower of the ninth month and also represents longevity because of its hardiness. The first character of its name, *ju*, is a pun for 'dwell', *ju*, see Bartholomew, *Hidden Meanings in Chinese Art*, p. 175, 7.11.

Hua Yun, the artist who presumably made the bottle but who certainly wrote the inscription, is un-recorded.

The quality of the carving on this bottle surpasses that of the previous example despite its 'rustic' charm. The running script calligraphy is well spaced and fluid. This is remarkably difficult to achieve with so hard and uncompromising a material as crystal, where one mistake remains etched for a lifetime. The carving of the chrysanthemum whilst simple is not simplistic, essential rather than rudimentary. The spacing across the face of the bottle is well achieved to form a pleasant asymmetric design that balances well with the slightly unusual serpentine curve of the 'rings' that form the lower portion of the lion-mask handles. The neck has the appearance of being 'waisted' because of the interior cutting of the mouth that leaves a 'waisted' outline visible through straight-sided cylindrical walls.

For an example of an Imperial Qianlong ceramic snuff bottle with chrysanthemum on one side and a poem that references Tao Yuanming on the other, see Hughes, *The Blair Bequest: Chinese Snuff Bottles from the Princeton University Art Museum*, pp. 164-165, no. 203.

(CBL C 876)

117 (two views)

118 (two views)

119

Crystal, of fruit shape, carved in low relief on each main face with a bat swooping above waves and rockwork, the narrow sides beveled flat with simple narrow vertical handles that are pierced horizontally, all below a wavy collar which forms the neck, the rim deeply concave, a large mouth and quite well hollowed and very lightly 'frosted' interior, the bottom cut flat with an oval foot ring and a deeply-cut concave base

1750-1850

Stopper: crystal as a twisting twig with leafy foliage (possibly original)

Height: 5.9 cm
Mouth: 0.8 cm
Neck: 1.6 cm

Although ostensibly a fruit-shaped bottle of compressed pear shape, it is possible, particularly if one removes the stopper which may not be original anyway, that the form might simply represent a gourd vessel like the one depicted alongside the wine immortal in No. 108 in this publication; the wavy collar of this bottle, which may represent calyx, is clearly very similar to the collar of that vessel. The addition of two very simplified vertical handles however would certainly not be appropriate on the group of purely naturalistic fruit-shaped bottles that this bottle might otherwise be grouped with (see the entry for No. 38 in this publication). On a wine vessel to be carried it would certainly make more sense. Possibly it depicts a leather pouch form of the kind worn by rural dwellers and horsemen. Certainly the rather poor quality finish to the piercing of the simplified handles gives it a nomadic feel.

The depiction of bats, *fu*, is a popular motif for 'blessings' and 'riches'. According to Bartholomew, *Hidden Meanings in Chinese Art*, p. 170, 7.3.11, bats hovering above waves or the sea, *hai*, forms the rebus 'May your blessings be as deep as the Eastern Sea', *furu donghai*, or 'May you be blessed by the mountain of longevity and sea of blessings', *shoushan fuhai*. The subject was a popular one on ceramics of the Yongzheng and Qianlong period made for the Imperial court. The depictions of the swooping bats and rockwork, which are simply but exquisitely wrought from the hard stone, differ slightly to each main face of our bottle which adds a nice asymmetry to the whole. The waves gently follow the outline of the curve of the bottle and are neatly finished at the base. The stone is actually of great clarity but the buffing or 'frosting' to the interior somewhat conceals this. The quality of workmanship, the degree of hollowing and the sensitivity of the lapidary's vision suggest that this bottle may well be a product of the second-half of the eighteenth century.

(CBL C 881)

120

Crystal, the main faces plain, each narrow side carved in high relief with a *chilong* climbing to the shoulder their bifurcated tails forming the foot ring, the neck cylindrical, the rim flat and the mouth large and cut very slightly off centre, the interior well hollowed, the clear stone with some crystalline inclusions to one side

1770-1880

Height: 6.5 cm
Mouth: 0.65 cm
Neck: 1.2 cm

The *chi* dragon, *chilong*, has a long history in Chinese hard stone carving. The impish light-hearted lizard-like dragon with bifurcated tail and feline features can be found on jade carvings, certainly as early as the Han period, 206 BCE-220 CE, and would certainly have been associated with antiquity by the scholar class, see Rawson, *Chinese Jade from the Neolithic to the Qing*, pp. 297-302, 21.6-21.16, for sword paraphernalia from Han tombs. There is no doubt that the *chilongs* of our bottle are indebted to this ancient source.

Moss, Graham, and Tsang, *A Treasury of Chinese Snuff Bottle: The Mary and George Bloch Collection*, Vol. 1, Jade, pp. 242-245, no. 99, discuss the subject of the *chilong* in the context of Court design on snuff bottles. Whilst examples of *chilong* as secondary elements in the design on multiple wares in the Imperial collections abound, their use as a primary element are far fewer. The authors believe there is enough evidence to suggest that the *chilong* was a particular favorite of the Court during the Qing dynasty, probably particularly so during the Qianlong period and probably far less common from centres other than the Palace workshops, but allowing that the Court could also dictate the use of the subject from any of the distant facilities producing for the Court.

The question arises whether the *chilong* of our example can be considered the primary or secondary element. Whilst certainly the only element of the decoration, one could argue that as they form the handles they should be considered secondary. They are assuredly of merit, the carving is well rendered and the animals have good movement, not only in their twisting and sinuous bodies but also in relation to each other. Each moves in the opposite direction, whilst their tails coil together at the base of the bottle to each form a part of the foot ring, which neatly anchors them. The bottle is of compressed shape and has been illustrated at an angle to allow the reader to see the *chilong* to best advantage.

For a bottle that otherwise has a good degree of hollowing and formal integrity, it is not only odd but also somewhat discouraging that the lapidary has cut the mouth very slightly off centre.

(CBL C 889)

119

120 (two views)

121

Crystal, two bats carved in low relief around the tapering cylindrical body, one swooping down from the rounded shoulder, the other flying up from the lower third of the bottle, a short tapering neck with a flat rim and very large mouth, the interior well hollowed but stopping well short of the foot and 'frosted', a flat uneven oval foot ring and concave base, a few flaw lines in the clear stone

1780-1880

Stopper: green glass of twisting twig form imitating emerald or jadeite

Height: 9.5 cm
Mouth: 0.7 cm
Neck: 1.1 cm

The bat or *fu*, as previously noted, is a motif for 'blessings' and 'riches'. When the bat is shown upside down, *dao*, as on one side of our bottle, it is a pun on the word 'arrived', *dao*, and when depicted as such they can mean 'blessings have arrived'. When a pair, *shuang*, of bats is depicted it forms the rebus 'May you have double blessings', *shuangfu*. See Bartholomew, *Hidden Meanings in Chinese Art*, p. 22, no. 1.1.2

The lapidary has rather sensibly stopped short of hollowing out the bottle the entire way down, as is usually the case on crystal bottles, to avoid an imbalance in weight distribution. Here there appears to be no doubt that the slender nature of the bottle with its small oval foot required that the lapidary leave enough 'weight' at the base of the bottle to enable it to stand successfully. This is somewhat aesthetically displeasing on a purely transparent material but appears unavoidable for the bottle to stand on its own.

Another unusual feature is the atypically large mouth in relation to the small size of the neck. Whilst allowing greater access to the interior, it is not a hallmark normally associated with the crystal group. The rare occasions when a large mouth is a feature is on a group of highly Imperial jade bottles. Many of these utilize a yellow or spinach jade, and very often are of vase form. It is possible that the group in some way influenced this bottle. For an example of such a bottle carved from spinach jade with three bats at the shoulders and a large mouth, see Moss, Graham, and Tsang, *A Treasury of Chinese Snuff Bottle: The Mary and George Bloch Collection*, Vol. 1, Jade, pp. 202-203, no. 82.

For a smoky crystal bottle of rectangular shape carved with a single bat, see Nicollier, *The Baur Collection*, pp. 234-235, no. H 93.

(CBL C 882)

122

Crystal, carved in a continuous scene in low relief with a female immortal standing on waves pouring the contents of an amphora, a large fish rises from the waves below cleverly utilizing an orange-brown inclusion in the stone, breaking frothy waves rise to the narrow sides which continue to the other main face, below a hilly island shoreline, the neck cylindrical, the rim slightly concave, a regular mouth and quite well hollowed interior, the base carved with waves

Possibly the School of the Rustic Crystal Master, 1750-1880

Stopper: glass imitating rose quartz, metal collar (oxidized silver), the silver spoon with stamped seal on reverse side of long scoop (not illustrated)

Height: 5.5 cm
Mouth: 0.7 cm
Neck: 1.8 cm

Whilst the subject matter and the medium-relief carving is not wholly indicative of that found on a wide-ranging group of quartz bottles that have been assigned to the School of 'The Rustic Crystal Master' by Moss, Graham, and Tsang, *A Treasury of Chinese Snuff Bottles: The Mary and George Bloch Collection*, Vol. 2, Part 1, Quartz, pp. 194-205, no. 254-257, there seem many other tangible reasons why this particular bottle might be assigned to the group. The school is discussed in the entry to No. 109 in this publication. The subjects most closely associated with this school are primarily painterly low-relief landscape scenes, influenced by the literati painting tradition. However, the school tackles a number of other subjects and sometimes uses a slightly higher form of relief carving. The school also features the creative use of flaws in the material. Many of these flaws take the form of misty white inclusions, which are quite useful when the subject matter is a winter landscape. However, when the flaws take the form of discoloured flaws of a yellow or brown nature, they must be handled with a different approach. Here the figure of the female Daoist immortal He Xiangu (or possibly Guanyin) holds a vase containing the elixir of life or soothing holy water, which she pours on to troubled brewing waters, from which a fish, emblematic of harmony and abundance, rises. The rather unsightly negative brown flaw suddenly becomes a powerful and positive lucky symbol. The carving on the reverse side is more in keeping with the regular subjects of the school, depicting a hilly island shoreline. For a depiction of He Xiangu in ceramic from Fujian province, see Donnelly, *Blanc De Chine*, fig. 100, and also Kerr & Ayers, *Catalogue*, Blanc De Chine Porcelain from Dehua, no. 6, for a figure of Guanyin also depicted with a pouring vessel. Such figures as these were particularly popular during the seventeenth and eighteenth century in the south of China and perhaps this may be a clue as to one possible centre of production for the school (Huzhou or Wuxing near Lake Tai being another). Interestingly, as mentioned in the entry for No. 109 in this publication, Moss, Graham, and Tsang, *A Treasury of Chinese Snuff Bottles: The Mary and George Bloch Collection*, Vol. 2, Part 1, Quartz, pp. 194-196, no. 254, offer a tentative attribution to Zhangzhou and Zhangbu in Fujian province as a possible centre of production for such crystal bottles.

The seal marks on the spoon can be read as *Xu — Feng* (a shop name or maker) followed by *Zu Wen* (100 percent silver)

A paper label glued on the reverse of the bottle reads 'D322/ I 2-10.

(CBL C 905)

121

122

123

Crystal, of compressed form, carved in low relief on each main face with a *Da* character in the upper bulb and a *Ji* character in the larger lower bulb, each character dividing two descending mythical feline creatures, a mixture of *chi-long* and tigers, the lower gourd with a wish-granting pearl, *baozhu*, below the *Ji* character, the neck very slightly everted, the rim slightly concave, the mouth small and a very well hollowed and lightly 'frosted' interior, a narrow flat oval foot ring and simple concave base

1750-1850

Stopper: jadeite with metal collar (oxidized silver)

Height: 6.3 cm
Mouth: 0.5 cm
Neck: 1.5 cm

See Bartholomew, *Hidden Meaning in Chinese Art*, p. 61, no. 3.3 for an explanation of the gourd as an important auspicious symbol. It is a natural symbol of fertility because of its numerous seeds. Combined with the two characters *Da ji* ('great luck') the positive aspects are reinforced.

Moss, Graham, and Tsang, *The Art of the Chinese Snuff Bottles: The J & J Collection*, Vol. 1, pp. 177-178, no. 98, illustrate an almost identical bottle. They tentatively attribute the bottle to the Palace workshops on three grounds. First, the popularity of crystal at Court; second, the popularity of the double-gourd form at the palace workshops, primarily on glass and enamel-wares; and third, the Qianlong emperor is known to have loved formalized designs of this type and ordered many bottles to give on special occasions. All three are perfectly acceptable arguments but perhaps more important still is the quality of the work. The hollowing is sensational. The difficulty that the lapidary had to overcome is astonishing. Not only did he have to work through a relatively small mouth but also had to find a way to carve out the upper section of the lower bulb past the narrow confines of the tightly pinched 'waist' at the centre of the bottle. It is perfectly achieved and we are left with a wonderful gourd form that is light due to the extraordinary degree of hollowing that barely allows the viewer to judge the walls thickness. The design of dragons, which have a definite feline quality, are carved in very low relief but enough to stop the bottle slipping in the hand. The neck of the bottle is not quite cylindrical. It has a very subtle flare that is more discernable when the stopper is removed.

It is exactly the same height and has almost the same size neck and mouth as the J & J bottle. The creatures on that example are simply called *chi* dragons. It does appear that the use of hatched lines on the backs and legs of the creatures might suggest a more feline tiger beast, although they do have bifurcated tails not normally associated with tigers. According to Bartholomew, *Hidden Meanings in Chinese Art*, p. 80, no. 3.28, the tiger teams up with the dragon to represent the yin and yang guardians protecting palaces as well as tombs. Perhaps this representation is a combination of the two.

For another almost identical example see Sotheby's New York, 17 March 1997, lot 149. For a plainer smoky crystal bottle of gourd shape decorated only with the *Da ji* characters, see Hall, *Chinese Snuff Bottles II*, p. 58, no. 40. See also a realgar glass bottle no. 186 in this publication, which also has a *Da ji* inscription on one side.

(CBL C 888)

123 (two views)

124

Crystal, of compressed form, both main faces carved in very low relief, one with a large fiery sun with flaming surround above a scene of a stylized rock battered by breaking frothing waves with bubbles, the other with the moon with a cloud-like surround, above a scene with further clouds, the narrow rounded sides carved with crane and musical stone handles, the neck very slighted waisted, the rim very slightly concave, a flat oval foot ring and deeply cut foot

1750-1850

Height: 5.5 cm
Mouth: 0.7 cm
Neck: 1.6 cm

The moon, *yue,* represents the essence of the female or negative principle in nature, just as the male or positive principle is embodied by the sun, *taiyang.* Therefore it symbolizes a celestial balance. A number of the clouds that support our depiction of the moon may actually represent waves, as the Chinese understood the moon's influence on the tides from an early age and the lunar calendar is still in use alongside the Gregorian calendar, see Williams, *Outlines of Chinese Symbolism and Art Motives.*

According to Bartholomew, *Hidden Meanings in Chinese Art*, pp. 107, 128, and 286 the Chinese associate the roundness of the moon, *yueliang,* with the cohesion of the family. A rising sun brings a new day and good fortune and can represent a rise in prosperity, rank, and career. The crane, *he,* is perhaps the most celebrated bird in Chinese art after the phoenix, *feng,* and was a popular subject as the aerial carrier of the immortals. It is a symbol of longevity and is also a symbol of high rank at Court; it ranks first of the nine civil official rank badges. Flying cranes, *yipin niao,* form the rebus 'May you rise high and become an official of the first rank', *yipin gaosheng.* Depicted here, nestled between the sun and the moon, it is fair to conclude that they do represent high fliers. Combined with the stone chime, *qing,* a pun for 'celebrate', also pronounced *qing,* and 'auspicious happiness', the good wishes are further emphasized.

But for the addition of a few minute inclusions to the otherwise clear stone and one small area of misty inclusions at the foot, one could easily mistake the material for glass. It is extremely light in the hand and does warm quite quickly in handling, a feature more readily found in glass bottles. However the extreme thinness of the cutting allows for this particular anomaly. Once again we have a masterfully produced bottle that must have been made at a high-ranking workshop. The thinness of the walls is unmatched by any other crystal in the collection and when the slightly bulbous main faces are viewed from narrow sides the form perfectly echo the spheres of the heavenly bodies. The foot of the bottle is nicely balanced against the tall neck, being neither too large nor too small.

(CBL C 891)

124 (side view)

124 (two views)

125

Crystal, carved in high relief on one main face with a European gentleman standing before a large rocky outgrowth looking at an elephant, the other face carved in lower relief with further rockwork and bamboo, some simply incised, rounded shoulders and a large cylindrical neck, a very slightly concave rim and small mouth, a quite well hollowed interior, large rounded oval foot ring and regularly cut base, the clear stone with a very slightly yellow tone, and some 'sea-spray' misty inclusions

1750-1860

Stopper: jadeite, gilt metal collar

Height: 7.5 cm
Mouth: 0.8 cm
Neck: 2.5-2.6 cm (very slightly oval)

This is a remarkable bottle and despite its generous hollowing is still very heavy in weight. This is understandable, given its massive overall size and need for a thick and wide foot to support it. The carver has very cleverly combined the form of the elephant with a misty inclusion within the stone to give an impression of the hide of the animal which is further emphasized by the carefully carved and engraved wrinkles in the skin at the neck and legs. The elephant is actually quite comical and seems to be as amused at the sight of the oddly dressed Westerner as the Westerner is amazed at the sight of the mysterious large beast.

The Westerner is depicted wearing a low felt or bowler hat, long cape, long-sleeved jacket, breeches, and boots and might be Dutch or Portuguese. The inspiration for the bottle is probably that of the fascination that the West had with the 'exotic' animals of the East.

Gschwend, in a chapter entitled 'Exotic Animals in Sixteenth-Century Europe' in the catalogue, *Encounters, The Meeting of Asia and Europe, 1500-1800*, notes 'that wild and domestic animals from Africa and Asia formed a large percentage of the cargo that Portuguese ships brought back to Lisbon during the sixteenth century. Exotic animals and the formation of princely menageries and aviaries became a fundamental part of the self-imaging of Renaissance courts. The more exotic the animal, the more highly it was prized. The acquisition of foreign, often bizarre, animals became synonymous with the level of luxury and majesty that courts cultivated.'

Whilst this bottle was probably made for 'local' consumption, as a depiction of strange Western dress and habits, there is a possibility, that a Western patron commissioned it, to show the exotic nature of the East. Regardless, it is a tour-de-force of the genre. The carving on the other main face of the bottle is much more in keeping with a classic Chinese scene, and shows delicately bending exposed bamboo caught in a breeze near low rockwork. The delicate nature of the scene mirrored in the delicate quality of the low-relief carving and light engraving. An appropriately large oval foot causes no imbalance in the overall form. The neck, which is very slightly oval in shape, is actually quite small for the large size of the neck, making the hollowing even more remarkable.

(CBL C 902)

125 (two views)

125 (detail)

126

Crystal, of compressed form, each main face carved in low relief with a circular panel, one depicting a lone figure walking in a landscape, the other with a leafless winter tree dividing bamboo, rockwork, and grasses, the rounded narrow sides with lion-mask ring handles below a flaring neck, flat rim, a regular mouth and a relatively well hollowed very lightly 'frosted' interior, a large flat oval foot ring and shallowly cut base

The School of the Rustic Crystal Master, 1780-1880

Height: 5.5 cm
Mouth: 0.55 cm
Neck: 1.8 cm

The carving style on this bottle is certainly comparable to the hands at work in the School of the Rustic Crystal Master. However the form is divergent from that normally associated with it. The formalized circular panels that frame and enclose the scenes carved on each main face are more 'constricting' than one would expect, which when coupled with the formalized lion-mask handles and the overall compressed neat shape, suggest that this is perhaps a mid-to-late period manifestation of the school. Certainly the depictions of wintry scenes is very much in keeping with the school which so often evoke the wish of the high-minded individual to escape the drudgery of city life for one of introspection away from the never-ending woes of the 'real' world. The simple lone figure on our bottle set against a vast mountainous backdrop, hunched over his trusty staff, pulling his weary body towards his insignificant but warm hamlet nestled under trees, represents the perfect metaphor for this. The other scene depicting a leafless tree, its bare branches towering over a large rock with sprouting bamboo, represents longevity. The interior has been 'frosted' to highlight the panels on each side. The stone is otherwise 'clear as crystal'.

(CBL C 899)

127

Crystal, the main faces carved in low relief in imitation of an eight-reales coin, a profile portrait head on one side, a Spanish-coat-of-arms on the other, both surrounded by an inscription, rounded narrow sides below a cylindrical neck, a flat rim and quite well-hollowed frosted interior, an extremely narrow oval foot with shallow concave base, the stone with a slightly pale brown hue

1790-1880

Height: 4.8 cm
Mouth: 0.65 cm
Neck: 1.6 cm

During the nineteenth century, Spanish dollars were common currency in China, especially in the sea ports, and many snuff bottles (mostly made from hard stones) incorporated their designs. The coins most usually copied depict either Charles III (1760-1788) or Charles IV (1788-1808) of Spain.

Unfortunately this is a rather poorly executed crystal bottle. The carving is often of the very finest quality with precisely and correctly copied inscriptions based on the Spanish silver dollar (eight-reales or piastres), see the upcoming entries Nos. 128-129 in this publication. Here, however the inscription is badly transcribed by the craftsmen unfamiliar with the latin language.

The inscription around the portrait appears to read 'DE GR II88 DOSE' and around the royal coat-of-arms on the other side reads 'IS ETID E 88 RE'. Neither inscription appears to make real sense, though the DE GR, probably is a shortened version of DEI. GRATIA found after the king's title and before the date on the silver coins. The number '1188' is probably a misreading of 1788. The name of the king, which always appears on the silver coins has been omitted. If the date is 1788 then the depiction could be either Charles III who died in 1788 or that of Charles IV who ascended the throne in the same year. The depiction of the king looking to his right rather than his left implies that the carver was working from an impression of the coin rather than the coin itself. Another rock crystal example depicting Charles IV and also carved with the king looking to his right was illustrated by Hui, Kwong and Sin, eds., *A Congregation of Snuff Bottle Connoisseurs*, pp. 174-175, no. 215.

The carver has made a rather sloppy attempt to imitate the millwork found at the edge of the coin and has lazily attempted the cursory Spanish coat-of-arms and portrait bust. This almost certainly suggests that is a late production when details mattered less and when sloppiness might easily creep in to the workshop. That it might have been copied from a badly rubbed or defaced coin seems unlikely given the number of coins in circulation.

The fairy clear pale brown stone has the appearance of deeper colour due to the 'frosted' interior surface.

Interestingly, as mentioned in the entry for No. 122, a suggestion of Fujian province as a possible centre for the production of crystal bottles was offered. How further compelling is this suggestion when we see a correlation between crystal coin bottles and the southern trading ports where the currency entered the country via the Western shipping merchants?

(CBL C 906)

126 (two views)

127 (two views)

128

Crystal, the main faces carved in low relief in imitation of an eight-reales coin, a profile portrait head on one side, a Spanish-coat-of-arms on the other, both surrounded by an inscription, the rounded narrow sides with high relief descending bats holding rings forming the handles, below a cylindrical neck, concave rim and extremely well-hollowed 'frosted' interior, a flat oval foot ring, the base appears to be a glass replacement

1798-1850

Height: 6.0 cm
Mouth: 0.6 cm
Neck: 1.9 cm

The inscription around the portrait reads DEI GRATIA . 1798. CAROLUS IIII . and around the royal coat-of-arms reads HISPAN . ETIND . REX . M . 8R . F. M.

This bottle copies a Charles IV silver dollar minted in Mexico City, the mint indicated by the letter M and the initials F.M. are those of the master of the minting workshop. The degree of accuracy in copying the coins varies greatly from bottle to bottle. This is an example of the absolute finest and most accurate of the group and relates very closely with two other examples bearing a coin date of 1798, one illustrated by Nicollier, *The Baur Collection*, pp. 232-234, no. H 92, and another attributed to the Imperial Palace workshops illustrated by Moss, Graham, and Tsang, *A Treasury of Chinese Snuff Bottles: The Mary and George Bloch Collection*, Vol. 2, Part 2, Quartz, pp. 422-425, no. 336.

What makes all these bottle distinctive is the fact that the coin image is superimposed on a standard snuff bottle shape, complete with foot and raised ring handles. In our case and the Baur bottle the use of a bat handle rather than the ubiquitous lion-mask type appears to be unique. The crystal used in all three bottles is also of the most flawless type. Moss et al, argue most convincingly for a Palace attribution, based on all the reasons that make the bottle distinctive, including the form, the circular panels, the extreme degree of hollowing, the thickness of the foot, and the use of mask handles of the kind one would expect to find from a courtly workshop.

According to Moss, Graham, and Tsang, ibid, Vol. 2, Part 1, Quartz, pp. 154-157, no. 238, the earliest 'coin' bottle bears a date of 1780 and the latest 1801, with many examples from the years 1789-1798, which coincides almost exactly with the period when commerce between China and the United States first intensified and the first American trading vessel arrived in Guangzhou in 1785. They continue, 'After the American War of Independence, the United States accepted the eight-reales coins as their official currency. It was not until 1785 that a new American-style silver dollar was approved by Congress but no coins were struck until 1794. American traders to China would have been using mostly Mexican dollars (Spanish dollars minted in Mexico) in their early trading years and were almost certainly the main impetus behind this new type of snuff bottle.'

It would seem most likely that the majority of this group of bottles, certainly the better quality examples, were made in the two or three decades after Americans first arrived in China.

For an explanation of the inscriptions, the dates, and the designs, see Victor Graham, 'Coin Snuff Bottles', *JICSBS*, Spring 1998, pp. 4-10.

The bottle is extremely well hollowed and what is otherwise a clear stone has a slightly misty appearance because of the 'frosted' or buffed interior. The quality is extraordinary and clearly carved by a master lapidary even down to the minute detail of the millwork on the edge of the coin. Of the three coin bottles in the collection this is easily the finest example in terms of quality of carving and must have appealed greatly to Mr. Beatty despite the unfortunate foot damage, of which he may not have been aware. At some point in its history the bottle lost its original base, since restored though inserted rather unevenly using a glass replacement.

(CBL C 907)

129

Crystal, the main faces carved in low relief in imitation of an eight-reales coin, a profile portrait head on one side, a Spanish-coat-of-arms on the other, both surrounded by an inscription, the narrow sides flattened below a flaring neck, flat rim and a quite well-hollowed 'frosted' interior, a simple shallowly cut base

1780-1850

Height: 5.7 cm
Mouth: 0.6 cm
Neck: 2.1 cm

The inscription around the portrait reads DEI GRATIA. 1780 . CAROLUS III . and around the royal coat-of-arms reads HISPAN .ETIND . REX . M . 8R . F . F .

This bottle copies a Charles III silver dollar from Mexico City, the mint indicated by the letter M, the initials F.F. are those of the master of the minting workshop and 8R refers to eight reales ("pieces of eight"). The degree of accuracy in copying the coins varies greatly. This is an example of the middle ground of the group. Of the three coin bottles in the collection this is the second finest example. The detailing of the portrait of Charles III is far less detailed than in the previous example; the laurel band in the hair is more simply indicated, as is the ribbon and the clasp that holds his tunic at the shoulder. The scale of the depiction, here slightly oversized, does not fit the space comfortably. Having said this, the bottle is dated 1780, which is the earliest recorded date on the bottles of this group.

For examples of eight reales coins minted in South America, including Bolivia and Chile, see Calico, Calico and Trigo, *Monedas Espanolas desde Juana y Carlos a Isabel II, 1504 a 1868*, pp. 373-374.

For further discussion see Victor Graham, 'Coin Snuff Bottles', *JICSBS*, Spring 1998, pp. 4-10.

For another crystal example from the Humphrey K.F. Hui Collection copying a Charles IV coin of 1789, see Hui, Kwong and Sin, eds., *A Congregation of Snuff Bottle Connoisseurs*, pp. 174-175, no. 215.

(CBL C 908)

128 (two views)

129 (two views)

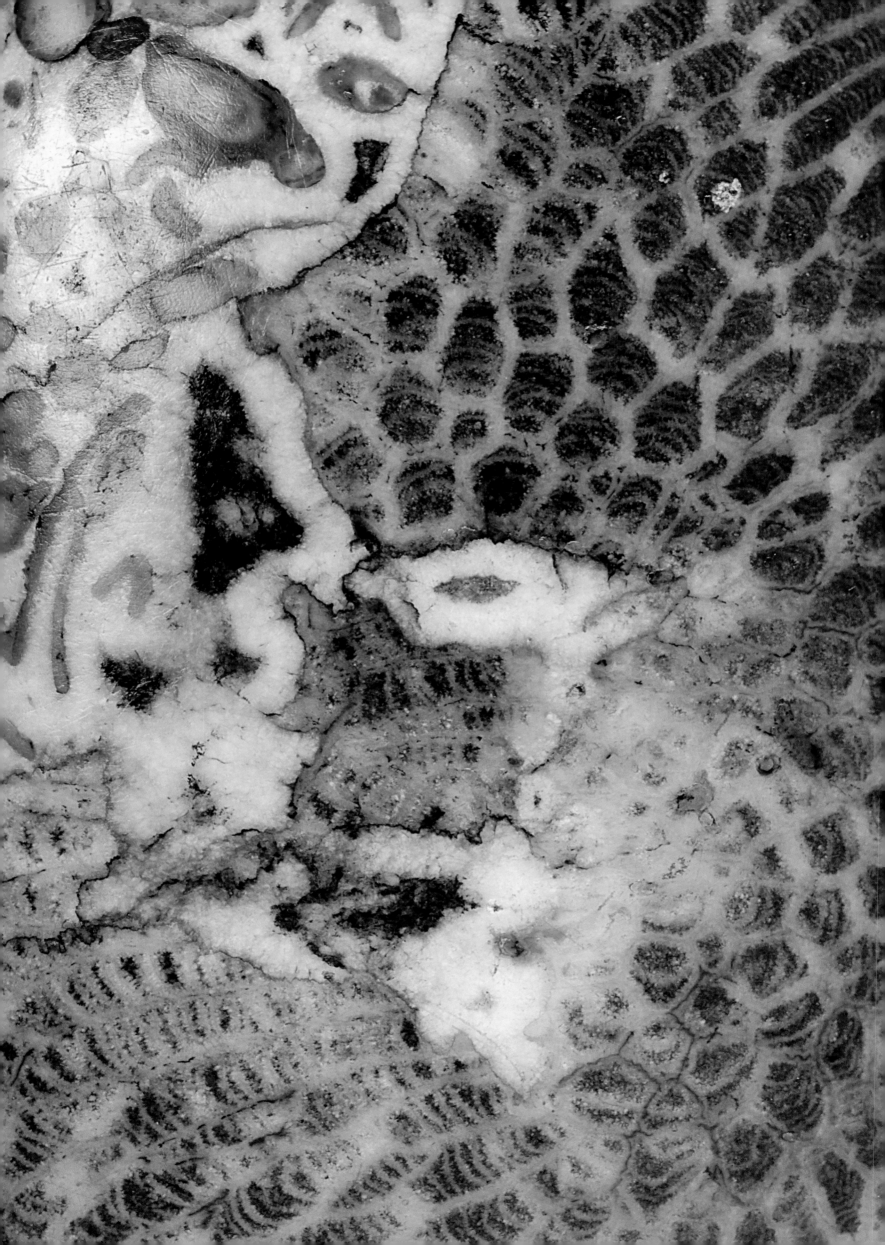

OTHER STONES

130

Lapis lazuli, of compressed form, the stone of exceedingly strong blue tone with pale mottling throughout and a light 'dusting' of gold particles and striations, the stone with natural fissures running vertically throughout the width of the bottle visible as crescent-shaped faults on one side, the neck tall and cylindrical, the rim flat, the mouth quite large, regular hollowing, a short oval foot shallowly concave

1770-1850

Height: 4.7 cm
Mouth: 0.7 cm
Neck: 1.3 cm

The most likely source of the best lapis lazuli in the Qing dynasty was from the inhospitable Hindu Kush mountains in the northeast of Afghanistan in the Kokcha River valley of Badakhshan province, where mines had been in existence for well over 5,000 years. The valley had also supplied lapis to the ancient Egyptians and Mesopotamians, and later the Greeks and Romans. The name 'lapis' is, in fact, the Latin word for stone, and 'azula' the Arabic for blue. In Renaissance painting, the ultramarine blue that radiates off the canvases and surfaces of numerous religious and secular paintings is nothing less than powdered lapis lazuli combined with binding agents. In the nineteenth century deposits were found around Lake Baikal, in upper Burma, and according to Moss, Graham, and Tsang, *A Treasury of Chinese Snuff Bottles: The Mary and George Bloch Collection*, Vol. 3, Stones Other than Jade and Quartz, pp. 126-127, no. 414, in Xinjiang province, access to which improved after the conquests of 1759.

Lapis lazuli, though considered a gem in its own right, is in fact a rock made up of several minerals, lazurite being the main component. The prized gold flecks that are clearly visible in our bottle are inclusions of pyrite, and the pale mottling, usually more prevalent than in this example, is calcite.

The shape of this bottle is an inverted spade and therefore a more or less standard shape turned on its head. It is perhaps surprising that so attractive a form as the 'tear-drop' is not more plentiful. The weight of the stone, so to speak, is below the centreline, where the body 'sags' giving a sensual bottom-heavy effect.

Of the ten recorded lapis lazuli bottles in the Imperial collections today, only one of the eight in Taipei can be considered close in shape, see *Snuff Bottles in the Collection of the National Palace Museum*, p. 262, no. 396 and neither of the two in Beijing are, with one purse-shaped and the other a fruit form. However, all use a remarkably similar looking material of strong rich colour with similar inclusions. This may be a clue to Courtly interest but does not necessarily mean a palace workshop provenance.

Another similar bottle is illustrated by Hall, *Chinese Snuff Bottles II*, p. 50, no. 35.

The material of this bottle (and indeed No. 132 in this publication) is amongst the finest and purest blue to be found in this material in snuff bottle production The richness and depth of colour is unsurpassed. The uniformity of the stone is perfect. As a mineralogist Beatty must have been aware of the rarity.

A late-eighteenth-century date is a distinct possibility for this bottle.

(CBL C 690)

131

Lapis lazuli, the stone of rich blue colour with gold and white flecks within the matrix of the entire stone which appear to run horizontally around the stone, one side with a crescent-shaped white inclusion below the everted beveled neck, the foot shallowly cut with a very narrow oval foot ring

1750-1830

Stopper: clear quartz with rose quartz, metal collar (oxidized silver)

Height: 5.5 cm
Mouth: 0.55 cm
Neck: 1.5 cm-1.95 cm (oval)

A lapis bottle, of slightly more elongated shape but essentially a flattened high-shouldered form that tapers to the foot, is illustrated in Moss, Graham, and Tsang, *A Treasury of Chinese Snuff Bottles, The Mary and George Bloch Collection*, Vol. 3, Stones Other than Jade and Quartz, pp. 130-131, no. 415, where the authors note the similarity of the shape with that found on nephrite bottles with Imperial poems inscribed on them and also with a well-known group of late Qianlong and early Jiaqing porcelain bottles, see no. 226 in this collection. Therefore, the shape was quite obviously a popular one at Court and if, as seems most likely, the porcelain examples post date the nephrite examples, presumably the same can be said about the this example. We can probably date this bottle to the last quarter of the eighteenth century or the first quarter of the nineteenth century at latest.

The stone is a very fine blue though not quite as rich in depth as the previous example. The uniformity of the stone is near perfect, with only one small crescent fault on the reverse face below the neck. The pyrite and calcite inclusions that run through the stone do so in an even and uniform pattern that runs horizontally across the bottle. The form is very satisfying and the hollowing sufficient.

Other than the Imperial porcelain bottle already noted above, two other bottles in the collection of similar shape should be noted. A rose quartz example, no. 134, and an amber bottle, no. 153.

(CBL C 692)

132

Lapis lazuli, the main faces carved in low relief with scrolling leafy floral sprays, probably hibiscus, the narrow rounded sides with handles formed as musical stones suspending twin-fish, the neck waisted, the rim rounded, severe sloping to the mouth interior, the stone of exceedingly rich blue colour, one side and one narrow rounded edge has inclusions of a paler blue-white colour, a few pyrite flecks dotted through the stone, a flat oval foot ring and a regularly cut base

1830-1900

Stopper: Four-petal flower-head shape and probably not original to the cylindrically-necked bottle, pearl finial

Height: 6.7 cm
Mouth: 0.6 cm (uneven deep sloping mouth interior)
Neck: 1.7 cm

Published: Chapman, 'The Chester Beatty Collection of Snuff Bottles', *Arts of Asia*, March-April, 1988, p. 61, fig 11.
Horton, *Alfred Chesler Beatty: From Miner to Bibliophile*, p.17 and front cover (with different stopper)

It is a great shame that this most magnificent of stones found its way into the hands of a shoddy workshop. The material itself is amongst the finest and purest blue. The richness and depth of colour is unsurpassed but here it is unfortunately diminished by the addition of poor quality floral decoration. The shape, oval in cross section is quite unusual and normally associated with quite late production, which appears to be corroborated by the rather poorly executed carving to the surface. Beatty almost certainly bought the bottle based on the quality of the material rather than on aesthetic grounds. He unquestionably had an eye for quality and the sloppy workmanship both on the surface and to the interior hollowing, cannot have passed by his critical gaze. Even the treatment of the mouth drilling, basically a deep sloping cone, would have stood out as lackadaisical and functionally compromised.

According to Bartholomew, *Hidden Meanings in Chinese Art*, p. 148, no. 6.21, the hibiscus, *mufurong*, is one of the nine flowers of autumn and is especially plentiful in Chengdu, the capital of Sichuan, which to this day is called the 'City of Hibiscus'. The flower grows near water and is often depicted with a kingfisher or dragonfly. Here the use of a twin-fish handle may be a reference to this fact. The twin-fish motif, *shangyu*, when combined with the stone chime, *qing*, as in this depiction, forms the rebus 'May there be a superabundance of auspicious happenings', *jiqing youyu*. It is also one of the eight auspicious symbols of Buddhism, *Ba jiaxiang*, representing freedom from restraint.

(CBL C 693)

130

131

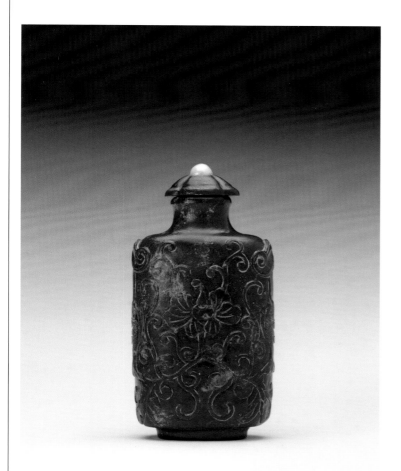 

132 (two views)

133

Lapis lazuli, one main face slightly convex and incised with a 31-character poem in clerical script, the other face engraved with leafy peony sprigs rising from rockwork, one peony head cleverly repaired, the narrow sides flattened, the neck tapering very slightly, the rim flat, the mouth small, the interior with regular hollowing, the stone of dark rich tone with minor gold pyrite flecks and fissures running through the material, the base has a narrow oval foot ring and is shallowly cut

1750-1800

Stopper: gilt-metal flower head

Height: 5.4 cm
Mouth: 0.5 cm
Neck: 1.2 cm

The inscription reads:
Yu zhi shi
Hua da ru bei jin zuo shi
Guan guan rui lu zan qun zhi
She yun ni xian nan shan shou
Wei shi hua feng lao suo chi

This can be translated as:
By Imperial command and written by the emperor
Flower as big as a vessel of gold colour
Early heavy dew like water boiling, vessel
Like the cloud, gives to longevity (Southern Mountain)
Story of longevity without understanding

In the hierarchy of Imperial marks the *Yu zhi shi* designation is considered the most important, as it infers direct Imperial involvement. For a full discussion see Hugh M. Moss, *By Imperial Command*, pp. 13-86.

Interestingly, on a bottle with an Imperial inscription, there is an area at the neck on one side that has visible original cutting lines from the tools used, which have not been polished out as one would expect on something that would be sent to Court. Similarly, a small oval flaw about 0.9 cm by 0.6 cm, appears to one side, and may even have once popped out and been re-inserted. The carver has cleverly integrated this flaw, however, in to the design of the flower heads. Presumably the stone was of such good colour it was deemed impossible to simply discard it. Perhaps lapis lazuli was much harder to work than previously recognized, particularly in a material, like this one with additional fissures running through the stone, which might have compromised the integrity of the stone during carving.

The quality of the inscription and carving cannot be questioned, and almost certainly relates to a known group of similar bottles, mostly carved from nephrite, with floral depictions on one side and Imperially inscribed poems on the other, See the entry for another lapis lazuli bottle No. 131 in this publication, and also the Imperial rephrite examples Nos. 8 and 9. See also Moss, Graham, and Tsang, *A Treasury of Chinese Snuff Bottles: The Mary and George Bloch Collection*, Vol. 1, Jade, pp. 260-263, no. 107, for a full discussion of the group.

The flowers of the herbaceous peony, *fuguihua*, and the tree peony, *mudan*, are almost indistinguishable, however the leaves and stems of the tree peony differ in being lobed and woody, see Bartholomew, *Hidden Meanings in Chinese Art*, p. 123, no. 5.26. It is considered the 'king of flowers' equivalent to the first rank among officials. Its Imperial associations go back to the Sui and Tang dynasties when it was grown in the royal gardens. It is a favorite theme in paintings, essays, drama, and poetry.

(CBL C 689)

134

Stained quartz, the main faces plain and slightly convex, the narrow sides sharply rounded, the neck edge beveled, the rim flat, the mouth small and the hollowing rather shallow and not broad like the bottle, a fairly rich-coloured transparent quartz paling towards the foot, some yellowish inclusions at the centre and a barely discernable 'turnip' matrix throughout, flat oval base

1790-1860

Stopper: glass imitating rose quartz

Height: 5.6 cm
Mouth: 0.5 cm
Neck: 1.95 cm-2.2 cm (oval)

The shape of the bottle can be favorably compared to the lapis lazuli example No. 131 in this collection (although this bottle is slightly less compressed in shape), and there is a similarity of shape to nephrite bottles inscribed with Imperial poems. This shape was quite obviously a popular one at Court and whilst we cannot be sure that this bottle was made at the same time as the nephrite examples, it may be the case. A jade or hard stone lapidary may well have enjoyed the opportunity, using a less often seen material and in this the result is extremely satisfying. The stone, which does appear to be stained in some way, is very rich in colour, generally evenly distributed but slightly paler towards the foot. Some yellowish inclusions do not detract in the slightest from the overall gem-like quality of the stone and that actually add some depth to the matrix. The final polish is also of the highest quality.

According to Moss, Graham, and Tsang, *A Treasury of Chinese Snuff Bottles: The Mary and George Bloch Collection*, Vol. 2, Part 1, Quartz, pp. 42-43, no. 195, there are two forms of rose quartz found in snuff bottles. The natural variety, which is milky-pink in colour and usually flawed, was used primarily towards the end of the nineteenth century. The bottles are usually of poor workmanship. The other type of material is quartz stained pink through a process which probably involved heat (and which might account for the underlying yellow tone within the matrix), where the staining accumulates to some degree in fissures and flaws. Many of this type appear to convincingly date from at least the last quarter of the eighteenth century, if not earlier. The authors illustrate a beautiful bean-pod shaped bottle whose colour and markings bear a strong resemblance to ours including the slight yellow tone to parts of the matrix. It is a convincing imitation of the rarer gemstone tourmaline, which it no doubt mimics.

The most comparable bottle to ours, also spade shaped but of more bulbous form, is illustrated by Kleiner, *Precious Playthings: Important Chinese Snuff Bottles*, p. 78, no. 52 and a pink-stained quartz twin-bottle of baluster shape is illustrated by Hall, *Chinese Snuff Bottles XII*, p. 47, no. 68.

It is most unusual to find a quartz used to such advantage and of the few-recorded examples besides those listed above, most tend to be fruit or animal shaped. A late-eighteenth-century date should not be ruled out.

(CBL C 841)

133 (two views)

134 (two views)

135

Sapphire, of bulbous form, with waisted neck, the deep azure blue stone with the usual crystalline matrix running in sweeping fissures across the bottle and with some darker brown and white inclusions particularly at the shoulder and neck on one side, the surface is very minutely pitted even though well polished, some fractures to the foot and shoulder, a flat rim, small mouth and remarkably well hollowed, a slightly uneven oval foot ring and shallowly cut depression at the centre

1770-1850

Stopper: glass imitating rose quartz, gold or gilt metal collar

Height: 5.3 cm
Mouth: 0.6 cm
Neck: 2.1 cm-2.2 cm (very slightly oval)

Published: Chapman, 'The Chester Beatty Collection of Snuff Bottles', *Arts of Asia*, March-April, 1988, p. 61, fig 10.

Moss, Graham, and Tsang, *A Treasury of Chinese Snuff Bottles: The Mary and George Bloch Collection*, Vol. 3, Stones Other than Jade and Quartz, pp. 96-97, no. 405, illustrate a similar sapphire bottle, and note that it is one of the best of a series of early sapphire and ruby bottles which essentially are the same compressed spherical form as this example. They go on to list five other sapphire examples, including the Beatty example, one illustrated by Hamilton, *Oriental Snuff Bottles*, p. 55, no. S-58, another by Ford, *Fine Chinese Snuff Bottles: The Edward Choate O'dell Collection*, of different shape, one offered at Sotheby's Hong Kong, 28 October 1992, lot 422, with mask handles and lappets around the base; and finally a fruit-form bottle illustrated by Stevens, *The Collector's Book of Snuff Bottles*, no. 632. To these should be added a silver-mounted bottle with irregular-shaped sapphire in the Linda Riddell Hoffman Collection; a sapphire and ruby silver-mounted bottle of similar type that sold at Sotheby's New York, 17 September 1996, lot 212; and two much smaller examples of pebble shape, one from the Alex S. Cussons Collection, offered at Sotheby's Hong Kong 3 May 1995, lot 481 and another Sotheby's Hong Kong, 3 November 1994, lot 918, though these two might be considered converted gemstones rather than bottles.

Moss et al, op cit, pp. 97-98, mention Kashmir, Burma, or even Thailand as possible sources of the material. Burma seems to be the most likely origin, particularly as relations between China and Burma normalized in 1784, and which may have led to the sudden interest in jadeite also mined there. Further cementing this link is the fact that many of the corundum bottles that are recorded are of the same basic shape as their jadeite counterparts.

Sapphire is one of the hardest gemstones; rated 9 on the Mohs scale and indeed is exceeded only by diamonds. It belongs to the corundum group, which is basically a crystallized aluminum oxide, with the presence of small amounts of other elements, especially iron and chrome, which colour the stone. Ruby is also corundum, coloured red by the addition of chrome.

Of all the compressed spherical bottles mentioned above, ours is perhaps the most satisfying shape, due to the soft transition between the shoulder and the neck and amplified by the 'waisted' centre and slightly flaring rim which all add a delicate concave counterpoint to the convex curve of the bulbous body. A late-eighteenth-century date is certainly a distinct possibility.

(CBL C 697)

136

Ruby, with cylindrical neck, flat rim, wide mouth and remarkably well hollowed to the interior, the rich red colour of exceptional strength and transparency in places, a very pitted and fractured surface and a characteristic fine webbing of crackle all over the stone, an uneven oval flat foot ring and deeply concave base

1770-1850

Stopper: stained crystal or rose quartz, gilt-metal collar

Height: 5.6 cm
Mouth: 0.6 cm
Neck: 2.1 cm

Published: Chapman, 'The Chester Beatty Collection of Snuff Bottles', *Arts of Asia*, March-April, 1988, p. 60, fig 9.

Just as the previous corundum bottle, this material is heavily fractured, particularly so around the mouth. The bottle is extremely heavy in the hand and not so well hollowed as the sapphire example due to the desire not to waste the precious material. There is a tremendous amount of light refraction from the various fractures in the stone, not unlike that found on tiger's eye material.

The stone is of the deepest richest colour with exceptional areas of great transparency but amongst these very rich areas of colour there are also some misty parts.

There appear to be fewer ruby bottles recorded than sapphire ones. Besides ours there is the Count Blucher example illustrated by Moss, *Snuff Bottles of China*, no. 103, a peach-shaped bottle illustrated by Moss, Graham, and Tsang, *A Treasury of Chinese Snuff Bottles: The Mary and George Bloch Collection*, Vol. 3, Stones Other than Jade and Quartz, pp. 100-102, no. 406 and also illustrated by Hall, *Chinese Snuff Bottles*, pp. 172-173, no. 85, a sapphire and ruby silver-mounted bottle of irregular shape that sold at Sotheby's New York, 17 September 1996, lot 212, another irregular-shaped silver-mounted bottle in the Linda Riddell Hoffman Collection (not published), and a small fruit-form bottle from the Victor Topper Collection sold at Sotheby's 3 May 1995, lot 480.

Like the previous corundum bottle the most likely source of the material was Burma, but it may have come from Kashmir or Thailand. To this might be added Vietnam or India where rubies were also mined. The term 'corundum' is derived from the Sanskrit word 'kuruvinda'.

The gemstone ruby is one of the hardest in existence, indeed, like sapphire, is exceeded only by diamonds. It belongs to the corundum group, which is basically a crystallized aluminum oxide, with the presence of small amounts of other elements, which colour the stone. Ruby is corundum coloured red by the addition of chrome; all other corundum is classified as sapphire. The close relationship between the two gems has really only been understood since the beginning of the nineteenth century, up to that time red garnets were often confused with rubies, and occasionally still are to this day.

(CBL C 921)

139 (two views)

140

Limestone breccia, of pebble shape, the exceedingly attractive stone with dark striations and 'webbing' in black on a variegated grey ground with the areas edged in russet, the natural striations remarkably suggestive of bamboo stems to each side with further dense smaller branches and roots, a small mouth and regularly hollowed interior, does not stand unaided

1750-1880

Stopper: jadeite bud-form

Height: 6.1 cm
Mouth: 0.6 cm (very simple mouth edge)
Neck: 0.7 cm

This is one of the glorious natural masterpieces of the genre. It is hard to believe that there are not more bottles cut from this extraordinary stone that must have amazed the lapidary as he worked through the material. The natural inclusions so resemble bamboo that it is hard to believe that they are not actually painted on to the surface. If ever there were a petrified bamboo forest, here it is. Even the nodes (intermittent ridges) that one finds on bamboo culms are here miraculously present. The entire surface appears as bamboo in rapid growth, with roots tracing outwards and the background material has the appearance of a misty monsoon deluge.

The material appears to be a limestone breccia, although no other bottle of this particular type appears to be recorded. A breccia is formed when movement along a fault disassembles the matrix of the limestone forming fragmented jagged inclusions. Limestone contains silica as well as clay, silt, and sand as disseminations, nodules, or layers within the rock. Limestone rocks are sedimentary rocks made from mineral calcite with the primary source being marine organisms.

As a longevity symbol the bamboo is immediately recognizable. How fitting then that this particular example is fossilized? The additional meaning would have been much appreciated. Whilst basically of pebble form, another possible reading of the shape is that of a bamboo shoot, this would certainly add yet another layer of meaning. According to Bartholomew, *Hidden Meanings in Chinese Art*, p. 230, no. 8.2, with its straight exterior and hollow culm, it also symbolizes humility and fidelity. To this can be added integrity for it bends in the wind but does not break. The joints (or nodes) are present inside the bamboo shoot before it emerges from the ground, and the character for joints, *jie*, is pronounced the same as the one for 'moral integrity', *jie*.

For an example of a pebble utilizing a similar stone described as 'Rain Flower Pebble', see *China's Rare Stones*, no. 117. Amongst stone collectors, these pebbles, which are tiny enough to be fondled on the palm, are prized.

A bottle from the Ko Family Collection, of baluster form and catalogued as puddingstone and where the markings are described as 'leafless trees in winter' but which resemble the markings on our bottle, albeit with colours transposed was illustrated in a sale catalogue, Christie's London, June 18 1973, lot 157.

(CBL C 698)

140 (two views)

141

Fossiliferous limestone, of compressed form, the main sides very slightly bulbous, and the narrow edges beveled flat below a slightly spreading small neck, the rim flat and partially concave at mouth edge, the mouth large, the hollowing shallow, the variegated grey, black, and white stone with irregular markings, the foot shallowly cut with concave oval base

1790-1890

Height: 6.4 cm
Mouth: 0.75 cm- 1 cm (angled mouth)
Neck: 1.4 cm

Here we apparently have a mixture of different limestone types including fossiliferous, conglomerate, and possibly breccia. A stone with gravel-sized clasts can either be conglomerate or breccia. Generally the conglomerates have rounded clasts, whilst if the particles are angular, the rock is usually called breccia. There also appears to be some fossiliferous material within the matrix as well.

The marking on this stone are a wonder of nature. They could not conjure a more evocative scene of an ornamental garden with *taihu* rockwork or old knotted trees if they had been painted.

The idea of a stone imitating a rock is such a powerful conceit that this bottle must have mesmerized the owners whose hands it passed through, including Beatty. As a geologist he must have been doubly entranced. The *taihu* rocks are represented by the darker grey areas of the stone with the paler ground representing gravel, sand, or even the garden pools, the reverse side can again be read as rockwork but also as an old knotted tree. The markings in the stone duplicate so closely the bizarre characteristics of *taihu* rocks such as being unusually and dramatically vertical with a combination of jagged projections, undulating surfaces, deep heavily eroded crevices, and weathered perforations that it is astonishing to think that Mother Nature was the artist millions of years earlier. Even the brittle quality of the rocks, which after all are limestone anyway, is somehow captured in the 'depiction'.

Of the variety of rocks available to the Chinese, the *taihu* rock is especially prized. It comes from Lake Tai, west of Suzhou in Jiangsu provence. They were treasured from at least the Tang dynasty as symbols of wisdom and longevity as well as reliability and toughness and were seen as miniature representations of the five sacred mountains of China, the abode of the immortals, see Mowry, *Worlds Within Worlds*, pp. 16-309, for numerous examples. They formed the centrepiece of many an ornamental garden and when small in size were brought indoors and used as scholars' rocks for contemplation.

The shape of this bottle is slightly unusual, in being both an almost circular spade shape and having such a short and small neck. The main faces are very slightly bulbous whilst the narrow edges are beveled flat. A nineteenth-century date is most likely.

(CBL C 700)

141 (two views)

142

Limestone conglomerate, the main faces slightly bulbous, the narrow sides rounded, the neck waisted and flaring, the rim flat, the mouth regular and adequate interior hollowing, the irregular shaped chips (clasts) which make up the matrix of the stone mostly black and grey on a cream-white ground, the base is cut with a shallow depression which forms a narrow oval foot rim

1770-1880

Height: 6.3 cm
Mouth: 0.7 cm
Neck: 1.7 cm

Limestone conglomerates are made up of flat, gravel-sized chips of limestone in a lime mud matrix. Clasts form when tidal flats covered by lime mud dry up, crack, and break in to flat, gravel sized chips. These chips are redistributed by the tides, and accumulate to form conglomerate limestone.

The attractive markings at the centre line of one side of our bottle, with some imagination, suggest a standing smiling bearded figure, viewed in profile clutching a massive triple gourd vessel, the size of his upper torso, in front of him. The reverse side appears like a rocky ravine, a mountainous landscape or a rock-strewn riverbed. The possibilities are endless and no doubt gave owners of this bottle hours of interpretive pleasure. The surface of our bottle has quite a lot of minute pitting and scratching but also a soft polish from years of loving attention. Due to a poor degree of hollowing to the interior of this bottle it is uncannily heavy when held.

The shape however is most pleasing with the concave profile of the neck balancing very nicely the convex profile of the bulbous sides. It may date to the late eighteenth century but with so little else but the shape, degree of hollowing, and the foot as clues, a nineteenth century dating could also be likely. The foot is a simple depression, usually associated with later bottles; it is a far easier and quicker way to terminate a bottle than cutting a foot ring, though not exclusive to it.

For a similar shaped bottle, though carved with a foot, utilizing a similar material, see Sotheby's London, 24 April 1989, lot 238 and for a slightly taller slender octagonal bottle, see Hall, *Chinese Snuff Bottles XI: The Snowy Peaks Collection*, no. 74.

(CBL C 699)

143

Limestone (marble) or quartz, one main face carved in mid relief on an abstract opaque white inclusion with three fish amidst waves and lotus tendrils, the other face plain and with concentric swirls of orange-brown, yellow, red, and cream inclusions, the narrow sides rounded with visible striation bands running vertically through them, the neck cylindrical, the rim flat, the mouth and interior hollowing regular, a short oval foot and shallowly-cut concave base

1800-1900

Stopper: variegated green glass imitating jade

Height: 6.45 cm
Mouth: 0.5 cm
Neck: 2.0 cm

Previously catalogued as being limestone or alabaster, which still might be the case, the vertical bands that run through the depth of the narrow sides do show a certain quartz-like crystalline structure suggest that it might be a form of quartz, perhaps even quartzite. It might also be a marble resulting from the metamorphism of limestone and composed mostly of calcite. For an example in marble of similar colour and with the same crystalline structure visible on the narrow sides, see Moss, Graham, and Tsang, *A Treasury of Chinese Snuff Bottles: The Mary and George Bloch Collection*, Vol. 3, Stones Other than Jade and Quartz, pp. 35-37, no. 387.

The bottle is unusually heavy for its regular size despite acceptable hollowing. The shape is a standard one for mid- to late-Qing production and the carved decoration, though pleasant, is not finely wrought. It almost has the quality of a glass overlay. The russet areas found on the fish and lotus appears to be original to the stone rather than staining but overall the depiction lacks real power and the white inclusion that frames the fish and lotus serves no real purpose. Patently the lapidary could not remove it without seriously compromising the surface of the bottle.

There are a large number of possible readings of the subject of three fishes and lotus amongst waves. The obvious one simply being that the collective word for fish, *yu*, is a pun for abundance, *yu*. According to Bartholomew, *Hidden Meanings in Chinese Art*, p. 112, no. 5.10.1, a large fish accompanied by small fish amongst waves can be read as 'Leading one's sons to Court', *daizai shangchao*, The waves represent the tide, *chao*, a pun for Court, *chao*. The expression is a euphemism for sons following in their father's footsteps and becoming high officials. A third possible reading of three fish, *sanyu*, is 'Three Leisures', *xuezu sanyu*, This motif refers to spending one's leisure time in studying, the Three Leisures being spare time in the day, the month, and the year.

The reverse side of the bottle is basically beige and yellow concentric inclusions that with a little imagination might be read as a floating figure of Damo, wearing one shoe, and riding the waves on his journey to the Western Paradise.

(CBL C 702)

142

143

144

Fossiliferous limestone, the stone a matrix of primarily small grey chips with a fine white webbing, an attractive patch of slightly larger reddish-salmon-coloured pebbles to the upper left quadrant on one main face, the reverse face with some wavy red-brown inclusions, the narrow sides rounded and with large white tubular markings, the neck cylindrical, the rim flat, the mouth and hollowing regular, the short oval foot with shallowly-cut concave base

1800-1900

Stopper: glass imitating jadeite or tourmaline, green jadeite frog finial with tourmaline cabachon, oxidized metal collar

Height: 6.4 cm
Mouth: 0.5 cm
Neck: 1.5 cm

The material appears to be a mixture of fossiliferous and conglomerate limestone. The grey and white area of stone, which covers the entire reverse face of this bottle as well as three-quarters of the main face, may be coralline as suggested by the tubular markings that 'stretch' around the narrow sides. The salmon coloured pebbles are more reminiscent of conglomerate material.

The juxtaposition of colours is glorious. The upper left quadrant could well represent a coastline whilst the grey and white material would represent the waves. The head of a fish rising from the waves is definitely readable at the centre of the bottle and below it one can also imagine the head of dragon with a plume of vapour escaping from its flattened jaw. The story of the carp swimming upstream in the Yellow River, fighting against the opposing current that must leap the rapids and transform in to a dragon, immediately springs to mind (see the entry to No. 24 in this publication). This story is a metaphor for a poor scholar who, by passing the civil services exams, raises himself to the status of high official.

For other bottles made from fossiliferous limestone of similar type, though obviously not the same 'decoration' see Moss, Graham, and Tsang, *A Treasury of Chinese Snuff Bottles: The Mary and George Bloch Collection*, Vol. 3, Stones Other than Jade and Quartz, pp. 82-93, nos. 400-403. Once again due to the lack of many stylistic identifying features, the date range for this group of bottle is left fairly wide.

(CBL C 546)

145

Quartz conglomerate (puddingstone), the main faces of slightly bulbous shape, the narrow sides rounded, the neck cylindrical, the rim slightly concave, the mouth small and well hollowed to the interior, the stone with a variety of large and small irregular pebbles and chips ranging from black, grey, red-brown, beige, and white all within the café-au-lait ground-matrix, a very narrow oval foot ring, barely noticeable, and a shallowly-cut concave base

1770-1880

Stopper: amber on oversize gilt-metal collar

Height: 5.3 cm
Mouth: 0.5 cm
Neck: 1.8 cm

This bottle should of course be in the quartz section of this publication having originally been mistakenly listed as a limestone conglomerate rather than a quartz conglomerate, a quite different mineral. Whilst snuff bottle collectors sometimes classify limestone conglomerate as a puddingstone, and indeed it does have a very similar appearance, it is of course a much softer stone. Oddly enough a common misconception is that the porcelain vessels made during the reign of the Qianlong emperor that imitate 'puddingstone' were imitating the quartz conglomerate material (as used in this bottle) when in fact they were copying the far more common limestone material, used since the Tang dynasty in sculptures and vessels and in the furniture trade since the Ming dynasty. Quartz conglomerate is a mixture of differently sized irregular quartz pebbles and grains held together by a finer matrix of quartz sand.

This bottle has one circular chip rising from the surface of the bottle with additional infill. This is a feature common to this stone, where some pebbles do appear to work loose from the matrix that normally cements them.

For a formally very similar bottle, utilizing a similar coloured stone though with larger pebbles, see Moss, Graham, and Tsang, *A Treasury of Chinese Snuff Bottles: The Mary and George Bloch Collection*, Vol. 2, Part 2, Quartz, pp. 454-455, no. 349. The authors note that whilst the material and the form are probably Imperial, plain bottles because they are devoid of carving, are more difficult to establish as such. However they note a large number of jadeite examples of similar shape were a staple at Court in the mid- Qing period. Certainly the quality of the workmanship on our bottle, including its remarkable hollowing, which gives it a relatively light weight, its neat foot and balanced form are all good indicators of a possible royal connection.

Another of similar type from the Carl F. Barron collection is illustrated by Moss, *The Barron Collection: Illustrated Handlist*, ICSBS Convention, Boston, 2008, p.10, no. 4294.

(CBL C 828)

144

145

146

Antigorite (serpentine), one main face carved in low relief with two birds in flight, the upper two-thirds of the stone semi-opaque olive-green-brown above a thin beige band and a darker brown lower band which is lightly incised with short horizontal strokes to indicate land or possibly water, the other face with a pair of similar pair of ducks on waves, the upper two-thirds of the stone an opaque reddish-brown, above a thin beige band and a darker brown lower band engraved with waves, the neck cylindrical, the rim slightly concave, the mouth and hollowing regular, a rounded oval foot ring and regular cut base incised with a four-character hallmark

Xingyouheng Tang (Hall of Constancy), 1800-1854

Height: 6.2 cm
Mouth: 0.8 cm (slightly concave)
Neck: 2.4 cm

The hallmark *Xingyouheng Tang* incised to the base of this bottle identifies it as having been owned by the fifth Prince Ding, Zaiquan, the brother of the Daoguang emperor. He was a published poet and collector. A wide range of objects bearing his hallmark are recorded; though some of these may be spurious marks added to enhance the value of an item. However, there is every chance that the inscription on our bottle is bona fide. First, the style and the spacing of the calligraphy is acceptable; second, the obviously old wear partially conceals two of the characters, which would be unusual for a counterfeit bottle, and perhaps most importantly, the bottle probably entered the Beatty collection well before the importance of the Hall of Constancy itself was fully recognized in the West.

On snuff bottles, the mark appears on jade, agate, glass, crystal, and serpentine examples, whilst other vessels that bear the mark include Yixing stoneware, gourds, soapstone, boxwood, and Duan stone. For a full discussion see Tsang and Moss, *Arts from the Scholar's Studio*, pp. 138-139, no. 108.

Within the serpentine group, owing to a wide range of admixtures, there are as many as twenty varieties, not all that easy to distinguish, but really only one of the polymorphs, antigorite, concerns us. It can be found in a range of hardness from the soft variety as demonstrated by our material and found in a wide colour range or in its harder form, bowenite, it is usually found in the green-yellow range. The beauty of the stone as far as the lapidary was concerned was that it is easily carved and polishes beautifully. Unfortunately the benefits of its relative softness for the carver are also its disadvantages when it comes to its life span. It damages easily and from the example here when can see that the surface decoration is worn. Perhaps this is one of the reasons that so few bottles in this material now exist.

The subject on the bottle appears to be pairs of ducks. The two flying birds whilst not appearing especially duck-like at first glance, are on careful examination, engraved with webbed feet rather than claws and the treatment of the heads, beaks, and eyes are identical to the two ducks on the other side. Assuming this is the case, they almost certainly represent paired mandarin ducks, *yuanyang*. These ducks mate for life and so represent marital bliss. This bottle would therefore have made a suitable wedding gift.

The inclusions within the stone have been carefully matched to the decoration. The carving style appears rather cursory but this is partly due to the extensive wear. The surface has a pleasant soapy appearance often associated with the material.

According to Moss, Graham, and Tsang, *A Treasury of Chinese Snuff Bottles: The Mary and George Bloch Collection*, Vol. 3, Stones Other than Jade and Quartz, p. 34, no. 386, 'China probably had fairly extensive deposits of serpentine and it was certainly found in large quantities in the Xinjiang region conquered by the Qianlong Emperor between 1757 and 1759. Another indigenous source was apparently in Hunan province'. Bowenite is sometimes referred to as 'Suzhou jade' so we can probably surmise from this that deposits may have been found in Jiangsu province.

For a green and brown jasper bottle somewhat similarly carved with three quail, one which is flying, see Lawrence, *Miniature Masterpieces from the Middle Kingdom: The Monimar Collection of Chinese Snuff Bottles*, pp. 112-113, no. 50.

(CBL C 923)

147

Bowenite (antigorite serpentine), the main sides slightly bulbous and plain, the narrow sides rounded, the neck cylindrical and short, the rim flat, the mouth large and the interior exceedingly well hollowed, the stone of pale yellow-green tone with some darker russet inclusions, the flat oval foot with a very shallowly-cut and remarkably thin concave base

1760-1850

Height: 5.5 cm
Mouth: 0.9 cm
Neck: 2.3 cm

For an explanation of this mineral see the previous entry, No. 146, in this publication.

This is a miraculous bottle. The stone has been hollowed to an almost paper-thin degree. Even the thickness of the foot, which is normally left with a quite deep thickness to give sturdiness to bottles, has in this case been left only marginally thicker than the sidewalls. The rust-red-brown markings on this bottle are quite magical in the manner in which they are confined to the lower portion of the bottle, allowing the yellow-green stone above to 'breath', as it were. They are suggestive perhaps of a forest canopy, a misty landscape, or waves beneath an open never-ending sky. The misty inclusions within the matrix of the stone merely add to the haunting imagery.

This bottle mimics jade to such a degree that without handling one could easily mistake it for such. The colour range for bowenite also mimics nephrite across the spectrum, and here clearly resembles yellow jade. The only noticeable difference is the surface of the material, which like the previous bottle has a pleasing soapy appearance. It is also distinctly softer then nephrite.

The shape of this bottle—a truncated circle with an atypically broad foot—is highly unusual. Interestingly, though perhaps not coincidentally, a unique nephrite jade bottle (in fact the only one recorded), that is incised with the highly Imperial reign mark *Qianlong yuzhi*, designating that the piece was made by Imperial command, bears a striking resemblance to this bottle, see Moss, Graham, and Tsang, *The Art of the Chinese Snuff Bottle: The J & J Collection*, Vol. 1, pp. 81-84, no. 32. The nephrite material, if it were bowenite, might have been cut from the very same stone; so similar is the juxtaposition of the yellow and russet areas. If the nephrite example were devoid of decoration, the profiles, though slightly different from each other, are so distinctly different from any other examples, as to indicate they may be related in some way. So what is the possibility that they share a pedigree? It is probably unlikely, as bowenite is not generally considered an Imperial material. However, it is an intriguing possibility, given that the workmanship on this 'secondary' material is of a 'first-rate' calibre. An early date of production, perhaps just after the Xinjiang province was opened to trade with China, is not out of the question.

(CBL C 926)

146 (mark)

146 (two views)

147 (two views)

148

Serpentine (antigorite) of irregular pebble shape, softly carved over the entire surface with a variety of dragons, nine in total, all appearing and disappearing amidst swirling cloud forms, with a lustrous primarily black-brown colour with soft soapy sheen

1750-1850

Height: 10.0 cm
Width: 5.5 cm (at widest point)
Mouth: 0.5 cm
Neck: No neck but 2.3 cm across at the shoulders

This is a most unusual bottle, both in form, material, and decoration. The material appears to be an antigorite, sometimes called 'noble' or 'precious' serpentine, which is one of the harder stones of serpentine family and often used in gem carvings. Here the surface definitely has a soft soapy sheen and has the appearance of a very hard stone closer to nephrite. Some of the natural fissures or cleavage cracks in the stone have been cleverly integrated in to the design and when they have not, they are so small that they are barely noticeable to the naked eye despite running through the entire surface. Some of the fissures appear as faint red-brown veins. The stone warms quickly with handling and appears to be in its natural form rather than being shaped. Another bottle that immediately springs to mind, partly because of its similar irregular shape but also its colour, is a limonite bottle illustrated by Moss, Graham, and Tsang, *A Treasury of Chinese Snuff Bottles: The Mary and George Bloch Collection*, Vol. 3, Stones Other than Jade and Quartz, p. 34, no. 386. It is cut from a much harder stone hematite, which is an ore of iron. Whilst not drawing any link, other than a visual one between these two bottles, attention should be drawn to comments by the authors regarding a reference by Zhou Jixu in his critique of the nineteenth-century *Yonglu xianjie* (see *JICSBS* Summer 1995, p.9) which states, 'Hollow stones (*kongxinshi*) come from Langqung county, Yunnan; these are all pebbles, whose colour is like that of Duan Brook stone (*Duanxishi*), but they are harder. The big ones can be made into little jars and wine cups, and the little ones can be made into snuff bottles. One grinds into them, following the natural shape of the stone, and makes a mouth. The interior is empty and extremely smooth, so there is no need to do any cleaning or drilling.'

The authors suggest that the hollow stones referred to are limonite. Whilst this very well may be the case, it is also tempting to suggest that it might refer to our stone also, as the information included in the series of works is often rather ambiguous. Certainly, the reference to the colour of Duanstone could apply to our bottle, particularly the interesting purplish red-brown inclusions on one side. Our stone is certainly harder than Duanstone also and is of pebble form. The last reference made is to the stone being naturally hollowed. Unfortunately with a mouth just 0.5 cm across, it is impossible to know to what extent our bottle may be naturally hollow or not. Still it is a tantalizing possibility even if limonite is probably the more likely candidate.

This bottle may have started life as a scroll weight, fondling piece, or even as a brush-rest for a scholar's table as suggested by the fact that it does not stand unaided, has no neck and a very small mouth. The decoration consists of nine dragons: two phoenix-headed dragons, two twin-horned dragons, and five single-horned dragons cavorting amidst cloud forms that appear to follow a more horizontal format when the stone is lying on its side. The dragons are of course, a popular Imperial subject and the use of nine here may well suggest an Imperial connection. It is certainly one of the most exciting carvings in the collection and worthy of Palace workmanship.

The dragons move with such ease and grace amidst delicate swirling clouds, appearing and disappearing seemingly at will. Some also have c-scrolls carved to their bodies, which adds an archaizing quality to the finished bottle. The intriguing subtle purplish red-brown markings within the matrix of our black stone could also be described as being extremely reminiscent of 'temmoku' tea wares of the Song dynasty, a fact that would not be missed by scholars or the Court.

(CBL C 935)

148 (two views)

148 (detail)

149

Turquoise, the stone with attractive dark and pale turquoise irregular-shaped chips which deepen in colour at their very edges, almost as if outlined, the chips ranging in colour from blue-green to pea-green and with a black and russet matrix ground, the narrow sides rounded below a shallow shoulder and slightly tapering cylindrical neck, regular mouth and regular hollowing to the interior, a simple flat oval base

1830-1900

Height: 5.5 cm
Mouth: 0.6 cm
Neck: 1.3 cm

Turquoise, here in its matrix nugget form, has a long history. It is certainly recorded in ancient Egypt and Persia. It is a copper aluminum phosphate with a hardness of 6 on the Mohs scale. The blue tones in the stone are a result of copper, whilst the green is a mixture of iron and chrome. Deposits are found in China, and the source for this bottle was probably indigenous. The stone has a tendency to absorb the natural oils of the hand and in doing so slightly alters the surface colour of the stone producing an even pale green and sometimes yellow-green patina to the centre of the chips. That effect is evident in this bottle, with the result that the chips appear to have been outlined purposefully. The tendency with pebble-shaped inclusions is that they are read as just that, natural pebbles, perhaps in a riverbed setting, however the reverse side of this bottle is perhaps more suggestive of a rock face covered with scree. This bottle does stand unaided but is not perhaps the most attractive form, appearing, almost certainly coincidentally, like a European powder flask. It is not particularly well hollowed and the neck has an almost unfinished appearance. The colour where the matrix is thinnest is extremely bright and a good example of the brightest colour turquoise can achieve.

However a nineteenth-century date of production is almost certain for a bottle like this and most likely the second half at that.

(CBL C 930)

150

Turquoise, of pebble shape, the stone with attractive soft pea-green colour chips and a black matrix webbing throughout, a short cylindrical neck, an uneven rim a large mouth, and a regularly hollowed interior, a flat foot of irregular shape

1800-1900

Height: 5.0 cm
Mouth: 0.8 cm
Neck: 1.8 cm

See the previous entry for a discussion of the stone. It is quite unusual for a pebble-shaped bottle to be carved with a neck like this example. Usually, the lapidary would simply drill a small hole at the terminus of the pebble to retain the overall integrity of the pebble shape. Here, however, the craftsman has taken the unusual step of carving out a short cylindrical neck. In fact, this approach is quite pleasing, as we have a bottle with dual intentions, a pebble on the one hand and yet obviously a bottle on the other. This would have appealed greatly to a Daoist philosopher with the school's fundamental concern with duality. Combine this with the duality of material as represented by the black matrix that holds together the brilliant turquoise chips which could easily represent clouds or stars in a pitch-black night sky or rocks in a river-bed and we have a most mesmerizing bottle. In fact the pebble shape is not entirely 'natural'. The original nugget has been very carefully carved in some areas to augment the 'pebble' shape.

The bottle has a lovely soft patina and like the previous example, the turquoise chips have taken on a soft waxy sheen and pea-green colour as a result of the oils of the hands that have held it. The black matrix is unusually dark and even. Often the matrix of turquoise will have russet or paler inclusions that can deprive the chips of the stark silhouette that so enhances this bottle.

Once again, the likelihood is that this bottle dates to the second half of the nineteenth century, though the first half cannot be ruled out.

For other pebble-shaped examples, see Hughes, *The Blair Bequest: Chinese Snuff Bottles from the Princeton University Art Museum*, p. 88, no. 85 and Moss, *The Barron Collection: Illustrated Handlist*, ICSBS Convention, Boston, 2008, p.10, no. 50, from the Carl F. Barron collection.

(CBL C 931)

151

Turquoise, the stone of extremely rich green turquoise colour with a light unobtrusive matrix of black, russet, and some grey webbing, some areas of pale-olive-green and pale yellowish misty markings, a short cylindrical neck, flat rim, a small mouth and the interior quite well hollowed, the foot is a simple shallowly-cut concave oval

1800-1900

Stopper: Turquoise (probably not original) with metal collar

Height: 6.3 cm
Mouth: 0.5 cm
Neck: 1.3 cm

This bottle is massive but nevertheless stunning in its colour and form. What stands out is the wide, thin, and delicate nature of the matrix itself which is unusually web-like in its appearance. Only one slightly wider grouping on the upper portion of one side allows for a reading of the turquoise areas as chips. It can be read perhaps as cracked-ice, a pattern familiar to the Chinese. It might also be read as multiple-branch lightning caught at the moment of its most intense ferocity as it hammers its way through the clouds. More prosaically perhaps would be a spider's web or a fisherman's net. All would have made perfect sense to the original owner. The bottle has a lovely patina but interestingly some of the more yellowish patches on the stone appear to be their original colour rather than having been caused through the oils of the hand, true of some turquoise bottles as discussed in the previous entry.

The form of this bottle, basically a massive flattened spade shape, presumably was cut to make the most of a patch of turquoise from a larger nugget that may not have been so bereft of the dark matrix as this particular section. Interestingly there are a number of quite large turquoise bottles recorded so perhaps this was a particular caprice of the workshop that produced them. A quite similar bottle also of large format is illustrated by Moss, Graham, and Tsang, *A Treasury of Chinese Snuff Bottles: The Mary and George Bloch Collection*, Vol. 3, Stones Other than Jade and Quartz, pp. 143-145, no. 419, which is also beautifully marked by varying thickness of dark matrix which the authors compare to the energetic pulsating lines of an artist's brushstrokes.

Our bottle is actually remarkably light in weight for its massive size. This we can put down to the very high degree of interior hollowing, which might suggest an early date of production, though we cannot be sure in this case and leave a wide margin of choice in its dating.

For a more rounded ovoid shaped turquoise bottle see Hui and Lam, *The Imperial Connection: Court Related Snuff Bottles, The Humphrey K.F. Hui Collection*, no. 101, that has a seal '*Mingke*' of a Qing government official Zhang Huixian (1761-1802).

(CBL C 932)

149

150

151 (two views)

正元二年
辛亥
甲午三書日

召宗
并

丙辰
癸上
元

髦
漢人
識
印

ORGANIC

152

Amber, carved in fine low relief with a yin-yang symbol at the centre of each main face surrounded by two layers of stylized petals forming a flower head, a leafy bud rising from this with scrolling foliage spreading to either side to surround it, another bud descending from it, all within a spade shaped panel with raised edges, the narrow slightly rounded sides are carved in low relief with a dragon amongst clouds which extend to the shoulder, the evenly coloured dark orange-red amber slightly transparent, the neck cylindrical, the rim flat, a regular mouth and well hollowed interior, a simple flat oval foot

1770-1830

Height: 6.1 cm
Mouth: 0.6 cm
Neck: 1.8 cm

Amber is a fossilized tree resin. In its original state it is a sticky semi-liquid amorphous organic resin secreted in the pockets and canals within the cell formations of plants and trees and which over time centuries hardens into amber. It occurs in a wide range of colours, far more than just the orange-brown or yellow colours described as 'amber'. It can be found in an almost white colour through lemon to brown and even black. Rare and uncommon colours include red, green, and even blue. It can be transparent or opaque, the opacity due to numerous minute bubbles within the material. The surface is often resinous. In Asia amber is found primarily in Burma and would have been available in larger quantities after the normalization of relations between Burma and China in 1784, but almost certainly in smaller quantities before then. In this and the following bottle, the amber material from which the bottles were carved must have been of a relatively large size, certainly larger than most examples, in order to produce such a broad body. It is a relatively soft material to carve, but despite this, of the many examples that exist, few exhibit the technical and artistic merit of this and the following bottle.

It certainly seems possible, if not likely, based on the imperial style of this bottle that the lapidaries who worked the jade workshops also tried their hand at carving amber. Indeed as a 'fossilized' tree resin, one could argue that it does come close to a 'stone' designation (despite the fact that it is not truly a mineral) and such a possibility is not out of the question. Interestingly Moss, Graham, and Tsang, *The Art of the Chinese Snuff Bottle: The J & J Collection*, Vol. 2, Part 2, p. 488, no. 288, discuss the same possibility with regard to a bear-shaped amber that closely resembles a number of nephrite bottles of the same form.

There may even be an influence from the imperial jade workshops working in the 'Hindustan' style. See the entry for the following bottle for further discussion.

Besides a few small variations in design on each main face, the main differences between this and the following bottle are the treatment of the neck and narrow sides. Here the sides have been entirely carved with dragons and clouds which extend to the shoulders, whilst they are beveled and plain on the other.

(CBL C 512)

153

Amber, carved in fine low relief with a yin-yang symbol at the centre of each main face surrounded by two layers of stylized petals forming a wave-like flower head, possibly peony, a further flower head probably hibiscus rising from this with scrolling foliage and further hibiscus spreading to either side to surround it, another descending from it, all within a spade shaped panel with raised edges, the narrow slightly rounded sides are beveled and plain, the evenly-coloured dark orange-red amber slightly transparent, the neck cup-shaped, the rim flat, a regular mouth and well hollowed interior, a simple flat oval foot

1770-1830

Stopper: jadeite

Height: 5.8 cm
Mouth: 0.6 cm
Neck: 2.1 cm

There may well be some connection between the decoration on this bottle and that found on jade carving in the 'Hindustan' style as the Chinese know it or 'Mughal' style as it is more familiarly known in the West, either directly or more likely indirectly through the glass workshops.

Hindustan literally means 'land of the Indus (river)', and historically can be placed geographically in the Ganges Plain of North India between the Himalayas and the Deccan Plateau. The term Hindustan jade used at the Court of Qianlong referred to a style of jade that was in general very thinly cut and often covered in a profusion of extremely fine relief-carved floral designs, some with gem-insets, mostly in the form of bowls and other vessels, that were imported or given as gifts from India and Turkey. The term Mughal jade is interchangeable with it, Hindustan having mostly fallen under the control of the Persian Muslim rulers known as the 'Mughal Empire' in the late sixteenth century until well into the nineteenth century. The term was also used to describe jades carved in the Hindustan style by workshops set up by the Qianlong emperor to emulate them, some time after 1759 when nephrite from Xinjiang province in Chinese Turkistan became plentiful.

The wave-like central flower head is probably a peony (though it may be a stylized chrysanthemum), which is surrounded by hibiscus. The use of a yin-yang symbol at the centre does tell us that the design was not copied exactly from a Hindustan precursor. We must be careful to not fall in to the trap of assuming that all formalized floral designs were influenced by the Hindustan style of jade carving, though here it seems as likely as not.

The cup-shaped neck gives this bottle a greater level of formal integrity than the plain neck of the previous example.

There are a number of reddish-brown monochrome glass bottles with stylized floral motifs, dated to between 1740 and 1790 that may also have influenced the carver of this and the previous amber bottle, for an example see Moss, Graham, and Tsang, *A Treasury of Chinese Snuff Bottles: The Mary and George Bloch Collection*, Vol. 5, Part 2, Glass, p. 368, no. 841 which is carved with the so-called 'Indian lotus'.

In shape alone, both in terms of its face and in profile, this bottle compares remarkably well with a wonderful flawless crystal bottle illustrated by Moss, Graham, and Tsang, *A Treasury of Chinese Snuff Bottles: The Mary and George Bloch Collection*, Vol. 2, Part 2, Quartz, pp. 416-418, no. 334, which is a likely candidate for Palace workshop production and another example illustrated by White, *Snuff Bottles from China*, pl. 43, no. 2, decorated with a formalized floral design derived from Hindustan jade decoration.

See also the entry for No. 131 in this collection regarding the similarity of shape with that found on both hardstone bottles with Imperial poems inscribed on them; and also with a well-known group of late Qianlong and early Jiaqing-marked porcelain bottles with moulded borders on their main faces and flat beveled narrow sides, see Chang Lin-sheng, *Snuff Bottles in the Collection of the National Palace Museum*, p. 117, nos. 79 and 80, and also No. 226 in this publication). The shape was obviously a popular one at Court and it seems likely that the porcelain examples post-date the hardstone ones. Most likely this bottle was made at the same time period as the porcelain examples, appearing as they do to follow the earlier hardstone precursors. We can probably safely date this bottle to the last quarter of the eighteenth century or the first half of the nineteenth century at the latest and whilst probably Imperial, it may even be from the Palace workshops.

(CBL C 513)

152 (two views)

153 (two views)

154

Amber, the main faces plain and flat, the narrow sides rounded and carved with exceptionally fine high-relief lion-mask and ring handles, the shoulders steep below a cylindrical neck, the rim flat, a regular mouth and regular hollowing, the amber of a rich even red colour, an unusually short flat oval foot ring and a shallowly cut base

1770-1880

Height: 6.2 cm
Mouth: 0.5 cm
Neck: 1.6 cm

The amber used in this particular bottle is quite rare being unusually deep red and extremely transparent. Quite why such a fabulous material was used on such a standard-shaped bottle is uncertain. However what the shape lacks in inspiration, the handles more than make up for in distinction. They really are of the highest calibre to be expected and a textbook case of the best lapidary skills brought to bear in another medium. Once again we almost certainly have a bottle that is heavily influenced by the jade workshop production, and if ever a 'handle' could be attributed to possible imperial workshops, this surely must be a top candidate. Whilst lion-mask ring handles are found on a large number of bottles definitely connected to the Court they were certainly not exclusive to it.

The lion-mask ring handles on our bottle are cut to sit on the very edge of the shoulder where it meets the side and appear to hang precariously from it like epaulettes on an officer's uniform. The lion masks have been very carefully articulated with friendly chubby faces and tidy curling manes and the rings that hang from their mouths appear realistically and firmly gripped in clenched jaws.

Interestingly a large group of monochrome glass bottles that might be attributed to the Imperial workshops, some of which are rectangular in shape and which are plain except for lion-mask ring handles may be indirectly connected to this type of amber bottle, see Moss, Graham, and Tsang, *A Treasury of Chinese Snuff Bottles: The Mary and George Bloch Collection*, Vol. 5, Part 1, Glass, pp. 244-262, nos. 771-78.

(CBL C 509)

155

Amber, carved on each main face with a central *shou* character surrounded by five bats, the narrow sides beveled flat below a short flaring cylindrical neck, the rim flat, the mouth small and slightly countersunk, the interior with regular hollowing, the amber of an opaque orange-red-brown colour, a simply cut flat oval foot

1800-1900

Height: 6.0 cm
Mouth: 0.45-0.6 cm countersunk
Neck: 1.35 cm-1.7 cm slightly oval

The subject of this bottle is longevity, embodied in its very material. As a fossil, and therefore millions of years old, amber has always been considered a material associated with longevity. Here the subject embodies the wish for longevity. The central character is a *shou* which signifies longevity, and the five bats that surround it, *wufu*, signify the Five Blessings: Old age, wealth, health, love of virtue, and a peaceful death. According to Bartholomew, *Hidden Meanings in Chinese Art*, p. 23, no. 1.1.6, the Five Blessings were first mentioned in the chapter on *Hongfan* (The Great Plan) in the ancient text *Shangsu*, compiled in the Warring States period (475-221 BCE).

Together with the *shou* character they form the rebus *wufu pengshou*, 'May you be granted longevity and the five blessings'. The word for bat, *fu*, is the same word though written differently for blessings or happiness, *fu*, and encompasses all that is auspicious.

For an amber bottle, mistakenly called beeswax, in the Imperial collections, decorated with five bats around a *shou* character, but of less fine quality, see Chang Lin-sheng, *Snuff Bottles in the Collection of the National Palace Museum*, p. 260, no. 391.

(CBL C 518)

156

Amber, carved in high relief in a continuous scene around the body, one main face with a large figure of an elderly robed gentleman utilizing a dark inclusion in the amber, and holding a brush or fly-whisk, standing under a paotong (paulownia) tree set amongst serrated rockwork, the other main face with a robed female figure in a similar setting with pine, the narrow sides with well-carved high-relief lion-mask ring handles above a continuation of the rockwork from the main scenes, a cylindrical neck, a flat rim, regular mouth and hollowing, the amber of variegated orange-brown colour with large black inclusions, a tall foot, rounded oval foot ring and shallowly cut base

1800-1900

Height: 6.7 cm
Mouth: 0.7 cm
Neck: 1.85 cm

As mentioned in a previous entry, the carving of amber towards the end of the Qing dynasty appears in general to be overwrought and over thought. The material is more a vehicle for story telling than for aesthetic pleasure. The bottles tend to the larger size and have an oddly lumpy quality to them. Whilst the artist here is definitely striving to produce a classic design; cleverly utilizing 'Suzhou'-style serrated rockwork and exploiting dark inclusions within the material, and whilst the details are sometime mesmerizing and of a very high quality, the overall effect is slightly unsatisfactory. In this case the over-sizes handles are partly to blame as they break the line of the profile, appearing more like large door knockers than delicate handles. Whilst they would certainly function admirably, they do add yet another layer of relief to an already rather busy surface. Still it is a noble attempt by the lapidary to mimic an archetypal 'shadow' agate from the Suzhou school and may be an indication of the location of the workshop, though we cannot be sure. What is indeed a very poor or rather flawed amber material has been adroitly and inventively manipulated to produce a quirky though perfectly acceptable mid-range bottle.

It is difficult to be sure of the subject matter on this bottle. However, if the object held by the male figure is indeed an artist's brush, which dangles in his hand above a piece of rockwork, then we probably have a depiction of Mi Fu (1050-1107 CE), or Mi Fei, as he is sometimes known. He was a Northern Song Dynasty literatus and considered one of the four 'Song Masters'. He was born in Taiyuan, Shanxi province and was known for his reverence, one could say addiction, to these strangely shaped rocks. He was a famed poet, calligrapher, and painter and hugely influential figure in the literati world.

If it is a fly whisk rather than an artist's brush then a very different interpretation makes more sense. Whilst it might simply depict a Buddhist priest or acolyte, it more likely depicts the Daoist immortal Lu Dongbin, who is always shown holding a flywhisk but usually with a sword tied to his back, which might be the case here, though it is difficult to make out in this depiction. Assuming this to be the case, then the female figure on the other side of the bottle, must represent one of the female Daoist immortals, Lan Caihe or He Xiangu, though impossible to name without attributes to guide us. It might also represent Magu, a goddess of longevity, usually depicted with a peach, which here might be substituted by another longevity symbol, the pine tree under which she stands.

(CBL C 523)

154 (two views)

155

156

157

Amber, of irregular triangular section, the amber of clear pale orange-red tone, carved in high relief in a continuous scene around the body with a boy leading a mule on which is seated the figure of Meng Haoran or possibly Huang Chenyang under a prunus bow, the other side with a boy clutching at his master Lu Dongbin's cloak sleeve, whilst the master points at three gold ingots lying on the ground, one marked with the character *ji* (gold), the scene again under prunus branches, shallow hollowing to the interior, the base flat and irregular shape

1790-1850

Stopper: twig-form glass imitating agate

Height: 6.9 cm
Mouth: 0.5 cm
Neck: 1.1 cm

The figure depicted on one face of this bottle is the Daoist immortal Lu Dongbin who is usually shown dressed as a scholar, holding a fly whisk in one hand and with a sword on his back. According to Bartholomew, *Hidden Meanings in Chinese Art*, p. 196, no. 7.36, the willow spirit, Liushujing, a half-naked demon-like man with a willow tree growing from his head, sometimes accompanies him. Whilst our accompanying figure is not half-naked, he is certainly demon or dwarf-like in his appearance and three willow branches above him that appear to rise from the tied bun of hair on his head verify the attribution. However, clinching the attribution is the inclusion of three gold ingots at their feet, one even inscribed with the character for gold, *ji*. This relates to one of the many stories concerning this immortal, Lu Dongbin. He failed on a number of occasions to pass the top-level civil service exam, but rather than become dispirited he used the failure as a stepping-stone to his own immortality. His transformation is told in a tale called the 'Yellow Millet Dream'. In this tale he puts on a pot of millet, to cook and then coaxed by an old man, who will turn out to be his future teacher, Zhongli Quan, he falls asleep. He dreams he has passed the exam, risen to fame, and has a happy family life. However as the dream continues, his life falls apart through missteps and unfounded accusations and he losses his wealth, his status and his family. When he wakes from the dream, in which he has lived an entire life, he finds that his millet is still not cooked. The insights he gained led Lu Dongbin to become a pupil and disciple of Zhongli Quan, the official leader of the eight immortals.

Zhongli Quan teaches him an alchemical formula that can turn ordinary stone to gold. The only drawback being that after five hundred years the gold reverts to ordinary stone. Lu Dongbin in a remarkable ethical move refuses to use the formula because he felt it would be unfair to the person who owns the gold five hundred years later.

The subject on the other side of the bottle is most likely the Tang dynasty poet Meng Haoran and his assistant, or possibly Huang Chengyan and his assistant, from the epic story *Sanguo yanyi* (Romance of the Three Kingdoms). Both are usually depicted riding a donkey in a winter landscape, and wearing hoods to protect them from the elements. Meng Haoran is normally shown holding a whip, which he may be in this portrayal and his assistant is usually shown carrying a plum blossom (prunus) which he apparently does not on this bottle, although the figures are surrounded by plum trees in bloom; whilst Huang Chengyan's assistant is normally shown with a double gourd vessel of wine, which doesn't appear to be the case here.

For a lengthy discussion of these figures and many more associated with this iconography, see Tsang, 'Who is the Rider on the Donkey? Some New Observations,' *JICSBS*, Summer 1994, pp. 4-16, and also the entry to No. 91 in this publication.

The shape of the bottle, as much a miniature mountain as a pebble, is actually quite pleasing, and serves as a suitable backdrop to the pastoral scenes. The bottle is not particularly well hollowed though sufficiently so to make it functional. The amber has some inclusions but in general is of an even transparent colour.

Interestingly this bottle may belong to a distinctive group of irregular or pebble-shaped amber bottles as discussed by Moss, Graham, and Tsang, *The Art of the Chinese Snuff Bottles: The J & J Collection*, Vol. 2, pp. 502-504, no. 297, which may all be the product of the same workshop, although they vary considerably in quality. It is interesting to note that the subjects depicted are often very similar, or at least have a similar Daoist or scholarly theme. The J & J Collection bottle, like ours, has a figure on a donkey being led by the reins by a boy servant, set below over-sized blossoming prunus. Though the amber is of a paler opaque kind and the carving far more three-dimensional, the overall concept is actually quite close, and three other bottles mentioned in the text depict the same subject. It is possible, given the wide ranging Daoist subject matter of a lot of amber bottles that a particular workshop, perhaps part of a Daoist community, was the leading producer and that they found the mystical qualities of the 'fossilized' resin material somehow in balance or accordance with their own alchemical leanings.

(CBL C 524)

157 (two views)

158

Amber, of irregular shape, the main body carved as a large rising sun above waves and rockwork and surrounded by high-relief clouds with a large menacing dragon on each of the narrow sides coiling in and out of the swirling cloud design, a cylindrical neck, a flat rim, a regular mouth and quite well hollowed to the interior, the amber of variegated colour ranging from dark orange-red and semi-transparent to honey and opaque, the irregular flat base carved with a continuation of waves, clouds, and a claw

1770-1870

Height: 8.0 cm
Mouth: 0.6 cm
Neck: 1.9 cm

This is an exceedingly lovely bottle that intelligently uses a difficult variegated material. At first glance this large and somewhat clunky bottle is confusing to read but then a picture emerges of the rising sun, energetic waves, and the swirling dragons amidst a profusion of clouds. All is a melee of action. Part of the initial confusion in reading the subject is caused by the abstract markings of opaque material, some of which is found at the surface, whilst others float underneath transparent passages of material. The sun itself forms the container for the snuff and is cut with a slightly flaring cylindrical neck. The bottle itself then has the appearance of being encased within the dragon, wave, and cloud sleeve. The sun, *taiyang*, represents the foremost male principle, yang, and the rising sun brings a new day and good fortune. The dragon, *long,* is the most recognizable of Imperial subjects and is omnipresent in all the arts. It is a symbol of male vigour and fertility. See Williams, *Outlines of Chinese Symbolism and Art Motives*, p. 132, where he quotes a description of dragons, taken from Okakura, *The Awakening of Japan*, that could easily describe the subject of our bottle, 'The eastern dragon is not the gruesome monster of medieval imagination, but the genius of strength and goodness. He is the spirit of change, therefore of life itself…. Hidden in the caverns of inaccessible mountains, or coiled in the unfathomed depth of the sea, he awaits the time when he slowly rouses himself into activity. He unfolds himself in the storm clouds; he washes his mane in the blackness of the seething whirlpools. His claws are in the fork of the lightning, his scales begin to glisten….'"

It is also possible that the body of the bottle rather than representing the sun might be the wish-granting pearl, *baozhu*, one of the 'Hundred Treasures', *baibao*, symbolizing wealth, and which is often shown set between two fighting dragons contesting to grasp this treasure.

For another amber bottle using a similar variegated material, of transclucent reddish-brown colour mixed with rich opaque yellow-ochre areas, which is sometimes called 'root' amber, see Moss, Graham, and Tsang, *The Art of the Chinese Snuff Bottles: The J & J Collection*, Vol. 2, pp. 502-504, no. 297. Like the J & J example, our bottle belongs to a distinctive group of irregular or 'pebble-shaped' bottles of this style, which have the appearance of being enveloped by an outer layer of material. They may well all be products of the same workshop.

(CBL C 533)

158 (detail)

158 (two views)

159

Amber, carved as a four-lobed melon with a leafy branch with meandering tendrils, a flower head, two smaller fruit and a butterfly to one side, a regular mouth drilled at the terminus of the fruit and the interior quite well hollowed, the pale-orange amber transparent but with a fine network of crackle, the lobes form the foot of the vessel

Possibly Imperial, 1750-1830

Stopper: twig-form glass imitating jadeite

Height: 6.2 cm
Mouth: 0.5 cm
Neck: no neck

As mentioned in the entries for Nos. 161-162 in this publication, there seems to be a strong likelihood that the workshops that produced amber bottles of this type at least knew the products coming out of the nephrite workshops, if not having some formal relationship with them. The similarity of the handling of the materials is remarkably close; both in the very high quality and the subject matter to the group of well recorded 'naturalistic' jade bottles (also see No. 13 in this publication).

For a very similar melon form amber bottle in the Imperial collections which must surely be from the same workshop if not the same hand, see *Snuff Bottles in the Collection of the National Palace Museum*, p. 259, no. 388.

For a discussion on the subject of gourds (*gua*) and butterflies (*die*) see Bartholomew, *Hidden Meanings in Chinese Art*, p. 62, 3.3.4. The author notes that the gourd, melon, pumpkin, and squash were interchangeable as subjects when paired with butterflies, and that the rebus *guaddie mianmian* (may there be ceaseless generations of sons and grandsons) applies to all these combinations. She further adds that this auspicious phrase comes from the *Book of Odes*, the earliest collection of Chinese poetry and relates a charming New Year's Eve ceremony story regarding butterflies and melons. For an example of a gourd bottle with butterflies carved from an almost white nephrite see Moss, Graham, and Tsang, *The Art of the Chinese Snuff Bottle: The J & J Collection* Vol. 1, p. 46, no. 9.

The very attractive amber of our bottle is actually enhanced by the crackle, which resembles the 'crizzling' found in early glass products. In the case of amber it may be the effects of heat that cause the mistiness sometimes found in the matrix of the resin. The trailing tendrils are beautifully handled by the carver appearing to almost trickle like liquid down the sides of the fruit, and the additional young gourds that grace one side of the melon hang deliciously and are pregnant with growth. This bottle is almost certainly a product of an eighteenth-century workshop.

(CBL C 526)

160

Amber, of pebble form, one main face carved in relief with a *qilin* standing on waves emitting vapour supporting a yin-yang symbol, the reverse face plain but with some creamy-yellow misty inclusions, the amber a transparent pale-orange colour with some areas of minor crackle to the main face , a small mouth and a regular hollowed interior, a flat irregular oval base

1800-1880

Stopper: twig-form glass imitating jadeite

Height: 6.3 cm
Mouth: 0.5 cm just off circular
Neck: no neck

The Daoist subject on this bottle relates to that found on No. 85 in this publication which depicts a horse, rather than a *qilin*, seated on waves, a plume of vapour rising from its mouth but supporting a moon, rather than a yin-yang symbol. The *qilin* is a fabulous creature, which resembles a deer but has the hooves of a horse, the tail of an ox and the head of a lion. Its appearance is a good omen and it symbolizes longevity, felicity, and wise administration. The *qilin* is more often depicted spitting out a jade book, rather than a yin-yang symbol, that heralds the birth of a son.

Once again we have another very attractive nugget of amber which fortuitously is enhanced by 'crackle' which resembles the 'crizzling' in early glass. Accidental dents to the surface of the bottle have been cleverly edited in to the design. Overall it is quite a pleasing bottle, though the carving is satisfactory without being stellar. A nineteenth century date of production seems most likely.

(CBL C 528)

159

160

161

Amber, carved in high relief around the body primarily using the pale opaque areas of the amber with dense over-size plum blossom (prunus), a ribbon-tailed bird set amongst the branches, an area of transparent orange-brown amber left plain, a short cylindrical neck, a small mouth and quite well hollowed to the interior, a flat irregular base

1790-1880

Height: 6.7 cm
Mouth: 0.4 cm
Neck: 1.5 cm

Like No. 157 in this publication, this bottle may well belong to a distinctive group of irregular or pebble-shaped amber bottles as discussed by Moss, Graham, and Tsang, *The Art of the Chinese Snuff Bottles: The J & J Collection*, Vol. II, pp. 502-504, no. 297, which may all be the product of the same workshop, although they vary considerably in quality. It is interesting to note that the subjects depicted are often very similar, or at least have a similar Daoist or scholarly theme. The J & J Collection bottle, like ours, has over-sized blossoming prunus, has areas of pale opacity and is very three-dimensional in concept. It is possible, given the wide ranging Daoist subject matter of many amber bottles that a particular workshop, perhaps part of a Daoist community or perhaps serving a Daoist community, was the leading producer and that they found the mystical qualities of the 'fossilized' resin material some how in accordance with their own or their clients' alchemical leanings.

See Bartholomew, *Hidden Meanings in Chinese Art*, p. 212, no. 7.48, for a discussion on the subject of the plum, *mei*. The blossoms are emblematic of perseverance and purity, as they bloom on withered old branches. As the first tree to bloom, it is considered a herald of spring. Besides growing from old branches, its significance as a longevity symbol rests on the name *mei*, which is homophonous with the Chinese word for 'eyebrow', *mei*, a long or bushy eyebrow is considered a sign of wisdom and longevity. Lohan and wise men are often depicted with them.

A popular theme is the depiction of a ribbon-tailed bird, *shoudainiao*, standing on plum branches but with the addition of bamboo, *zhu*, which forms the rebus 'May husband and wife enjoy longevity', *qimei zhushou*. A few long leaves near the underside of our bottle, may in fact be an attempt at stylized bamboo, but if it in fact is not the case, then perhaps we are looking at a bottle of late production, where the carver was simply unaware of the protocol of the subject producing a perfectly fine decorative object. The carver has very carefully used the pale honey-coloured areas of the amber to depict the plum blossom and the bird, much like the lapidary using the skin on a nephrite bottle or the inclusions in agate. This high-relief decoration is then set against an area of transparent orange-brown amber that has been left plain, giving breathing space around the otherwise busy surface.

(CBL C 534)

162

Amber, the lumpy surface carved as a rock backdrop in a continuous scene around the variegated bottle with Meng Haoran riding his donkey in a winter landscape with his assistant trudging behind holding a plum blossom in one hand, opaque bands of yellow-beige inclusions running through the otherwise transparent deep reddish-brown amber have been cleverly carved as plum branches with a pebble-like section to one edge, a short neck, a flat rim, and appropriate hollowing, the amber primarily a clear deep reddish-brown colour with some opaque linear yellow-beige, an irregular flat base

1800-1880

Stopper: jadeite

Height: 6.5 cm
Mouth: 0.4 cm
Neck: 1.3 cm-1.4 cm (slightly oval)

The subject carved around this bottle is the Tang dynasty poet Meng Haoran and his assistant. He is usually depicted riding a donkey in a winter landscape, and wearing a hood to protect him from the elements. He carries a whip and his assistant is usually shown carrying a plum blossom (prunus). The scene is sometimes confused with that of Huang Chengyan and his assistant, in similar garb and settings but with the assistant carrying a double gourd vessel of wine. For a lengthy discussion of these figures and many more associated with this iconography, see Tsang, 'Who is the Rider on the Donkey? Some New Observations', *JICSBS*, Summer 1994, pp. 4-16.

The bottle actually takes the basic shape of an ovoid vase with a large pebble-like attachment or growth on one side. The carving tends to the slightly courser side but the use of the material itself is quite glorious. Of particular note here is the use of a small pale opaque inclusion for a blossom held by the boy assistant and the use of other winding bands of pale colour that are magically transformed into sweeping bending branches of blossoming plum.

See the entry for No. 157 in this publication for a discussion of a distinctive group of irregular or pebble-shaped amber bottles, which may all be the product of the same workshop. Although they vary considerably in quality, all have similar Daoist or scholarly themes, are often carved with over-sized blossoming plum, have areas of pale opacity and are often very three-dimensional in concept.

(CBL C 535)

161 (detail)

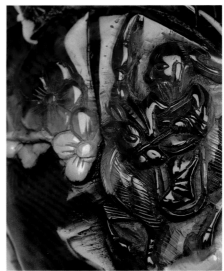
162 (detail)

161 (two views)

Amber, inscriptions carved on each main face and also the narrow sides in a variety of differing scripts, with rounded shoulders, cylindrical neck, regular mouth but well hollowed and lightly 'frosted' interior, the amber of clear red-orange colour with some black inclusions and natural flaws to one shoulder, an oval foot ring and shallowly cut base

One inscription signed Ran Dao Ren Shi and dated Bingchen year probably corresponding to 1856 (or possibly 1796) followed by the artist's seal, Shi Shou Shan Ren Zuo.

One inscription dated Xinwei year, probably corresponding to 1871 (or possibly 1811), and naming Shuzhong in Sichuan province.

One inscription Tongzhi Jisi year, corresponding to 1869.

Stopper: glass imitating coral surmounted by ivory bead imitating pearl

Height: 7.1 cm
Mouth: 0.65 cm
Neck: 2.0 cm

On one main face is a seven-character inscription in clerical script which reads:
Yan nian yi shou pi bou xiang

This can be translated as:
Long life, longevity, avoid bad things

This is followed by a smaller ten-character inscription in standard script followed by a seal that reads:
Bing chen chun zheng shan yuan Ran Dao Ren shi followed by the seal *Shi Shou Shan Ren zuo*

This can be translated as:
Bing Chen year (1856), Spring, inscribed by Ran Dao Ren (artist) followed by the seal 'made by Shishou Shanren (the Stone Longevity Hermit)'

The other main face has two horizontal inscriptions, the first larger and in seal script reads:
Shou kou ru ping

This can be translated as:
Keep mouth shut like a bottle

The second smaller-sized ten-character inscription in standard script followed by a seal reads:
Tong zhi ji shi jia ping shi you jiu ri followed by the studio seal *Wei ... ren zhai*

This can be translated as:
Tongzhi Jishi year (1869), twelfth month (December), nineteenth day followed by the studio seal, partially unreadable.

The large four-character inscription on one narrow edge in seal script can be read as:
Pin an ru yi

This can be translated as:
Peaceful and everything you want you get

The lengthy 11-character inscription in standard script on the other narrow edge can be read as:
Xin wei shi yue jiang jiu yan shu zhong Ji Chi

This can be translated as:
Xinwei year (1871), fourth month, Ji Chi (artist) inscribed this and will retire (or recover) in Shuzhong (Sichuan province)

It is difficult but not impossible to establish the order of the inscriptions on this bottle, despite having three cyclical dates but only one reign mark, Tongzhi, amongst the inscriptions, to guide us. What we can immediately establish from the Tongzhi cyclical date is that this particular inscription was engraved in 1869. Based on the shape and size of the bottle, coupled with the calligraphic style and the order in which they appear on main and subsidiary sides, a mid-nineteenth-century date of production seems likely. Assuming this to be the case, the two other cyclical dates would correspond to 1856, on the opposite main face, and 1871 on the narrow edge. This appears logical, as one would expect to find the earliest inscription (1856) on one of the main faces and the next dated inscription (1869), on the other main face. The latest date (1871) would logically appear on one of the narrow edges, as it does here. This being the case we can almost certainly attribute this bottle to Ran Dao Ren, otherwise known by his art name, Shishou Shanren, the Stone Longevity Hermit, and made in the spring of 1856.

Interestingly another amber bottle signed with the same art name Shishou Shanren, but without the real name, is published by Moss, Graham, and Tsang, *The Art of the Chinese Snuff Bottle: The J & J Collection*, Vol. 2, pp. 494-495, no. 292. It, too, is a bottle for the scholar class made in the literati taste and bearing clerical and standard script. The authors note that the art name is not recorded in biographical dictionaries, but that he was perhaps a retired scholar, probably a painter and calligrapher, and more likely a poet and musician as well.

A third example in amber also bearing the Shishou Shanren art name and an inscription from an archaic bronze is illustrated by Low, *Chinese Snuff Bottles from the Sanctum of Enlightened Respect III*, p. 313, no. 273 where the author mentions a fourth formerly in the Mary Prescott Wise Collection (and now the Bloch Collection and awaiting publication) which bears a cyclical date correspondint to either 1816 or 1876.

It is well established in Chinese art for paintings to 'collect' inscriptions during the artists' and collectors' lifetimes and afterwards. As this bottle is as close as we come to a calligraphic painting, it is probably safe to assume that the inscriptions were added over a few short years as the bottle gained provenance.

The bottle has a worthy formal integrity. The rounded shoulders and delicately curved lower portion of the body, coupled with the slightly bulbous main faces, form a perfect canvas for the literary inscriptions inscribed on them. The interior has a very high degree of hollowing and the interior surface has been 'frosted' to allow for a better reading of the calligraphy. Here we have a case that demonstrates that even when a bottle is of the very best quality it does not necessarily indicate an early production date and is also a reminder that a late date of production is merely a historical fact, and not necessarily a judgement of its quality.

(CBL C 515)

163 (four views)

164

Hornbill (*heding*), the two main faces plain and of even honey colour, the narrow sides carved from the orange-red sheath of the casque with coiling *chilong* handles in low relief, the dragons of sinuous form with curling leaves at the edges, sloping shoulders, a cylindrical neck, a flat rim, a regular mouth and hollowing, the high foot with a rounded oval foot ring and deeply cut base

1800-1900

Stopper: amber glass

Height: 6.1 cm
Mouth: 0.7 cm
Neck: 1.5 cm

Published: Chapman, 'The Chester Beatty Collection of Snuff Bottles', *Arts of Asia*, March-April, 1988, p. 61, fig 17.

The casque of the hornbill, *Rhinoplax vigil*, as vehicles for snuff bottles is a rather unstable material. In its natural form, attached to the beak and head of a large, comical looking, curved bill bird that once filled the skies of Borneo, it was most unusual. Unfortunately for the hornbills, the rather ugly but dense ivory-like casque was deemed highly valuable and used for ornamental carvings apparently from as early as the fourteenth century, although most examples that we see today appear to date from the Qing dynasty. The once plentiful birds have dwindled to the point where they are now on the endangered species list. Its use seems to have been confined to belt buckles, snuff bottles, jewelry, feather holders, thumb rings, and other small objects.

The most celebrated carver of casque items recorded appears to be the artist Baishi who signed with an artist's *hao*, rather than his real name.

His work is marked by a meticulous attention to detail in the pictorial scenes and an esotericism in the calligraphic passages. He often signed his work but few are dated. It is accepted that his working period was during the middle of the Daoguang period in the 1830s and 1840s.

A bottle from the Meriem Collection (formed by the Canadian collector Mary Margaret Young) that bears a striking similarity to ours, including the unusual treatment of the handles in which the dragons appear almost as sinuous foliage, was sold at Christie's, New York, 19 March 2008, lot 217. The footnote suggested that the handles so resembled others on signed works by the artist that a possible attribution to Baishi should be considered. Unfortunately most of the illustrations of side handles don't allow for quite so sweeping a judgement that on their own they are evidence to ascribe a piece to Baishi, though the possibility remains. There must have been a workshop producing a range of such bottles, that perhaps included a few artists, with Baishi as its leading light.

Another of spade shape is illustrated by Low, *Chinese Snuff Bottles from the Sanctum of Enlightened Respect III*, p. 328, no. 287.

A large crack that runs vertically through the entire bottle almost dividing the bottle in two is a classic fault of the material, where the natural lines of lamination within the beak separate. It is also visible but to a lesser extent on the following bottle. The basic shape of the bottle is a compressed, though not quite perfectly flattened, spade shape with unusual shoulders that continue in an unbroken line to form the neck. The exterior of the quite tall foot is slightly rounded and this unusual feature appears to be the case on quite a number of the recorded examples. A date of production in the mid-nineteeth century is certainly possible but a slightly wider dating range is probably more prudent.

(CBL C 547)

165

Hornbill (*heding*), the two main faces plain and of even honey colour with paler patches at the center, the narrow sides carved from the pinkish-orange sheath of the casque with robust ascending dragons in slightly rounded relief with *lingzhi* sprays issuing from their mouths, below sloping shoulders, a cylindrical neck, a flat rim, a regular mouth and hollowing, the high foot with a rounded oval foot ring and shallowly cut base

1800-1900

Stopper: turquoise and coral glass

Height: 6.1 cm
Mouth: 0.5 cm
Neck: 2.0 cm

Published: Chapman, 'The Chester Beatty Collection of Snuff Bottles', *Arts of Asia*, March-April, 1988, p. 61, fig 17.

See the previous entry for a discussion of hornbill.

The handles on this bottle show a significant enough difference from the previous bottle to indicate that a different craftsman worked on this bottle, even if he was perhaps from the same workshop.

The dragons are carved in slightly rounded relief, rather than the sharp flat handle of the previous bottle. They are altogether fatter dragons, have unusually large eyes, and their folds of belly skin and a long ridge that runs down each back has been thoughtfully engraved. Each holds a luscious *lingzhi* spray in its mouth. These are not mere handles but a vehicle for artistic endeavour.

For an almost identical example in regards to both the dragon handles and the overall shield shape, see Hall, *Chinese Snuff Bottles*, pp. 12-13, no. 3. Both bottles clearly appear to be from the same hand, one of a master of his craft.

Interestingly the majority of hornbill bottles illustrated in the numerous publications available to us today invariably are carved with either pictorial or figural scenes crammed with details or calligraphic passages that cover their entire sides. Few are quite as uncomplicated as the two examples in the Beatty Collection. Sometimes less is more.

Like the previous bottle, though less significantly here, a few cracks run vertically through the entire bottle, where the natural lines of lamination within the beak separate. The basic shape follows the previous bottle being of compressed spade shape. The shoulders also continue in an unbroken line to form the neck, which in this bottle is short and truncated. The foot exterior is similarly rounded, a particular feature of many hornbill bottles. The base, however, is far more shallowly cut on this bottle.

A date of production in the mid-nineteenth century is certainly acceptable but a slightly wider dating range is probably more prudent.

(CBL C 548)

164 (two views)

165 (two views)

166

Laque burgaute, one main face inlaid in mother-of-pearl, gold, and silver with an elegant lady in a garden setting, the other side painted in silver with a poetic inscription of four lines of seven characters each, the very narrow sides simply grooved and the rounded shoulder inlaid with six flower heads and a dense scrolling foliage, the cylindrical neck and stopper with simplified lappets and flower-head patterns, the lacquer of a dark brown almost black colour, the base with a spurious four-character seal mark

Qianlong mark, Ryukyu Islands or Japan, 1850-1920

Stopper: laque burgaute, original

Height: 6.3 cm with stopper
Mouth: 0.55 cm
Neck: 1.1 cm

Published: Chapman, 'The Chester Beatty Collection of Snuff Bottles', *Arts of Asia*, March-April, 1988, p. 60, fig 7.

The poetic inscription reads:
Xiang ru yong chuan you guang hui
He shi lan gan lei shi yi
Jui fu dong shan yu ji zai
Chong jiang ge wu song jun gui

This can be translated as:
Xiangru's story is handed down for 1000 years (lucky for the poor)
Why does it matter crying against the columns of the pavilion
Concubine is still in the old home at the East Mountain
Dancing and singing at home then a farewell party

Xiangru, mentioned in the first line of the poem, refers to Sima Xiangru, a Western Han dynasty dignitary (179-117 BCE). He was a minor official but known for his poetic skills. He wrote his poems in a very popular style of the day, a rhymed prose known as *fu*. His two most famous works were 'Ode of the Wide Gate', *Chang Men Fu*, and 'Rhapsody on the Son of Heaven on a Leisurely Hunt', *Tianzi Youlie Fu*. He was also celebrated as a fine *qin* player.

Usually when an inscription is placed on a bottle with a scene on the other side, they share a theme. If this is the case then perhaps the elegant lady holding a fan under the swaying branches of a maple depicts the concubine at the East Mountain. Perhaps the use of rockwork to her right is a subtle reference to the mountain and the trailing ribbons hanging from her robes are suggestive of a dance at the farewell party. The strange bird that flies off to her left may also be a reference to departure at a farewell party.

The use of the mother-of-pearl inlay on this bottle is stunning. The variety of colours and their perfect juxtaposition are mesmerizing. The beautiful blue of the robes are balanced by the shimmering gold of the skirt, the purple of her undergarment and fan, and the delicate green shading of the hair which also picks out her shoes. The rockwork too has elements of shimmering gold leaf to counterbalance the skirt and which is again used sparingly for the beak of the bird. It forces the eye to roam around the bottle and gives energy and spirit to the scene. The chief sources of this colourful inner shell layer of various mollusks are the pearl oyster, freshwater pearl mussels, and the abalone.

Interestingly, the 28-character inscription is not inlaid like the design on the reverse face, but is in fact written in a silver pigment and the decoration on the flattened rounded shoulders is a mixture of inlaid mother-of-pearl flower head dispersed amidst silver-painted scrolling foliage. This is an unusual feature, which might someday tell us something about its place of origin.

The material used for the body of the bottle is rather difficult to ascertain but because of the very slender knife-blade cross section formed by the convex sides (the narrow edges are unusually sharp), it would seem perfectly sensible to expect a metal body under the lacquer. However, there does not seem to be any indication of this. The overall weight of the bottle is extremely light and there seems to be no evidence of metal at the mouth or foot where one might expect to find it. This suggests a cloth or textile body. The arguments regarding the country of origin of a wide range of laque burgaute (some-

times spelled lac burgaute) bottles persist. In the early collecting days it was assumed that the majority were of Chinese origin. This probably stemmed from the long Chinese history of using mother-of-pearl inlay discovered in tombs that date as far back as the late Shang dynasty (twelfth to eleventh centuries BCE) in vessels from the Western Zhou dynasty (eleventh to tenth centuries BCE) and on mirrors of the Tang dynasty (mid-eighth century CE). From this date the technique seems to have spread, along with Buddhism, to Korea and Japan. By the time of the Southern Song dynasty (twelfth to thirteen centuries CE), the technique had been perfected; see Leidy, *Mother-of-Pearl: A Tradition in Asian Lacquer*, p. 22, fig. 16a, for the delightful colourful decoration on a lobed box. During the Yuan and Ming dynasties the tradition continued, as did the cross-cultural ties and influences, to the point where there is often debate about the origins of certain pieces of inlaid lacquer. By the seventeenth century, the technology reached its apogee and from this period on laque burgaute production in China, Japan, and the Ryukyu Islands (a chain of islands located off the west coast of Japan in the China Sea) followed extremely similar paths. Even the choice of subjects, most Chinese in origin, make it difficult to determine where individual pieces were created. A detail from a Kangxi period inlaid screen at the Metropolitan Museum, New York, see Leidy, op cit, p. 42, fig. 31b, highlights the inherent problems with dating and origin. If it were not for the minutiae of details on the robes of the elegant ladies set in a garden setting on the screen, there is little difference between the technical and aesthetic aspects of that scene with the one found on our bottle. However our bottle was probably produced at least one hundred, and possibly even two hundred, years later, in a different country, and herein lays one of the problems. The laque burgaute made in China, Japan, and the Ryukyu Islands from the mid-eighteenth century on happens to have reached its pinnacle at the same time and examples from all three areas have an extremely similar appearance. It seems that all three countries used both textile and metal carcasses for their lacquer vessels, though we tend to associate metal bodies with lacquer produced in Japan. This may be a misconception that needs to be corrected. For some reason, particularly in regards to snuff bottle production, the workshops that produced the bottles chose Chinese subjects for the decoration— a clue worth investigating. The Ryukyu Islands, which includes present day Okinawa, historically had very close political and economic ties with China, even after the Japanese annexed the islands. They are also famous for their fine mother-of-pearl lacquer wares many of which made their way to China as export items and indeed as Imperial gifts. Leidy, op cit, p. 68, no. 33, mentions at least three known occasions when lacque burgaute items were sent to the Chinese court (specifically dishes decorated with Imperial five-clawed dragons). Why not snuff bottles? It makes perfect sense that a gift to the Chinese court would inevitably pay homage to Chinese culture and thus perhaps the reason for the plethora of Chinese subjects on the lacquer. The inscription on our bottle would also be seen as a fitting tribute bearing homage to a famed Han poet. To confuse matters, however, the shape of our bottle (an elongated spade with arched shoulders), combined with its relatively large size are reminiscent of Japanese bottles made of ivory and cinnabar lacquer and the technique of inlay can be found on various Japanese wares including boxes and inro. Still, the Ryukyu Islands were absorbing influences from both countries and so perhaps, this is the source of our bottle. In all likelihood, we have a product made outside China, though possibly for a Chinese market, and probably in Ryukyu or Japan.

Another Laque burgaute bottle of broader form similarly decorated with a lady standing under a tree and attributed to Japanese workmanship is illustrated by Low, *Chinese Snuff Bottles from the Sanctum of Enlightened Respect III*, pp. 356-357, no. 309.

(CBL C 497)

166 (two views)

167

Cinnabar lacquer, deeply carved in a continuous scene around the body through a cinnabar red to a black ground with scrolling vine tendrils, flower heads, and numerous melons on a dark ground, all set between ruyi-head lappets at the foot and shoulder and key-pattern at the spreading neck, all on a metal ground visible at the mouth and the squared-off flat oval foot, stopper with chrysanthemum petals

1770-1830

Stopper: cinnabar lacquer and metal finial

Height: 6.2 cm without stopper; 7.5 cm with stopper
Mouth: 0.5 cm
Neck: 2.0 cm

With the recent re-attribution by Hugh Moss (see 'The Imperial Master', *JICSBS*, Spring 2007, pp. 4-15) of almost the entire group of Imperial ivory bottles that had for years been associated with eighteenth-century Chinese court production to a late-nineteenth-century date of Japanese production it is incumbent upon us to re-visit many of our assumptions about snuff bottle production particularly in respect of bottles that relate, albeit peripherally, to the ivory group. Like the Japanese ivory group, this lacquer bottle is of a shape and format that can be found in late Qianlong and Jiaqing moulded porcelain bottles.

One of the compelling reasons to believe the long-held view that this type of bottle is Chinese and of late-eighteenth-century production is the fact that examples of very similar type exist today in the Imperial Collections. This was not the case with the 'Imperial' ivory group. The downside to this particular theory however is that we do not know what date the cinnabar lacquer bottles entered the Royal collections. However we do know that two tributes of carved lacquer bottles (and cinnabar bottles are the only carved bottles that remain in the collection today) were made for the Court in 1798 and 1819 (see footnote to the following lacquer bottle in this publication). Still the fact that they do reside there is certainly an indication of Imperial interest. Six examples are illustrated in *Masterpieces of Snuff Bottles in the Palace Museum*, pp. 187-191, nos. 192-197, and each are dated to the middle Qing dynasty. It is quite possible that they appear on a dated Palace inventory that secures their dating. Unfortunately these inventories have not yet been published. The same publication, op cit, pp. 33-34, mentions the use of copper-bodies in early Qing Lacquer.

Another feature that might confirm a Chinese origin is the original stopper. The Japanese tended to design their own stoppers, both for the 'Imperial' ivory group and their cinnabar lacquer bottles. Our stopper, a chrysanthemum design of 'Official Hat' shape, is certainly found in profusion on porcelain bottles of the Qianlong and Jiaqing periods (but only occasionally on the Japanese ivories). The leaf lappets located at the shoulder and foot and the key-pattern band at the neck are certainly consistent with decoration found on cinnabar lacquer vessels in the Imperial collections, other than bottles, dated reliably to the eighteenth century.

That Japan had thriving lacquer workshops is well known. They produced very fine cinnabar lacquer bottles between 1860 and 1920. Most tend to the very large size and are generally broader than our example. The majority have busy pictorial scenes carved to the main faces. Whilst we cannot entirely rule out that copies of this group may have been made in Japan, there are presently enough indicators to argue more persuasively for Chinese origin.

The fruits almost certainly represent melons, though the artist has chosen to add a 'splitting' skin revealing interior seeds, normally a feature seen in the depiction of pomegranates. However the melon, like the pomegranate, produces numerous seeds and is often a symbol of progeny and perhaps explains this unusual detail. The trailing vine tendrils and large leaves with five petals each seem to confirm the melon attribution.

Another cinnabar lacquer bottle, also depicting splitting fruit is illustrated by Low, *Chinese Snuff Bottles from the Sanctum of Enlightened Respect III*, p. 320, no. 280, and given a possible Beijing palace workshops provenance. Another carved with butterflies and melon is illustrated by Mead, 'Cricket Mania', *JICSBS*, June 1980, pp. 9-10, figs. 5 and 6, and also *Snuff Bottles of The Ch'ing Dynasty*, p. 92, no. 136.

(CBL C 501)

168

Cinnabar lacquer, carved in high relief to both main faces with a lady greeting a fisherman on one main face and a robed male figure in a landscape setting on the other, with formalized diaper patterns grounds, one of the narrow sides with rockwork, the other with trees and rockwork, all below clouds at the shoulder and *shou* characters on a cell ground at the spreading neck, all on a metal ground visible at the mouth and flat oval foot, stopper with chrysanthemum petals

1770-1830

Stopper: cinnabar lacquer and metal finial

Height: 6.6 cm without stopper; 7.7 cm with stopper
Mouth: 0.5 cm
Neck: 2.0 cm

In general the remarks regarding the dating and place of origin of the previous bottle are relevant for this and the following two bottles. The only substantial difference between this and the previous bottle is the subject matter.

The unusual neck decoration on this bottle, a *shou* character set within a diaper cell ground, can also be found on a narrow side panel of a cinnabar lacquer bottle in the Imperial Collections, see *Masterpieces of Snuff Bottles in the Palace Museum*, p. 191, no. 196. As this design is not to our knowledge seen on either moulded porcelains or the Japanese ivory and cinnabar lacquer groups, where key pattern is the norm, we can assume that we are indeed dealing with a Chinese lacquer example here.

The same publication, op cit, pp. 33-34, mentions that 'during the Qing dynasty, production of lacquer arts and crafts spread all over half south China. The production centers mainly include Suzhou, Yangzhou, Fuzhou, Guizhou, and Jiujiang, and the lacquer workshop in the Imperial Court as well as government-run workshops in Suzhou' It continues that in 1758 the Emperor Qianlong 'had ordered several times that lacquer snuff bottles be encased, (presumably boxed) Whether they are tributes or made in the Imperial Court is not definitely recorded'.. They continue that only twice are tribute bottles in lacquer recorded in the archives; one in 1798 when Li Penghan (an unidentified official position) paid tribute of ten carved lacquer snuff bottles; and in 1819, when Zhao Shen, the provincial governor of Guangxi, paid tribute of nine carved lacquer snuff bottles. They further record that there are four types of lacquer bottles in the collection amounting to sixty in total. (At least six of these are cinnabar red lacquer and very similar to Nos. 167, 168, and 169 in the Beatty Collection). The authors conclude that 'their style and features' show that none are products of the Imperial Court but do not expand further to explain the reasoning behind their statement. They continue that all the red-carved lacquer snuff bottles are copper-bodied and that the group carved with historical figures and stories have good layouts and clever compositions to form complete pictures. They were definitely carved by a master hand. They conclude that an analysis of the bottles' style and features suggest they are products of a Suzhou lacquer workshop.

The scene depicted on this bottle is almost certainly taken from a popular novel or drama. A woman with hands raised and open mouth gesticulates to a male figure in a boat at the shoreline or river's edge, whilst on the other side the same open-mouthed female figure appears to be in conversation with a male figure supporting a halberd. The appearance of the same figure twice suggests that the scene should be read sequentially rather than continuously.

For a similar bottle, see Hughes, *The Blair Bequest: Chinese Snuff Bottles from the Princeton University Art Museum*, p. 98, no. 102 and White, *Snuff Bottles from China: The Victoria and Albert Museum Collection*, nos. 1 and 2.

(CBL C 505)

167

168 (two views)

169

Black and cinnabar lacquer, deeply carved with a continuous lotus pond scene with a kingfisher on a lotus pod and an egret wading in the water, the water carved with a dense wave design in black lacquer, stylized leaf lappets at the foot and shoulder, key pattern at the neck, all on a metal ground visible at the mouth and flat oval foot

1770-1850

Stopper: metal

Height: 6.5 cm
Mouth: 0.5 cm
Neck: 1.6 cm

This is quite an unusual lacquer bottle. Its shape is quite different from the majority of published Chinese lacquer bottles. It is a tall baluster shape rather than a spade; its formalized long lappets are quite unlike the more common short cloud-shaped lappets; and it is two-coloured rather than the ubiquitous single colour of cinnabar red. Despite these differences from the norm, it is still likely to be a product of the same workshop as the entire group. The construction appears to be identical and the styles of carving and fairly extensive wear are extremely comparable.

In the snuff bottle world we have become used to the idea that two- or three-coloured lacquers were the products of Japanese workshops. Understandable as this is when we see how few Chinese bottles in this technique are published, we must remember that the tradition of using two- and three-coloured lacquers was in fact a Chinese one that continued throughout the Ming dynasty and in to the Qing in the lacquer arts. There is no plausible reason to suppose that bottles were never made in these dual or triple colours. Another dual-coloured lacquer bottle is illustrated by Hughes, *The Blair Bequest: Chinese Snuff Bottles from the Princeton University Art Museum*, p. 99, no. 104, which reverses the ground to red and the scene to black, and which was catalogued as Chinese rather than Japanese.

The scene was a popular one in the Chinese decorative lexicon and can be found in multiple media, including painting and ceramic production. The symbol of an egret can be read in many ways according to Bartholomew, *Hidden Meanings in Chinese Art*, p. 90, no. 4.10. Because of its clean, white feathers, it is often compared to an honest and incorruptible official. A 'single egret', *liyu*, and lotus seeds, *lianzi*, form the rebus 'May you pass your exams all the way', *yilu lianke*. According to Williams, *Outlines of Chinese Symbolism and Art Motifs*, p. 241, the plumage of the kingfisher vies for notice in the colour of the sky and the green tints of the hills and has become a popular emblem of beauty. Perhaps only coincidently the pied kingfisher is a native of Fuzhou, one of the lacquer manufacturing centres.

Whilst the baluster shape of our bottle can be found in the moulded porcelain bottles produced during the Qianlong and Jiaqing periods and mentioned in the previous entries, the design and the lappets do not seem to feature in any of the published examples. This might indicate that this bottle is later than the moulded bottles but also suggests that it is not a Japanese copy, which tended to rely on the porcelain models for inspiration. Whilst the wear and style is not inconsistent with the Chinese cinnabar group, it may well be that this is simply a later development within the same or related workshops.

A similarly-shaped cinnabar lacquer bottle carved with horsemen from the Avrina Pugh Collection was sold at Sotheby's New York, 1 April 2005, lot 423.

A later metal stopper rather poorly attempts to imitate the cinnabar original.

(CBL C 502)

170

Cinnabar lacquer, carved with a continuous landscape scene, one main face with a seated gentleman below maple, the other main face with a gentleman seated under pine pulling at his beard, his youthful assistant standing behind him with formalized diaper-pattern grounds, clouds carved at the shoulder and a key-pattern band at the flaring neck, all on a metal ground visible at the mouth and flat oval foot, the shoulder and foot have the addition of unusual circular eyes for suspension

1770-1830

Stopper: cinnabar lacquer and metal finial (not original but period)

Height: 5.8 cm without stopper; 7.0 cm with stopper
Mouth: 0.6 cm
Neck: 1.9 cm

Published: Chapman, 'The Chester Beatty Collection of Snuff Bottles', *Arts of Asia*, March-April, 1988, p. 61, fig 18.

Once again we have a bottle, which to all intents and purposes follows the identical format of the well known group of Chinese cinnabar lacquer bottles discussed in the previous entries but with the addition of metal 'eyes' at the shoulder and foot for suspension. The 'eyes' at the shoulder look as though they could have been attached at a later date whilst the 'eyes' at the foot appear to be an integral part of the construction. Even the traces of gilding that linger on the foot and the eyes appear to bear consistent wear, suggesting that these were always an intended part of the original bottle. Presumably a cord was threaded through them to make the bottle easier to carry.

The bottle must be a product of the same workshop, but perhaps made to special order. The construction appears to be identical and the styles of carving and fairly extensive wear extremely comparable. They also all demonstrate the same formalized diaper pattern grounds representing earth, water, and sky, which can be found on a host of Ming and Qing lacquer wares. Land is usually carved as hexagonal flower-head cells; water as diamond-shaped cells with squared waves; and air as grooved brick-like continuous cells. The scenes are invariably cut on two or more basic planes rather than fully in the round. On this bottle we again probably have two scenes from the same story, as the elderly bearded figure appears to be the same in each depiction. This is often the case on bottles that depict popular novels or dramas. The two scenes are cleverly joined on the narrow sides by the inclusion of rockwork and trees, which continue on the main faces.

Attention should be drawn to the stopper on this bottle that whilst probably not original to this bottle (it is 2.0 cm in diameter as opposed to the 1.9 cm diameter of the neck) is probably a period stopper from a slightly larger bottle. Three of the six bottles in the Imperial Collections have an identical stopper, see *Masterpieces of Snuff Bottles in the Palace Museum*, p. 189-191, nos. 194, 195, and 197.

(CBL C 503)

169

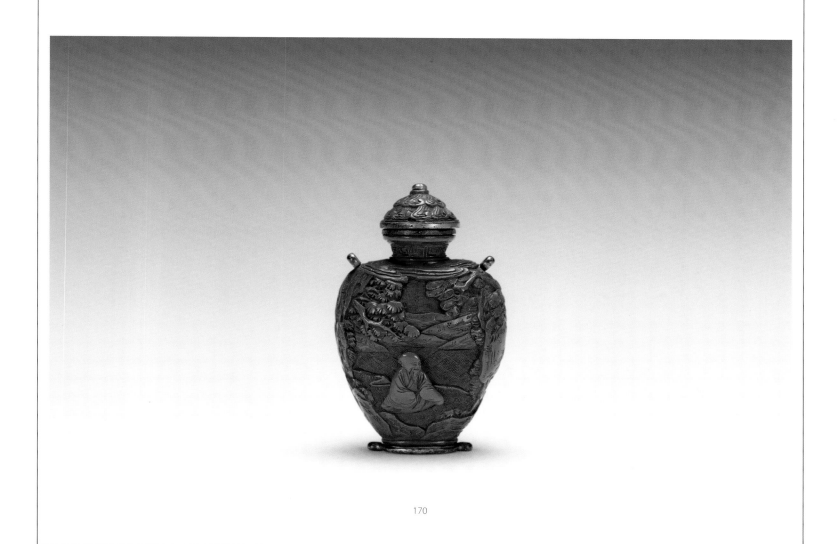

170

171

Mother-of-pearl, carved on one main face in low relief with a long-tailed bulbul, *baitouweng*, with head raised standing on the branch of a flowering plum, the bird cleverly utilizing a single black-brown inclusion, the reverse side with a ten-character inscription followed by two indistinct seals within a double-lined oval panel, the neck cylindrical and the foot oval and shallowly cut

1780-1880

Stopper: horn

Height: 5.8 cm
Mouth: 0.5 cm
Neck: 1.3 cm

The poetic inscription of two lines of five characters each reads:
Chang jin yi tian wai
Wan gong guai fu shan

This can be translated as:
Long sword leans against the heaven
Curved bow hangs on tree (mulberry)

The two seals that follow the poem are indistinct.

It is difficult, given the few lines of what was probably a much longer poem, to understand the full meaning of the inscription.

Normally one would expect the scene on one main face of a bottle to echo the sentiment of the poem or inscription written on the reverse side. This is not the case here, though that's hardly surprising given the cryptic nature of the poem extract. The tree in which the bulbul sits is definitely not a mulberry, *fusang*, but probably a plum, *mei*. The flowers of the mulberry tree hang as catkins and here we have the ubiquitous plum (prunus) as indicated by the five-petalled flowers. The bird depicted is almost certainly a bulbul, as indicated by the long tail, short wings, and the slightly elongated and slightly hooked beak. There is a wide variety of bulbul but some have a patch of white feathers on the top and back of the head and also a patch under the chin. As a result the Chinese named the bird 'white-headed old man', *baitouweng*. According to Bartholomew, *Hidden Meanings in Chinese Art*, pp. 173-174, no. 7.9, it symbolizes not only longevity but also a happy marriage in which the couple grow old together until their hair turns white as the head of a bulbul, *baitou xielao*. The plum, another longevity symbol, appears to confirm the symbolism.

Perhaps it was mere happenstance and perhaps it was the genius of the carver, but a flaw that runs through the material bisects the bird's head, forming a white patch under the chin, whilst a pale area at the top edge of the inclusion is used for a crown. The continuation of the flaw is disguised as it runs exactly down the spine of the bulbul and into the tail.

Another quite unusual feature of this bottle is its almost perfect compressed ovoid shape. As a result of the degree of difficulty in locating a section of mother-of-pearl large enough to carve as a complete snuff bottle, most examples are relatively small and more often than not, have a natural but nevertheless slightly peculiar, curved shape when viewed from the narrow side. The curve in our example barely registers. Yet another characteristic displayed in bottles cut from this material is the areas of honey and white discolouration that run through them.

In general the published examples invariably are carved with naturalistic subjects, primarily birds and animals, though at least three examples have additional figures on the other face. Perhaps this restricted subject matter is indicative of a school or workshop that has yet to be identified. It seems likely that a workshop producing mother-of-pearl would be located in a coastal region and if this was the case, it may well have been a Southern port city like Guangzhou, where we know many handicraft workshops existed catering to an Imperial and export market. It is interesting to note remarks regarding the pearl market in *Tributes from Guangdong to the Qing Court*, p. 59, 'Pearl comes from pearl oysters which are found in the warm seas along the coast of

Guangdong and Guangxi.... There are numerous varieties of pearls.... Southern pearls come from Hepu in Guangdong.... The people of Guangdong in the Qing dynasty were fond of pearls, placing them even above gold in value.... These pearls were either pierced and made into chains or used as an inlay material.' If a thriving pearl industry existed it seems highly probable, that the subsidiary mother-of-pearl market was located nearby.

For other bottles carved from this intriguing natural material see *Snuff Bottles in the Collection of the National Palace Museum*, no. 408, with a figural scene on one side; *Zhonguo Biyanhu Zhenshang*, no. 427; Hughes, *The Blair Bequest: Chinese Snuff Bottles from the Princeton University Art Museum*, p. 103, no. 111; *Snuff Bottles of the Ch'ing Dynasty*, p. 130, no. 250; Moss, Graham, and Tsang, *A Treasury of Chinese Snuff Bottles: The Mary and George Bloch Collection*, Vol. 3, Stones other than Jade and Quartz, pp. 192-195, no. 436; Moss, *Chinese Snuff Bottles*, p. 42, no. 152, which depicts a hawk and bear and uses a mother-of-pearl material that appears very close to ours; and Stevens, *The Collector's Book of Snuff Bottles*, p. 169, nos. 627 and 628, and p. 174, no. 668.

(CBL C 562)

171 (two views)

172

Ivory, in the form of a lotus bud or possibly a bamboo shoot, naturalistically carved with layers of leaves some very slightly unfurling in places, the ivory of a beautiful creamy yellow tone with areas of natural growth structure faintly visible within the carving mostly at the tip and base, the stopper at the thick base end of the shoot rather than the tip, a small mouth at the concave root and exceedingly well hollowed

Chinese, possibly Imperial, 1730-1780

Stopper: green glass twig form

Height: 6.8 cm
Mouth: 0.5 cm
Neck: No neck

Despite the recent re-attribution by Hugh Moss (see 'The Imperial Master', *JICSBS*, Spring 2007, pp. 4-15) of a large swathe of Qianlong-marked so-called Imperial ivory bottles, usually figural and of large spade shape, that had for years been associated with eighteenth-century Chinese court production, to a late nineteenth-century date of Japanese production, the door was not closed on other bottles made in ivory still being eighteenth-century and Imperial items. In fact the few examples that he cites as possible contenders for Imperial workmanship and eighteenth-century production included two in the form of bamboo shoots that really are far inferior to the present example, if indeed this bottle represents a bamboo shoot rather than a lotus bud. The others he illustrates are a bottle of bamboo-form, actually the stems with nodes rather than shoots; two other fruit-form bottles, a bitter-melon and a lychee, from the Palace Collection; and a series of three bird-form bottles. Moss, ibid, p. 13 also makes mention of the earliest archives from the Palace workshops during the Yonzheng period in which the records of 1724 for items from 'Miscellaneous Workshop' include 'four ivory snuff bottles in the shape of fruit on a zitan (wood) grape-leaf (shaped) tray' and the records for 1725 mention that the 'Ivory Workshop' was instructed to make 'one ivory snuff bottle in the shape of a Buddha's hand, coloured orange'.

There is a very good chance that our bottle should be a contender to join this elite group of Imperial fruit-or-flower-shaped bottles. The exceedingly high degree of hollowing to the interior of this bottle and the placement of the hole at the centre of the bulbous end without interfering with the petal design at all, suggest that this extraordinary carving was always intended as a snuff bottle and was not a later conversion. The 'nerve' of the ivory is right alongside the mouth opening and the chances are that if this were a conversion this might have been removed.

If our bottle represents a lotus bud, as seems most likely, the meaning is obviously quite different from that of a depiction of bamboo. The flower is widely used in Buddhist imagery to support seated and standing figures of Buddha and other bodhisattvas, and is a potent, almost omnipresent, symbol of purity, emerging as it does from muddy waters.

Should our bottle represent a bamboo shoot, then according to Bartholomew, *Hidden Meanings in Chinese Art*, p. 230, no. 8.2, with its straight exterior and hollow culm the bamboo also symbolizes humility and fidelity. To this can be added integrity for it bends in the wind but does not break. The joints (or nodes) are present inside the bamboo shoot before it emerges from the ground, and the character for joints, *jie*, is pronounced the same as the one for 'moral integrity', *jie*. The bamboo is also recognized as symbol of longevity due to its durability and to the fact that it is evergreen and flourishes throughout the winter. According to Williams, *Outlines of Chinese Symbolism and Art Motives*, p. 34, the bamboo shoot also figures in one of the 24 classic stories of filial piety (See No. 213 in this publication for examples of this subject on a porcelain bottle). The story goes, that one winter, a sick mother longed for a soup made from bamboo shoots. Her son, entered a bamboo grove to gather some shoots for her, only to find the ground frozen solid by the harsh frost and winter snow. He wept so copiously on her account that his warm tears softened the hard icy earth which caused the shoots to burst forth in reward for his pious affection.

(CBL C 551)

172 (two views)

173

Ivory, the entire body carved in high relief with dense design of nine bats flying amidst scrolling vine tendrils, five gourds, and various flower heads, buds, and leafy foliage, the bats highlighted in traces of red, added foot and stopper

Probably Chinese, 1750-1790

Stopper: ivory but later addition

Height: 6.8 cm without stopper, 8.3 cm with later stopper
Mouth: 0.5 cm
Neck: 0.7 cm (reduced across width)

We will probably never know if Chester Beatty was aware that this bottle had been 'improved' prior to its purchase. The body of the bottle itself is original. However the original foot is missing and has been replaced by a disc of bone imitating ivory. The neck was also reduced (shaved down) to form a standing cylinder in order to allow for the fitting of the substitute stopper, which is carved to slot over the neck and allow the scrolling tendril design to match exactly with the tendrils on the body. The gourd itself, due to the high degree of hollowing (not a feature common to Japanese ivory bottles made in the Chinese taste), has various pin-prick holes around the body and some repair to the waisted section at the gourds centre possibly hiding further losses.

The argument that the bottle might be Japanese because of the addition of a pigment to the bats, a feature often found on late Japanese ivory bottles, does not really carry much weight, as it is also a feature of the two Imperial ivory fruit-shaped bottles in the Palace Collection, a bitter-melon and lychee (see No. 172 in this collection). The fact that this bottle is indeed fruit-shaped might even indicate that it was following in the footsteps of the early Imperial bottles and may even be related to the group of naturalistic jade 'fruit-shaped' bottles that were being produced in the second half of the eighteenth century (see Nos. 13, 44-48). The carving style would certainly be acceptable on a nephrite fruit carving, with its delicate tracery of vine tendrils with undercutting and the exquisite balance of the overall subject which here also appears to include various flower heads including magnolia. The only real argument in favour of Japanese manufacture is the fact that the Japanese ivory bottles, once thought to be imperial Chinese production, seem, for the most part, to be direct or interpretive copies of Chinese porcelain bottles. The shape and decoration of our ivory bottle is certainly found first in porcelain models. However, there seems no good reason why the Chinese ivory workshops could not have followed a Chinese jade or porcelain model.

See Bartholomew, *Hidden Meanings in Chinese Art*, p. 23, no. 115, The subject of bats, *fu*, is synonymous with 'blessings', *fu*, and 'riches', *fu*. Here we have nine bats. Nine, *jiu*, as a number is most auspicious. Groupings of nine are a very common subject: nine peaches, nine cauldrons, nine coins, nine lions, nine plants of autumn, nine quail etc., although in the context of bats five is more common, *wufu*. Here the bats retain some of their original red pigment and the pronunciation of the word for red, *hong*, and vast, *hong*, are very similar and thus the subject can read as 'vast blessings or riches'. The gourd symbolizes fertility and good fortune thus complementing the meaning.

For a slightly more slender example from the American Museum of Natural History, New York, also carved with bats and gourds and flowerheads, see Stevens, *The Collector's Book of Snuff Bottles*, p. 201, no. 756.

(CBL C 552)

173 (two views)

Ivory, carved in relief with various elegant figures in a pavilion garden setting with ladies collecting lotus in canopied boats with further ladies and a gentleman awaiting their return on a terrace below weeping willow at a pavilion with tiled roofs against a background of waves, all between a band of leaf lappets at the foot and a *ruyi*-head band and a running scroll at the shoulder below key-pattern at the neck, traces of colour, primarily blue, green, red, and black, very finely cut slightly rounded foot ring and a flat base with a spurious Qianlong four-character seal mark in a square, a root visible

Japanese, 1854-1900

Stopper: ivory but later addition

Height: 7.1cm
Mouth: 0.6 cm
Neck: 1.8 cm

A recent lecture and article by Moss 'The Imperial Master', *JICSBS,* Spring 2007, pp. 4-15, has hopefully resolved a lingering question over the authenticity of a group of so-called Imperial ivory bottles, usually Qianlong or Jiaqing-marked, which tend to have figural scenes and, more often than not, are generally of large spade shape. The 'Imperial' ivory group has long been considered of mid- to late-eighteenth-century Chinese production with equivalent bottles produced in porcelain at Jingdezhen considered the copies of Imperial ivories. That assumption has now been turned on its head, and Moss, almost certainly correctly, believes the ivory bottles to be Japanese copies of (the now) earlier Chinese porcelain models from Jingdezhen. Their had always been a great deal of discussion and uncertainty about the ivory bottles that were published as Imperial, including on the part of this author, who somewhat hedged his bets regarding the correct classification of the group, see Hughes, *The Blair Bequest: Chinese Snuff Bottles from the Princeton University Art Museum,* p. 96, no. 98.

Moss's reasoning is extremely sound and resolves the niggling doubts that plagued the subject. To paraphrase his lengthy rationale and insight, Moss now believes that the entire group was made after the 1854 treaty that opened Japan to the outside world. He notes, rather interestingly, that the earliest record of the existence of the so-called 'Imperial' ivory bottles in a Western collection is a Chester Beatty Library handwritten list dating to 1914 (on that list nine ivory bottles are listed, though they cannot be accurately identified, they are almost certain to include the ivory examples published here). If we allow that Beatty probably did not purchase a snuff bottle before his tenth birthday, his earliest purchase would have been in 1885, though probably more likely after 1905 when he returned from Denver as a rich man. Moss also notes that no ivory bottles from this so-called 'Imperial' group can be found in the Palace Museum Collections in Beijing or Taipei, nor are there any stylistically similar ivory carvings made at, and for, the Court. One of the conundrums related to the entire group was the use of carelessly written marks to the base that, somehow, most specialists in the field simply overlooked, as poor rather than apocryphal. Knowing now that the marks were close copies of the porcelain examples, which also have rather poorly written iron-red marks, resolves this anomaly. Moss further studies a variety of salient points such as neck construction, hollowing, the similarity of certain ivory bottles with ivory dragon 'seals' that are now credibly assigned to late Japanese manufacture, and even stoppers, which in the case of Japanese bottles generally tend to the eccentric (though not in this particular case). However, it is really the shape and decoration that so clearly follows the porcelain bottles made during the late Qianlong and Jiaqing reigns, that is the clinching factor in the re-assessment. Moss's helpful new sobriquet for this group is 'The Imperial Master'.

The subject on our bottle is almost certainly copied from a Chinese porcelain bottle, though our example may be a slightly later stage in ivory production. What started as accurate copies of moulded porcelain bottles became more independently artistic in output as time progressed. Few ceramic snuff bottles in this shape exist bearing this form of decoration and it seems likely that the 'Imperial Master' combined the decoration on one bottle with the form of another. The theme of 'lotus-gathering' is fully discussed in the entry to No. 242 in this publication.

For a very similar example in ivory from the A.W. Bahr Collection, 1916, see Glickman, *Chinese Snuff Bottle Mania,* p. 49, fig 2.22.

(CBL C 557)

Ivory, carved in relief with a continuous scene of *arhat* or *lohan* amidst waves, one main face depicting a female immortal holding a book or box and offering or receiving it from another *arhat* with earrings standing alongside, she standing on frothy breaking waves on a backdrop of a calmer wave cell pattern below clouds at the shoulder, the other main face with three further *arhat*, one seated on a lion holding a rosary in his raised right hand, another standing with a staff and alms bowl, and a third looking on, all against the same calm wave cell pattern ground and below clouds, all between a key-pattern band at the foot and neck, the narrow sides with dense rockwork, one with a seated figure of another *arhat*, the neck rim everted, the shallowly-cut base with oval foot ring and incised and painted in red with a Qianlong four-character seal mark in a double square, a nerve ending visible at the inside edge of the foot rim

Japanese, 1854-1900

Stopper: ivory but later addition

Height: 6.3 cm without stopper, 7.3 cm with stopper
Mouth: 0.7 cm
Neck: 1.7 cm

Published: Chapman, 'The Chester Beatty Collection of Snuff Bottles', *Arts of Asia,* March-April, 1988, p. 60, fig 16.

Moss, 'The Imperial Master', *JICSBS,* Spring 2007, fig. 2.

See the entry for the previous bottle regarding the reattribution of this particular type of bottle to post-1854 Japanese production.

The scene depicted on this bottle is that of various Buddhist *arhat* (or *lohan*) dispersed amongst waves and clouds, with one either accepting a gift from a female immortal or in the act of presentation. According to Williams, *Outlines of Chinese Symbolism and Art Motives,* pp. 157-168, *arhat* or *lohan* have passed through the different stages of the Noble Path, or eightfold way, conquered all passions, and in effect attained nirvana. They can number as many as 1600 but the more standard depictions show between 18 and 500. Their images can be found arranged along the sidewalls of the second or main hall of Buddhist monasteries. It is said that of the 18 *arhat,* 16 are Indian and the two others were added by the Chinese at a later development of Chinese Buddhism. Williams illustrates a set of 18 and mentions that the images are mainly derived from the works of one or two Tang Dynasty painters and based on descriptions given in Buddhist records. However various conflicting depictions of the subject over many hundreds of years has rendered identification through their attributes extremely difficult. In our example only five *arhat* are depicted along with a female immortal.

The carving on this bottle is of extremely high quality. The *arhat* spring to life and one gets a feeling that the Japanese craftsman has taken his porcelain template and added a layer of depth that moulding does not allow for so easily. One can read three or four different plane levels from the lowest wave background, through the swirling clouds, the craggy rockwork to the figures themselves which jump to life with their trailing ribbons and sense of freedom.

Moss, op cit, p.9, fig. 14 also points out certain discrepancies in border design between the porcelain forerunners and the later ivories using a bottle from the Denis S.K. Low Collection as an example. It happens to be decorated with *arhat* in a pine grove, possibly by the same hand, the so-called 'Imperial Master', and has identical bands of decoration at the foot and neck. Whilst the upper band on ours is possibly Chinese in style the lower band has been simplified to a series of elongated S shapes, which is unusual for high-quality Chinese works of art. The depiction of the *arhat* and the tiger (or lion) to one side have a distinctly Japanese sensibility. If the neck is a separate attachment, which many of the Japanese necks are, the join has been cleverly hidden and must run exactly along the lower edge of the key-patter band. Presently the porcelain model on which this ivory was based has not been located.

Another ivory bottle from the Metropolitan Museum of New York illustrated by Stevens, *The Collector's Book of Snuff Bottles,* p. 206, no. 786 is similarly carved with groups of *arhat* and *lohan* as indeed are two others, one sold at Sotheby's New York, 15 March 1984, lot 127 and the other from the Denis S.K. Low Collection illustrated by Low, *More Treasures from the Sanctum of Enlightened Respect,* p. 276, no. 253.

(CBL C 555)

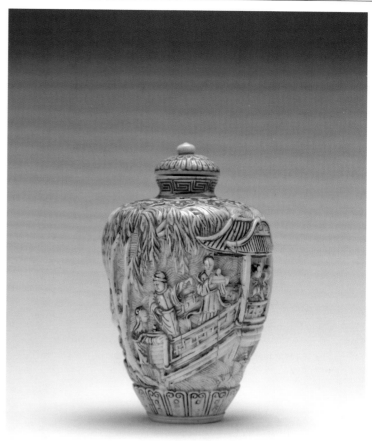

174 (two views)

175 (two views)

176

Ivory, carved in a continuous scene around the body with a scene from the 'Legend of the White Snake', depicting a bearded scholar, probably Xu Xian, riding a donkey on one side amidst a vapor plume rising from below on a dense wave ground surrounded by eight immortals amongst rockwork to either of the narrow sides, all wearing voluminous robes, one holding a large parasol, another a sceptre, some with their hands clasped together under their sleeves and watching a lady, Bai Suzhen, seated in the prow of a canopied boat heading downstream clutching at the supports of her canopy whilst her assistant attends to the rudder, a demon balances a basket of fruit on his head whilst wading in the frothy waves alongside, a chevron band at the foot and neck, flat oval foot ring and shallowly cut base incised with a spurious four-character Qianlong seal mark, a nerve visible in the corner of the seal

Japanese, 1854-1900

Stopper: bone or horn (later)

Height: 6.2 cm without stopper
Mouth: 0.7 cm
Neck: 1.8 cm

Published: Chapman, 'The Chester Beatty Collection of Snuff Bottles', *Arts of Asia*, March-April 1988, fig. 16.

See the previous two entries regarding the reattribution of this particular type of bottle to post-1854 Japanese production.

The subject of the 'Legend of the White Snake' was a popular one on ivory as evidenced by the numerous examples published (see Moss 'The Imperial Master', *JICSBS*, Spring 2007, pp. 10, figs. 16, 18, and 19, and Kleiner, 'Chinese Snuff Bottles', *The White Wings Collection*, pp. 204-205, no.143, now in the Denis Low Collection). The earliest examples appear to copy almost exactly the design from a well-known group of brightly enameled porcelains, which bear Qianlong or more often Jiaqing marks (see Hughes, *The Blair Bequest: Chinese Snuff Bottles from the Princeton University Art Museum*, p. 199, nos. 259-260, and Kleiner, *Chinese Snuff Bottles in the Collection of Mary and George Bloch*, pp. 324-325, no. 210). With slight variations, the porcelain examples depict a lady seated at the prow of a boat on one main face and a gathering of immortals on clouds and a promontory on the other. However the ivory examples, whilst usually depicting the lady at the prow of a boat on one main face, seem to differ considerably with the depiction on the other side. Ours is no exception, with a figure atop a donkey amidst swirling clouds, which appears to have no porcelain counterpart.

The plot of the 'Legend of the White Snake' is rather complicated. Simplified, the story is one of a young scholar, Xu Xian (probably the figure depicted atop the donkey on our ivory bottle), who falls in love with a beautiful woman, Bai Suzhen (probably the lady in the prow of the boat), unaware that she is a white snake demon who has taken on a human form in the hope of transforming into a goddess by completing good deeds.

Once again we have an unusual band of decoration at the foot and neck. Though this does have an equivalent in porcelain bottles, see Hughes, op cit, p.196, no. 255, it is the exception rather than the rule and it is unlikely that the carver was aware of this. Kleiner, op cit, pp. 474-475, no. 313, illustrates another ivory bottle formerly in the Frederick W. A. Knight Collection with the same subject of Bai Suzhen at the prow of her boat (though a different scene on the reverse) that utilizes the same neck band and Moss, op. cit, p. 8-9, fig. 12, bottom right, illustrates another from the Burghley House Collection. Kleiner, *Chinese Snuff Bottles from The Burghley House Collection, Stamford, England*, no. 142, illustrates a clearer image of the same bottle.

(CBL C 556)

176 (two views)

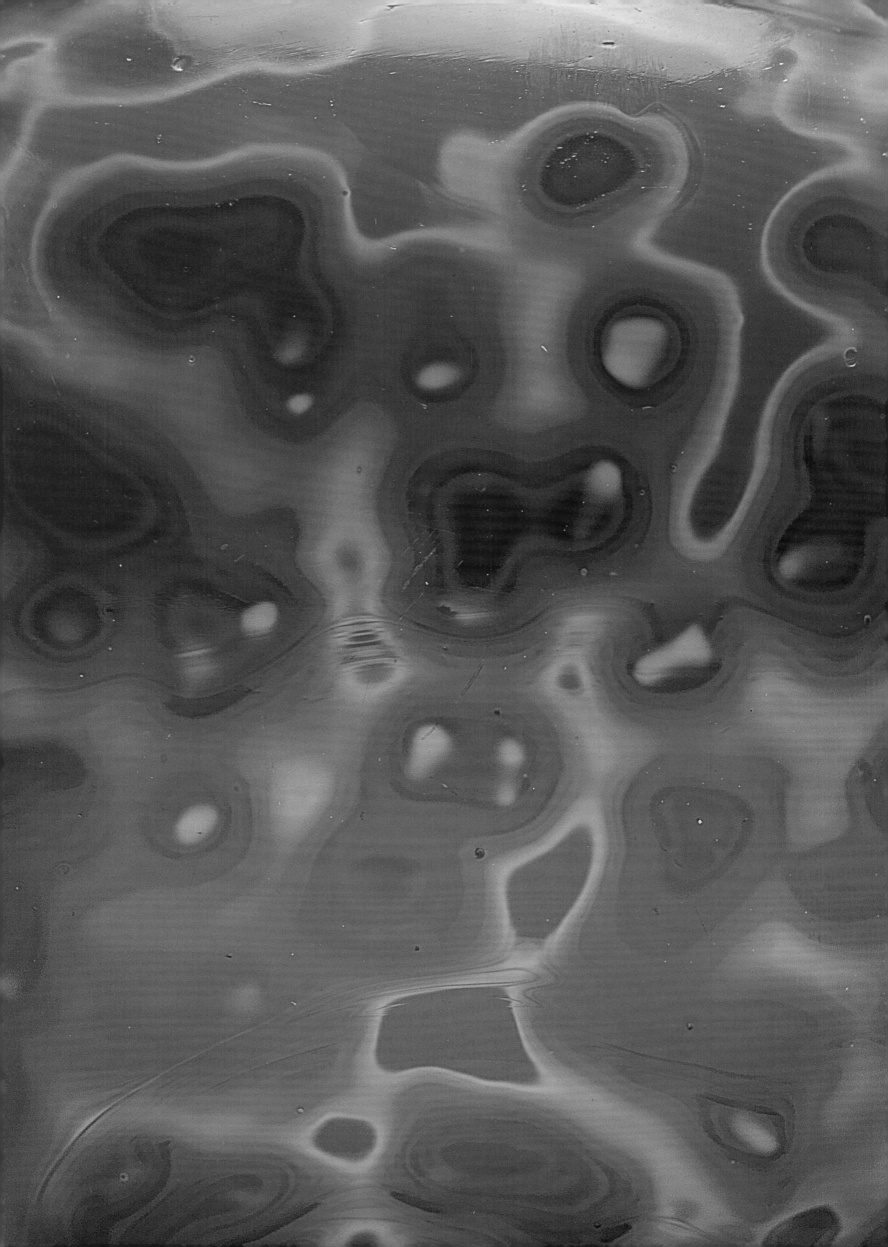

GLASS

177

Glass, of an unusual graduated semi-opaque sky-blue colour, darker at the neck, shoulder, and the lower third and with some misty areas at the centre, carved in relief with a stylized archaistic design suggestive of confronted *kui* dragons with further scrolling and lotus design and dot motifs framing a central motif of a stylized lotus bloom or a beribboned double-gourd, the narrow sides with lion-mask elongated ring handles, a rounded oval flat foot ring and shallowly cut base

Possibly Imperial, 1750-1830

Height: 6.0 cm
Mouth: 0.9 cm
Neck: 2.0 cm

The *kui* dragon was a popular motif at court and fitted neatly into the courtly and literati framework of archaism that persisted throughout the eighteenth century and pervaded much of snuff bottle production. Drawn as they were from the ancient bronzes, they were an exceedingly suitable subject. Here, admittedly, the *kui* dragons are at the very edge of formalization, appearing almost as nothing more than a scrolling foliate design. However there is little question that the design at the lower portion of the bottle does indeed depict the heads of confronted *kui*. See Moss, Graham, and Tsang, *A Treasury of Chinese Snuff Bottles: The Mary and George Bloch Collection*, Vol. 5, Part 2, Glass, pp. 334-335, no. 822, for an example of more slender shape in monochrome red glass and where the authors argue for attribution to the Imperial glassworks. Whilst the carving on ours does not quite match the same degree of quality exhibited by the Bloch bottle it does display another similar feature of a quite wide mouth that can be an indication of early production. The elongated lion-mask handles are also a feature common to many palace bottles.

The pale sky-blue colour of the glass is quite unusual. For a discussion of this as a possible candidate for the 'azure-blue' (or 'blue sky after rain') designation found in early Chinese sources and recorded as a colour produced at the Imperial glassworks as early as 1708, albeit by a Guangzhou glassmaker, see Moss et al, op cit, Vol. 5, Part 1, pp. 117-118, no. 690. It also appeared in the archives that have been published so far, six times between 1715 and 1728. Much about this bottle might be considered Imperial from the archaistic decoration to the handles and the glass itself, which has swirling variation of tone associated with early glass and the wide mouth previously mentioned. Whilst the shape and large size in glass production can often be an indication of later manufacture, it would not be true if the piece were jade. Interestingly and perhaps most importantly the snuff bottle that comes closest in shape and design to this bottle is in fact a nephrite example with a highly Imperial Qianlong *yuzhi* mark, see Moss, Graham, and Tsang, *The Art of the Chinese Snuff Bottle: The J & J Collection*, Vol. 1, pp. 81-84, no. 32. Not only is it carved with a similar pastiche of archaic designs, which bear the hallmark of florid ornamentation with rococo leanings, so beloved by the emperor Qianlong, but it also has the identical lotus bloom or be-ribboned double-gourd at the centre of the design. The authors note that the identical design appears on a group of cloisonné enamel bottles reasonably attributed to the Beijing Palace Workshops, and that this 'strange and distinctive motif, [was] not one likely to be picked up casually by some distant, unconnected workshop as a minor element of design. This may suggest a link with the Palace workshops at Beijing'. The authors further add that at the Palace, where a wide range of arts was produced, lapidaries would almost certainly have been supervised as they worked in a variety of media from jade to chalcedony and even glass. Furthermore, the *yuzhi* mark in form and style is executed in a similar fashion to that found on glass works attributed to the Palace glassworks.

See Tsang, 'Decoding Dragon Designs,' *JICSBS*, Autumn 2000, pp.16-33, where the author suggests that the joining at the head and tail of the dragon can signify longevity, like the unending Buddhist knot.

(CBL C 390)

178

Glass, the glass imitating white nephrite, carved in a continuous scene with a female immortal holding a *ruyi* scepter before a castellated fortress striding on waves with two boys, one holding coral, the other a scroll at play in the water nearby, one on a vessel the other amidst the waves on one main face, the other with a pavilion and pagoda on an island with pine to one side, a crane on one narrow side and clouds on the other, a flat oval foot ring and a slightly convex base

1750-1850

Stopper: rose quartz or tourmaline

Height: 5.8 cm
Mouth: 0.6 cm
Neck: 1.5-1.6 cm oval

Clearly the glass is meant to imitate a flawless white nephrite and may even have been based on a jade example. The choice of an opaque and quite 'dry' glass seems to corroborate this theory as most white glass bottles tend towards the slightly transparent white glass with a silky polish. The shape is also one more familiar in a jade context rather than glass.

The subject on this bottle appears to be a Daoist one as evidenced by the inclusion of a flying crane, the fortress rising from magical waves (Daoist Paradise), and the female immortal clutching a *ruyi* sceptre and standing on waves before two acolytes clutching a twig of coral and a scroll, all auspicious Daoist attributes. According to Little, *Taoism and the Arts of China*, p. 275, among the various religions of China, Taoism is distinguished by its emphasis on the vital role of the yin force–the feminine aspect of the world. It compliments the yang (male) force. They must be seen as mutually complimentary opposites whose interactions create all the mechanisms of the universe; one cannot exist without the other. Female saints have played a vital role both in popular and elite worship. From the second century onward, both men and women could be ordained into the Taoist clergy.

Exactly which deity this particular female represents in uncertain due to the lack of detailed iconography. However the general theme of longevity as attested to by the inclusion of the crane, *ruyi* scepter in the form of a *lingzhi*, and the ancient fortress is plainly clear.

The inclusion of a swastika flag, a symbol normally associated with Buddhism, can be easily attributed to the close ties between the two religions.

For another opaque white glass bottle imitating nephrite and depicting a large pagoda rising from a stormy sea on one side, see Holden, *Rivers and Mountains Far from the World*, pp. 292-293, no. 128.

(CBL C 789 II)

177

178

179

Glass, carved through a black overlay to a pale-coffee or caramel-beige ground with a continuous scene with the sleeping figure of Li Tieguai supported on his gourd vessel resting on his crutch dreaming as the vessel hurtles downstream, a wispy vapor rising from his gourd to join cloud swirls and bats in the sky above, the other side with a fisherman punting his craft down a rapidly running river beneath a crane amidst clouds and further bats, four in total, a basket in the prow of the vessel, various marine animals including a crab, a shell, a fish, and a mollusk appearing amidst the waves around the foot of the bottle, a flat oval foot with shallowly cut base

Li Junting School, probably Yangzhou, 1780-1830

Height: 6.0 cm
Mouth: 0.7 cm
Neck: 1.9 cm

Published: Chapman, 'The Chester Beatty Collection of Snuff Bottles', *Arts of Asia*, March-April, 1988, p. 60, fig 2.

This bottle forms part of a well-known group of bottles probably from Yangzhou and attributed to the School of Li Junting, working between 1780 and 1830.

They themselves form a part of the larger group of Yangzhou 'seal school' bottles (see the following entry). Many of these bottles bear cyclical dates (sixty year cycles) but, with few exceptions, no reign mark. The two exceptions are extremely helpful as they both bear Qianlong marks with identical cyclical dates, which place the earliest known bottles of the group to 1784. The similarity in style of these two Qianlong marked bottles with 'seal school' bottles bearing either the family name Li or the studio name *Jinyu Ting* (Pavilion of Today's Rain) associated with Li Junting, or both, confirms that they are most likely sequential. Typically, they are carved in low relief overlays with a single, double, or sometimes more overlays, usually silhouetted against a light or dark ground. Many include carving of the ground colour in addition to carving of the overlays. They are painterly in style often with inscriptions and seals, reflecting literati painting sensibilities. Their attribution to Yangzhou is discussed in detail by Moss, Graham, and Tsang, *The Art of the Chinese Snuff Bottle: The J & J Collection*, pp. 648-658, nos. 398-404, although as Moss et al discuss in a later publication *A Treasury of Chinese Snuff Bottles: The Mary and George Bloch Collection*, Vol. 5, Part 3, Glass, p. 693, no. 1008, the location of the bottles' workshops is unknown, though suggestions are made. They include the possibility that whoever started the school (be it Li Junting or another) learned his craft at Beijing, either working for the Court or in a private workshop, and then established his own glassworks in his native area. The other suggestion is that he began his career elsewhere, but that much of his production reflected the contemporary, courtly style. Interestingly Li Junting's earliest dated bottle is 1819 and other makers' names appear on 'seal school' bottles with earlier dates, suggesting that he was not the initiator of the school but simply its most famous proponent. (Interestingly, the 1819 dated bottle by Li Junting also bears the place name Jingjiang, situated about 20 miles from Yangzhou, see Moss et al, ibid, pp. 720-721, no. 1021.)

A strong link with Yangzhou was suggested by Gerard Tsang in an article in *JICSBS*, June 1979, in his reading of the seal, Xiaomei, found on many of the 'seal school' bottles, which was the art name of a painter from Yangzhou, Wang Su (1794-1879) and confirmed by a bottle illustrated by Hui, Polak, and Sin, *Hidden Treasures of the Dragon*, no. 225, with the inscription Xiaomei Wang Su zuo (made by Wang Su). See also Lawrence, 'An Analysis of the Seal School Group of Glass Snuff Bottles', *JICSBS*, Summer 1993, pp.10-11, where the similarity of subject matter on some of the 'seal school' bottles with the work of Hua Yan a celebrated painter from Yangzhou is discussed.

The subject of this bottle is most certainly inspired by Daoism as evidenced by the inclusion of the sleeping figure of Li Tieguai identified by his iron crutch and gourd and the crane, *he*, holding a tally or counter, *chou*, in its beak flying above the fisherman punting his craft. The tally is a small strip of bamboo for recording longevity, each notch representing a life span. Certain legends recount that the crane would drop such a tally into a magic vase to extend life expectancy (see Bartholomew, *Hidden Meanings in Chinese Art*, p.

221, no. 7.55.2.) The inclusion of the punting figure appears to be a generic one found on many bottles of the school and does not appear to figure into the story of Li Tieguai. Presumably, the fish and various crustacea carved to the lower section of the scene are connected to this fisherman. Interestingly, but presumably coincidentally, the unusual deeply cut areas of swirling clouds at the narrow sides are actually reminiscent of Suzhou nephrite lapidary work.

No other Li Junting School bottle appears to follow the exact design of our bottle though three bear similar scenes to at least one side. The depiction of the Daoist immortal Li Tieguai appears to be unique. For a cinnabar and black overlay with a similar scene of a fisherman punting his craft which bears the studio name of Li Junting, *Jinyu Ting* (Pavilion of Today's Rain), see Hughes, *The Blair Bequest: Chinese Snuff Bottles from the Princeton University Art Museum*, p. 147; and another is illustrated by Moss et al, op cit, Vol. 5, Part 3, Glass, pp. 699-701, no. 1011; another bottle with a *Jinyu Ting* studio name with a differing boating scene but with a opaque cafe-au-lait or caramel-beige ground is illustrated by Hall, *Chinese Snuff Bottles*, pp.86-87, no. 43; and various bottles with or without the studio name are known with this distinctive café-au-lait or caramel-beige ground colour.

(CBL C 406)

179 (two views)

180

Glass, very delicately carved through a black overlay to an opaque white ground on one main face with a horse rolling on its back near a thick coiling vine stem which rises upwards supporting a monkey in its slender leafy upper branches, the monkey keeping a watchful eye on a wasp flying nearby, alongside is a four-character inscription, the other side with two bushy-tailed dogs near lily and a prunus spray glaring at two butterflies, the narrow sides with simple mock-mask ring handles, a black overlay oval ring forms the foot with a slightly convex base

Probably Yangzhou, 1800-1880

Stopper: coral glass

Height: 5.5 cm
Mouth: 0.65 cm
Neck: 1.3 cm

The inscription reads:
Ma sheng hou feng

This may be translated as:
On the horse, a monkey

The depiction of a horse, *ma*, monkey, *hou*, and a wasp, *feng*, is a popular one on snuff bottles, particularly within the quartz group. Usually the monkey is shown seated on the horse or standing alongside it. This depiction with the monkey in the branches of a vine above a horse rolling on its back is singular. However the inscription clearly indicates the subject which can be read as 'May you immediately be conferred the rank of marquess' or 'May you immediately be appointed a high ranking position', *mashang fenghou*. The subject of two dogs, portrayed on the other side, may depict the Pekinese variety with their telltale small sizes and bushy tail, though here they do not have typical shaggy manes or floppy ears. The depiction of pairs of Pekinese dogs was particularly fashionable during the reign of the Daoguang emperor (1820-50), which would fit neatly into the 'seal school' time frame. They may also merely depict other dogs, here closely watching two annoying butterflies, which may well form a rebus that as yet is unidentified. Cats watching butterflies can of course be read as birthday wishes 'may you live into your seventies or eighties', *maodie*, though it is unlikely that the animals shown here are meant to represent cats.

The wider group of overlay bottles (and this includes the Li Junting School discussed in the previous entry) is generally known as the Yangzhou seal school. Characteristics include low relief overlay carving usually silhouetted on a different ground colour, a distinctive painterly style, and often seals and inscriptions. Their attribution to Yangzhou is discussed in detail by Moss, Graham, and Tsang, *The Art of the Chinese Snuff Bottle: The J & J Collection*, pp. 648-658, nos. 398-404. The decoration on this bottle of two separate scenes on either side of the main face rather than a continuous one, seems to fit with the general trend within 'seal school' bottles, though not applicable to the majority of signed works of the Li Junting school. The multiple overlays and this anomaly may indicate a slightly later production. The simple lion-mask ring handles and the foot ring on our bottle are also carved from the same overlay as the scene, and whilst the handles are neat, the foot ring is somewhat uneven, a feature common to the group though with no obvious explicable reason. The use of handles on the entire seal school group seems to be arbitrary, on bottles where handles would be appropriate, particularly in the demarcation of two different scenes, they are missing and where they do appear, they are sometimes unnecessary. Generally most lion-mask ring handles appear in the group of extremely low relief decorated bottles, quite often of smaller size, usually a more standard spade, rounded, or rectangular shape and again is possibly indicative of a slightly later production date. As one would expect on bottles with continuous scenes (more often than not this applies to the early Li Junting type bottles and the multiple overlays), handles are usually absent.

(CBL C 420)

181

Glass, delicately carved on one main face through a black overlay to an opaque white ground with the figure of an elderly man with a traveling case by his side, a staff with a gourd attached and a wine cup by his feet, gesticulating at a mule, all below a four-character inscription, the other side with a figure, possibly Damo, seated on a leafy fringed mat holding a staff possibly suspending four bells, three standing goats nearby and a fourth seen from behind lying nearby, two birds fly overhead, the narrow sides with simple mock-mask ring handles, the oval flat foot ring simply cut from the overlay

Probably Yangzhou, 1800-1880

Stopper: tourmaline and metal collar

Height: 5.4 cm
Mouth: 0.5 cm
Neck: 1.4 cm

The inscription reads:
Wei zhi qing wan

This may be translated as:
For enjoyment of Wei Zhi

Unfortunately we do not know who Wei Zhi, the recipient of this delightful bottle, is. Neither is it certain what the subject of the overlay depiction is either. Whilst the scene may simply be a generic one of a traveler with his donkey and a goatherd tending his flock, it is possible that there is a more specific story being portrayed. One possibility for the figure with the donkey is that it represents Huang Chengyan from the epic story *Sanguo yanyi* ('Romance of the Three Kingdoms'). Usually he is depicted riding a donkey in a winter landscape, with his assistant clutching a plum blossom and invariably shown with a double gourd vessel tied at his waist. Perhaps, this is a moment in the story when he has dismounted and sends his steed away. His assistant's gourd vessel is now tied to his staff. We certainly have a traveling case at his feet, which suggests the figure has been on a long journey, and a wine cup might indicate an invigorating drink to warm the weary winter traveller. For a lengthy discussion of such figures and many more associated with this iconography, see Tsang, 'Who is the Rider on the Donkey? Some New Observations,' *JICSBS*, Summer 1994, pp. 4-16, and also the entries to Nos. 91 and 157 in this publication.

The depiction on the other side may well be nothing more than a goatherd tending his flock but the addition of a leafy-fringed mat might suggest that this is a meditating figure, perhaps an arhat, with his Buddhist bells tied to his staff. The depiction of goats is usually found in groups of three, *sanyang*, under a sun, forming the rebus 'renewal and a change of fortune in the spring', *sanyang katai*. Here we have four goats and no sun, so this seems unlikely.

Like the previous bottle, this one displays the classic attributes of the Yangzhou seal school; low relief overlay carving silhouetted on a different ground colour, a distinctive painterly style, a seal-type inscription, and small neat mock-mask ring handles. The inclusion of pebbles at the feet of the goats is a clever use of the overlay, where the surface has been delicately cut away to simply leave dots of black overlay. The opaque white surface of this particular bottle has been rather carelessly left somewhat lumpy in the areas around the figural scenes giving a slightly unfinished appearance.

(CBL C 421)

180 (two views)

181 (two views)

182

Glass, a pale opaque pink overlay on an opaque white ground, one main face carved with an elegant lady holding a fan with rockwork at her feet to one side and a large curving tree branch rising from her feet at the other and extending to form a canopy above her, a cyclical seal alongside, the other main face of the bottle carved with a male figure on a mule followed on foot by an assistant clutching a wrapped *qin* with two birds flying overhead, the narrow sides with simple mask and ring handles, a long elegant neck, a flat oval foot ring and slightly convex base

Probably Yangzhou, dated Renwu year probably corresponding to 1822

Stopper: amethyst

Height: 5.3 cm
Mouth: unknown (stopper glued)
Neck: 1.1 cm

Like the previous bottle it is uncertain what the exact subject of the overlay depiction is though in this case a more generic interpretation seems likely. The figure of an elegant female, would actually appear to be no more than that, in a garden setting with *taihu* rock and a plum or cherry tree forming an arbour. The fan may be no more than a cooling device rather than a specific attribute. The two female immortals, He Xiangu and Lan Caihe, are sometimes shown standing on a boat made from a hollowed-out tree usually with branches still attached at the stern which might be the reference here, but the first is nearly always shown with the attribute of a lotus and the second with a basket of flowers.

The other side has a gentleman riding a donkey or a horse, looking back at his assistant carrying a *qin* wrapped in a cover for protection. Whilst the previous entry discusses the various possibilities of this particular subject in relation to various historical and legendary figures, the strong likelihood is that we have no more than an idyllic rustic scene of a scholar and his companion traveling through a landscape with birds overhead, a common enough theme in literati painting. Again we have the mask handles and rings, and the shoddy foot finish often found on Yangzhou glass bottles; here visible not only as a missing portion of overlay to the foot edge but also as careless pink glass trails across the entire foot base.

Pink glass as a ground colour appears to have been particularly popular in the early bottles of the Li Junting school dating from the 1780s onwards, especially with the high-relief multiple overlays, depicting fruit and silkworm subjects, see Moss, Graham, and Tsang, *A Treasury of Chinese Snuff Bottles: The Mary and George Bloch Collection*, Vol. 5, Part 3, Glass, pp. 686-698, nos. 1006, 1008-1010. It is seen occasionally, though rarely, as a ground colour on the more low relief decorated bottles that appear to date from the second decade of the nineteenth century, for example see Moss et al, ibid, p. 722, no. 1022, for a bottle signed Yunting though attributed to Junting, which is dated 1819 and another, p. 740, no. 1030, dated 1821, attributed to the same master. As a single overlay however it is quite rare. This may be due to the fact that the subjects and particularly small seals and inscriptions do not 'pop' so easily as more contrasting colours do.

(CBL C 453)

183

Glass, a transparent honey-coloured overlay on an opaque white ground, one main face carved with a figure of Mi Fu worshipping a large rock with grassy fronds at its base and tree branches behind, a four-character cyclical inscription alongside, the other main face with a quail standing alongside a group of various auspicious objects including a vase with prunus, a *ruyi* scepter, a wine pot and cup and a fruit, possibly a persimmon, apple, or an orange, a seal alongside, the narrow sides with simple mask and oval ring handles, a short cylindrical neck and a flat oval foot ring

Probably Yangzhou, signed Zheng Ke and dated Bing Shen year probably corresponding to 1836

Height: 5.3 cm
Mouth: 0.6 cm
Neck: 1.3 cm

The four-character inscription reads:
Bing shen chun yue and the seal as *Zheng Ke*

This can be translated as:
'Bing Shen year (probably 1836), spring month', and the seal of Zheng Ke, probably the maker's name

Unfortunately we do not have any information on the artist which is a great pity because he was a master of adding subtle colour variations on a single overlay through the judicious paring down to a variety of thicknesses to show depth and shading, particularly noticeable on the rockwork.

The depiction on one main face is that of Mi Fu, or Mi Fei, as he is sometimes known. He was a Northern Song Dynasty literatus and considered on of the four 'Song Masters'. He was born in Taiyuan, Shanxi province (1050-1107 CE) and was known for his reverence, one might say addiction, to these strangely shaped rocks. He was a famed poet, calligrapher, and painter and hugely influential figure in the literati world. Here he is shown worshipping a massive *taihu* rock characterized by its large cavities. A further rebus may be implied if the grasses at the base of the rock represent day lily, *xuancao*, and the leafy branches represent pine, *song*, or cypress, *bai*, which can be read as 'May Mount Song bring a hundred longevities', *Song Shan baishou*. (See Bartholomew, *Hidden Meanings in Chinese Art*, p. 212, no. 7.47.9.)

The other side is replete with numerous meanings. The vase, *ping*, apples, *pingguo*, and wish-granting wand, *ruyi*, can be read as 'May you have peace and fulfillment of all wishes', *ping'an ruyi*; the quail, *anchun*, bears the character *an* in its name which is a pun on peace, *ping'an*; see Bartholomew, ibid, p. 230, no. 8.1.2, and p. 244, no. 822; and the Yixing teapot, *hu*, according to Moss, Graham, and Tsang, *A Treasury of Chinese Snuff Bottles: The Mary and George Bloch Collection*, Vol. 4, Part 1, p. 129, no. 479, for happiness or good fortune, *fu*.

For a similar depiction of auspicious objects on a cinnabar overlay bottle see Hughes, *The Blair Bequest: Chinese Snuff Bottles from the Princeton University Art Museum*, p. 142, no. 173.

Again, we have the mask handles and rings, often found on this particular group (see Nos. 180-183 in this publication) but interestingly, and perhaps not surprisingly given the fine carving elsewhere on this bottle, the foot treatment is better than many whilst still leaving room for improvement. The colour of the glass overlay is most unusual and extremely rare on single overlays. Though it can be found in small areas of multiple overlay bottles, the inability of the colour to contrast sharply with the opaque white ground, just like the pink of the previous example, probably made the honey hue unpopular.

(CBL C 454)

182 (two views)

183 (two views)

184

Glass, with two overlays of semi-opaque pink and then transparent pea green on an opaque white ground, carved in high relief with a continuous scene of the 'Seven Worthies of the Bamboo Grove', each at various scholarly pursuits in a bamboo and pine setting with a pavilion and seating areas, a boy standing on rockwork on one narrow side holding aloft one end of an unrolled scroll for inspection, the lower layer of green used to carve the backdrop of the bamboo grove and leaves at the neck which has been reduced and fitted with a silver collar, a simple flat oval foot ring cut from the top pink overlay and then cut from the transparent green glass with a stylized coiled bird silhouetted against the opaque white ground

1780-1840

Stopper: pink glass

Height: 6.9 cm (to present collar)
Mouth: 0.55 cm
Neck: 2.1 cm (silver collar diameter)

The subject of the 'Seven Worthies of the Bamboo Grove' also known as the 'Seven Sages of the Bamboo Grove', was a popular one in literati painting as well as in other works of art. It can be found on porcelain brush pots, wall paintings, carved on bamboo brush pots, and many other media including glass and occasionally porcelain snuff bottles. According to Tsang and Moss, *Arts from the Scholar's Studio*, p. 146, no. 118 and Moss, Graham, and Tsang, *A Treasury of Chinese Snuff Bottles: The Mary and George Bloch Collection*, Vol. 6, Part 3, Arts of the Fire, pp. 896-897, no. 1426, the 'Seven Worthies' were famous literati of the third century and amongst the most influential men of their day and included ministers of state as well as poets, musicians, and artists. It is believed that the key members were Daoist followers. Their number included Xiang Xiu, Xi Kang (223-262), Liu Ling, Shan Tao (d. 283), Yuan Xian, Ruan Ji (210-263) and Wang Rong (235-306). They gathered, in Loyang (present day Henan province), to enjoy music, poetry, elegant conversation, contemplation and wine and to escape what they believed was the corruption at the Imperial Court during the Three Kingdoms period and the ensuing Jin dynasty. They relished a simple rustic life and rejoiced in nature, which would be illustrated metaphorically in the common theme of the 'Seven Worthies of the Bamboo Grove'. Although not the case here, the seven are often depicted with the additional figure of the fifth century BCE scholar Rong Qiqi because he was their role model for living naturally and spontaneously. He was a recluse known to have once met Confucius on his travels.

For similar scenes of the same subject, see Hughes, *The Blair Bequest: Chinese Snuff Bottles from the Princeton University Art Museum*, p. 155, no. 194, for a blue-and-beige glass example; and Moss, Graham, and Tsang, *A Treasury of Chinese Snuff Bottles: The Mary and George Bloch Collection*, Vol. 6, Part 3, Arts of the Fire, pp. 896-897, no. 1426, for a painted ceramic version.

The stylized bird to the foot initially looks like a yin-yang symbol but on close scrutiny is in fact a bird looking over its back with wings and tail swept upwards and legs set at one hundred and eighty degrees apart straddling branches above and below. It is a most unusual and rare feature. Unfortunately this particular bottle has suffered trauma over the years, losing the upper portion of the neck and receiving chips to the overlay.

184 (foot detail)

This bottle belongs to a distinctive group of bottles, all with double overlay in deep relief and a collar of pendant plantain leaves. These include the Princeton example mentioned above; one illustrated by Kleiner, *Chinese Snuff Bottles from The Burghley House Collection, Stamford, England*, no. 21; Hall, *Chinese Snuff Bottles II*, p. 144, no. 132; Stevens, *The Collector's Book of Snuff Bottles*, p. 73, nos. 229-230; and to Moss, Graham, and Tsang, *A Treasury of Chinese Snuff Bottles: The Mary and George Bloch Collection*, Vol. 5, Part 3, Glass, pp. 667-683, nos. 1002-1004; Moss, *The Barron Collection: Illustrated Handlist*, ICSBS Convention, Boston, 2008, p. 39, no. 2757 and others dotted around the world's collections. Moss et al, ibid, suggests that the entire group is linked to the Court probably originating from the Imperial glassworks or another such facility dominated by Court orders and style, though resisting a specific attribution. The authors qualify their belief that the earliest of the group probably dated to 1780 or earlier by comparing it to a dated overlay bottle of 1780, ibid, p. 558, no. 940 and others.

(CBL C 424)

185

Glass, an opaque dark olive-green overlay on an opaque dark pink-blush ground, both main faces carved with an up-turned carp jumping amidst waves, one supporting a moon or rising sun on vapour swirls emanating from its mouth, the other supporting a pavilion in the same manner, the narrow sides with rockwork, one with *lingzhi*, the other rock with a bat and crane, a slightly everted cylindrical neck with quite wide mouth, deeply-cut flat foot ring with convex base

1770-1850

Height: 5.7 cm
Mouth: 0.75 cm
Neck: 1.5 cm

The carp is the fish associated with motifs for passing the civil service examinations. The story goes, according to tradition, that a carp swimming upstream in the Yellow River, fighting against the opposing current must leap the rapids of Dragon's-Gate (Longmen) falls; the first to succeed transforms itself into a dragon. This story is a metaphor for a poor scholar who by passing the civil services exams raises himself to the status of high official, see Bartholomew, *Hidden Meanings in Chinese Art*, p. 92, 4.11.2. The depiction on one side of a pavilion above the carp may well be an allusion to this legend certainly a wish for advancement is generally associated with a carp leaping from water. Though unlikely on this particular bottle, the inclusion of two fish can also symbolize conjugal bliss. The various other motifs all form representations of longevity: the crane, *he*, carrying a tally in its mouth (see entry no. 179); the bat, *fu*; the *lingzhi* fungus; and the rocks.

For a red overlay bottle with a 'snowstorm' ground depicting very similar Daoist scenes on both sides but with books replacing the sun or moon supported on the vapour emanating from the carp, see Hughes, *The Blair Bequest: Chinese Snuff Bottles from the Princeton University Art Museum*, p. 136, no. 163. For another see White, *Snuff Bottles from China: The Victoria and Albert Collection*, pp. 190-191, pl. 3. For a red overlay glass bottle with one side depicting an upturned fish supporting a pavilion on a plum from the Carl F. Barron collection, see Moss, *The Barron Collection: Illustrated Handlist*, ICSBS Convention, Boston, 2008, p. 30, no. 4513.

The colour combination is unusual but not rare. Certainly it was a favorite of the early Li Junting School multiple overlays and perhaps this might be a clue as the origins and dating of this bottle, which has been given a wide dating range.

(CBL C 413)

184 (two views)

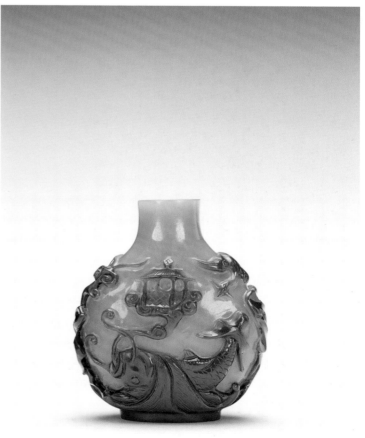

185 (two views)

186

Glass, of realgar type, of unusual flattened double gourd shape, of slightly irregular shape with a long everted neck, flat rim and regular mouth, the glass has a bright fiery red blotchy surface which disperses in areas to reveal yellow and mustard glass beneath and also a few small areas of swirling lime-green particularly at the base, the lobes of the gourd on one main face cleverly marked with the characters *Da ji* and on the other with the characters *Ping an*, a flat oval foot

1720-1830

Stopper: green glass

Height: 7.0 cm
Mouth: 0.55 cm
Neck: 1.5 cm

The characters *Da ji ping an* can be translated as 'Good Luck and Peace'.

The characters themselves seem to have been manipulated on to the surface of the bottle during the moulding process. Quite how is uncertain, but a close inspection of the glass surface is helpful. The glass was evidently blown in to a two-piece mould, as evidenced by an irregular line of 'revealed' yellow glass that runs vertically around the narrow sides of the bottle and across the base. It has the look of a mould line that appears on ceramic bottles made in two-piece moulds but, unlike those, is not ridged. Similarly, the main faces of the upper and lower gourds have a flattened disc exactly at the placement of the characters (not easily visible in the illustrations). This indicates that these discs are mirror images of the mould interior and that somehow, perhaps using wax resist, simply as a result of leaning up against a lightly raised negative character on the mould interior or some other 'secret' method, the yellow under surface of the glass has been exposed to reveal the inscription.

Whatever the exact method, it was ingenious and gives the appearance of having been calligraphically written on to the glass itself.

The neck of the bottle leans both forward and to the side, possibly as a result of some kind of twisting action in the manufacturing process, visible at the neck as twisting air-bubble channels and twists of colour or possibly because the neck was later annealed after or during the mould process. For a bottle that is in so many ways technically difficult to produce, it is a pity that it so lacks formal integrity. The gourds are not evenly shaped and the bottle leans rather dramatically.

See Bartholomew, *Hidden Meaning in Chinese Art*, p. 61, no. 3.3 for an explanation of the gourd as an important auspicious symbol. It is a natural symbol of fertility because of its numerous seeds. Combined with the four characters *Da ji ping an* the positive metaphor is reinforced.

For another plain realgar glass bottle of this rare gourd shape but of more compressed form, see Kleiner, *Chinees Snuff Bottles: The White Wings Collection*, p. 74, no. 43. For a crystal bottle with the same inscription, *Da ji*, on both sides, see No. 123 in this publication. Moss, Graham, and Tsang, *The Art of the Chinese Snuff Bottles: The J & J Collection*, Vol. 1, pp. 177-178, no. 98, illustrate an almost identical crystal bottle, which they tentatively attribute to the Palace workshops on a number of grounds, two of which are relevant in the context of this bottle. The popularity of the double-gourd form at the Palace workshops, primarily on glass and enamel wares and the formalized designs of this type with auspicious meanings were beloved by the Qianlong Emperor who is known to have had large orders made to give away on special occasions. Both are perfectly acceptable arguments for ascribing this bottle to the Palace workshops as well.

For a discussion of realgar and realgar glass see the following entry.

(CBL C 277)

187

Glass, of realgar type, delicately carved in low relief through the orange red surface with a continuous pond scene with five fan-tailed fish swimming amongst lotus and millet and small aquatic leaves, some small areas of swirling lime-green glass on one shoulder of the main face in particular but also trailing around to the other side and found in small swirl traces around the entire body, a concave shallowly-cut oval foot

1720-1830

Stopper: red glass imitating amethyst or ruby, metal collar and spoon, silver

Height: 5.3 cm
Mouth: 0.85 cm
Neck: 1.55 cm

Realgar is a toxic arsenic compound much valued in Daoist alchemical practice. Small amounts were mixed in drinkable elixirs to chemically transform the consciousness so as to enter a transcendent state. Its use as an actual material for snuff bottles proved almost impossible (there are only a few known examples including one in the *Shuisongshi shanfang* Collection), as the material had a tendency to decompose upon prolonged exposure to sunlight, hence its fractured appearance in other works of art made from the material, and perhaps more importantly because the material is very poisonous. For an example of a rare *ruyi* sceptre in this unstable material, see Christie's, New York, 19 September 2007, lot 27. However, once the glassmakers were able to produce a satisfactory and safe replica, so to speak, snuff bottles in the material appeared in fairly large numbers.

It is not unusual to find realgar glass bottles with carved surfaces though plain bottles, which rely on the colour of the glass alone for decoration, are far more prevalent. It seemed uncertain for some time if the red overlay was intentional or a result of the cooling process, which left the red colour on the surface and the yellow beneath it. However, extremely close observation of the entire core group by Moss, Graham, and Tsang, *A Treasury of Chinese Snuff Bottles: The Mary and George Bloch Collection*, Vol. 5, Part 1, Glass, 138-149, nos. 703-708, seems to suggest that it was indeed intentional, particularly as the red overlay appears to be a transparent ruby glass whilst the lower levels of colour are usually opaque. The ruby red colour sometimes appears opaque due to light refraction through the lower levels of opaque orange and yellow.

For another rare realgar glass bottle carved in low relief with fan-tailed fish, see Sotheby's, New York, 1 July 1985, lot 154, but where the overlay fish and the ground colours are reversed.

For other examples of carved realgar glass see, Hughes, *The Blair Bequest: Chinese Snuff Bottles from the Princeton University Art Museum*, p. 149, no. 185, with chrysanthemum and plum; Moss, Graham, and Tsang, *The Art of The Chinese Snuff Bottle: The J & J Collection*, Vol. 2, p.591, no. 354, with Buddhist lions with a possible Beijing Palace workshops' attribution; and Kleiner, *Chinese Snuff Bottles from the Collection of Mary and George Bloch*, no. 109, with pomegranate and melons.

Whilst it is commonly accepted that these bottles imitate realgar, the possibility that they imitate carved lacquer, bamboo, or even hornbill should not be ruled out.

The subject of fish is, of course, an emblem of harmony and conjugal bliss because they often swim in pairs and are happy in their own element. The fish, *yu*, and the lotus, *lian*, (the reverse side depicts a large lotus pad, buds, and stalks), together form the rebus 'May you continuously have plenty year after year', *liannian youyu*.

An x-ray analysis of this bottle (carried out by the museum many years ago) reveals that the constituents are mostly silicon, with very small amounts of potassium, calcium, and iron. Copper is also present in a slightly larger quantity. This analysis is the same as No. 188 in this publication.

(CBL C 415)

188

Glass, of realgar type, an orange-red mottling or blotches at the surface which disperses in areas to reveal yellow, mustard, green (particularly on one side), and brown-beige glass beneath, the narrow edges and base of the bottle revealing the darker brown-beige glass under surface as a result of the molding process, slightly everted tall neck with shallow concave mouth, flat oval foot very deeply cut and extraordinarily thin

1720-1830

Stopper: coral glass, green hard stone or glass disc

Height: 5.9 cm
Mouth: 0.55 cm
Neck: 1.6 cm

That realgar glass was amongst the earliest produced at the beginning decades of the eighteenth century seems fairly well established, see Moss, Graham, and Tsang, *A Treasury of Chinese Snuff Bottles: The Mary and George Bloch Collection*, Vol. 5, Part 1, Glass, p. 138, no. 703. Realgar glass with a Yongzheng mark (1723-35) is recorded in the Imperial Collection in Beijing and there is a set of ten realgar glass cups in the National Museum of Denmark, which were purchased in Guangzhou and taken back to Europe in 1732 (*Ethnographic Objects in the Royal Danish Kunsthammer 1650-1800*, Nationalmuseet, nos. Ebc 71-82, p. 218). The authors also note that for glass produced at this relatively early date, it is notable that none, with the exception of recently excavated examples, display the crizzling or internal disintegration common to early glass prior to the Jesuit influence at the Imperial glassworks in 1696. This would sensibly suggest that realgar glass was probably first made at the Imperial glassworks before spreading to other glass producing centers. Realgar glass was also bequeathed by Sir Hans Sloane to the British Museum collection in 1753 and must therefore have been produced at a date earlier than this.

This particular example has a wonderful variety of colours within its matrix, ranging from ruby red, orange, pale yellow, beige, and even green in a patch to one side, which swirl like oil on water. There seems to be a constant movement to the surface and numerous images seem to float within it. One can read gnarled root wood carvings, *taihu* rockwork, or even amoebic cells. The face of a Buddhist lion or Pekinese dog can also be imagined from the abstract makings on the reverse side.

The glass is blown to a remarkable thinness and but for a slight lean has a fine formal integrity. The spade shape is well balanced by the slightly waisted neck and the surface has a high degree of polish that helps to give brightness to the colours.

An x-ray analysis of this bottle (carried out by the museum many years ago) reveals that the constituents are mostly silicon, with very small amounts of potassium, calcium, and iron. Copper is also present in a slightly larger quantity. This analysis is the same as No. 187 in this publication.

(CBL C 827 II)

187

188

189

Glass, of *meiping* shape, a dark blood-red overlay on an opaque milky-white ground, carved in very high relief with full-faced three-clawed dragon coiled around the bottle above breaking waves, fire scrolls, and water splashes and contesting a flaming pearl with another dragon appearing from the waves on the other side, a slightly waisted cylindrical neck with quite large mouth and flat rim, a simple flat circular foot ring carved from the overlay, the base white glass

1730-1790

Height: 6.6 cm
Mouth: 0.6 cm
Neck: 1.2 cm

This is a very rare bottle, if not unique. Whilst the slender *chilong* or *kui* dragons are found in abundance on bottles throughout the eighteenth and nineteenth centuries, the use of an Imperial-type dragon with menacing demeanor that stares out directly at the viewer is most unusual. The high quality relief and rare subject matter are certainly suggestive of court production as is the fairly large mouth. There is every possibility that the maker of this bottle based his design on ceramic vessels seen in the Royal Collections within the Imperial Palace. During the reigns of the Yongzheng and Qianlong emperors, both ordered exquisite porcelains in blue and white and underglaze-copper-red from the workshops in Jingdezhen, which displayed full-faced dragons often in a contest with another for the magical flaming pearl. Some of these designs are so close to the format of our bottle it is hard not to make the argument that our bottle was ordered by someone with knowledge of the Imperial collection. However the lack of a reign mark, whilst undercutting this argument, does not entirely rule out the possibility that it might have been a private order for someone associated with the Court. This would certainly answer the niggling question of why the dragons on such a superbly crafted bottle lack the requisite five claws, expected on an Imperial bottle. However three-clawed dragons, as in our example, was the standard format of the earliest depictions up until the Yuan dynasty and early Ming when five claws became the Imperial norm.

For Imperial ceramic vessels that might have been the inspiration behind this bottle, see *Blue and White Porcelain with Underglazed Red (III)*, The Complete Collection of Treasures of the Palace Museum, pl. 213, for a moonflask, *magua ping*, that according to the Qing dynasty archives may have been ordered in 1742 from Tang Yin in Jingdezhen. It is painted with a superb full-faced (directly facing the viewer) dragon coiled around a flaming pearl in a rich underglaze-copper ruby-red colour on a white ground, with the waves picked out in underglaze blue. It bears a Qianlong sealmark. See also another Qianlong marked miniature vase, this time of very similar *meiping* shape to our bottle and only 11.4 cm. high painted entirely in underglaze copper-red with a five-clawed dragons above waves, Christie's, Hong Kong, Important Chinese Ceramics, 28 November 2005, lot 1385. Again one can clearly see how this might have been an inspiration to the snuff bottle workshop.

The subject of a dragon staring out directly at the viewer can also be found on cinnabar lacquer bottles and these may also have been a source of inspiration for the glass maker, and an example from the F.W.A. Knight Collection is illustrated in a sale catalogue, Sotheby's London, 9 June 1981, lot 58.

For a red overlay bottle carved with a five-clawed dragon, see Moss, Graham, and Tsang, *The Art of the Chinese Snuff Bottle: The J & J Collection*, Vol. 2, pp. 599-601, no. 360, which is attributed to the early phase of the Palace glass workshops in Beijing, partly because of the subject matter but also on the grounds of quality of carving and finish, degree of wear, the ground colour, which can clear or milky-white and often suffused with bubbles or 'snowflakes', and the overlay, which in the early phase was predominately ruby-red or sapphire-blue. The author's further note that overlay wares from the Palace workshops are recorded as early as 1708 and that during the reign of the Yongzheng Emperor (1723-35) the palace archives list 'red overlay water containers' and 'red overlay brush-washers'.

For another possibly related bottle in blue overlay on opaque white with two confronted dragon with four claws, see Hughes, *The Blair Bequest: Chinese Snuff Bottles from the Princeton University Art* Museum, p. 128, no. 149. And a more compressed red overlay opaque white glass bottle of *meiping* shape carved with dragons coiling around the body is illustrated by Low, *More Treasures from the Sanctum of Enlightened Respect*, p. 145, no. 134.

(CBL C 436)

189 (two views)

190

Glass, a dark cherry-red overlay on a transparent though slightly misty ground, well carved with a continuous monkey landscape scene, one main face with two monkeys peering up at two bees or wasps, one monkey with a stick poking at a nest hanging from a pine branch, the other side with three monkeys variously dispersed and each holding large peaches, the narrow sides primarily carved with idiosyncratic 'lumpy' rockwork outcroppings in deep relief which supports pine trees and which extend to frame the scenes on each main face below a short cylindrical neck and a regular mouth, a deeply-cut rounded thin oval foot ring and very slightly convex base

1730-1790

Stopper: coral glass, bone finial

Height: 5.4 cm
Mouth: 0.6 cm
Neck: 1.3 cm

The subject on this bottle is a popular one in the snuff bottle oeuvre appearing on a variety of media. Here, however, we have one of the earliest interpretations of the scene and an extremely exquisite example of an artist at the height of his powers in the wonderfully balanced asymmetry of design. Five monkeys are carefully placed within a rocky landscape scene. Two are teasing wasps to one side, one holding a stick and poking at the wasps' nest hanging from a pine branch above while two wasps defend their territory. The monkey, *hou*, is a pun for a high ranking noble, marquess, *hou*. The wasp, *feng*, and monkey together can form the rebus, 'conferring the rank of marquess', *fenghou*. Described as a wasps' nest, the irregular shaped package hanging, *gua*, from the pine branch might actually be an official seal wrapped in a cloth, *yin*. If this is the case the combination of the hanging seal (*guayin*), wasp (*feng*) and monkey (*hou*), forms the rebus 'may you rise to marquess status and be given the seal of office', *fenghou guayin*, see Bartholomew, *Hidden Meanings in Chinese Art*, p. 120, no. 5.21.5, where an agate snuff bottle depicting the scene is illustrated. The reverse side of the bottle depicts three monkeys each clutching a large peach. The monkey, *hou*, and peaches, *shoutao* forms the rebus 'sacred monkey offers longevity', *linghou xianshou*.

This is a fantastically well-carved overlay bottle. The allure of the idiosyncratic 'lumpy' rockwork craved on the narrow sides from the lustrous bright cherry-red colour balanced against the bubble-suffused transparent misty ground gives this bottle a masterful edge. The rockwork itself almost defies gravity in places with extraordinary overhanging ledges and precarious pinnacles of rock attached by the narrowest of craggy connections. The rock almost takes on an organic quality that would be very much in keeping with Daoist sensibilities of change and transcendence. Interestingly and presumably from the same workshop, a bottle illustrated by Moss, Graham, and Tsang, *A Treasury of Chinese Snuff Bottles: The Mary and George Bloch Collection*, Vol. 5, Part 2, Glass, pp. 437-438, no. 876, also a red overlay, depicts a similar scene on one main face, with a single monkey, a bee, and a wrapped seal hanging from a tree. It also has 'exuberant' rockwork on one narrow side and the authors comment on the possibility that the bottles might have been made at a glass workshop in Suzhou. Stylistically the rockwork would certainly fit in to the output of the hard stone carvings of the School of Zhiting as it would the broader range of jade carvings believed to be the output of Suzhou for the Qianlong Court. Conversely, it might also reflect Suzhou style at the Court influenced by the style imported to Beijing from the south.

The neck of our bottle is probably reduced.

(CBL C 441)

191

Glass, a transparent cherry-red overlay on a transparent misty ground lightly suffused with bubbles, each main face carved with an oval panel with a rope-twist border, containing a bucolic scene, one side with a figure crossing a bridge holding a fan and followed by a boy assistant, in the background framing the scene is a small building under pine on a rocky outcrop, the other side with a boy on a buffalo playing a flute whilst crossing another bridge under pine and swirling clouds, mask-ring handles on the narrow sides, a long slightly tapering cylindrical neck and quite wide mouth, a flat oval foot ring and slightly convex base

1750-1820

Height: 7.8 cm
Mouth: 0.7 cm
Neck: 1.9 cm

The subject on this bottle appears to be simply a bucolic one. On one side is the traditional theme of a boy riding a buffalo whilst playing a flute. The subject is certainly depicted as early as the Tang dynasty as a blue *sancai*-glazed pottery model of the subject in the Alan and Simone Hartman Collection in New York attests. It was popularized by the time of the Southern Song dynasty in academic painting and from that time on became common in Chinese art. The subject can be found on snuff bottles in overlay glass, chalcedony, porcelain, and lacquer. It frequently appears as a subject on inside-painted bottles by the Beijing School, in particular Zhou Leyuan and the Ye family and even in some rare examples by Ma Shaoxuan. The other main face shows a scholar and his assistant walking in a rustic setting. Both figural groups are shown crossing a bridge suggesting that a journey is underway. The scholar is even shown leaving his empty pavilion (perched precariously on a cliff edge) and his assistant carries supplies for the trip on his back. The scene evokes the wish of the high-minded individual to escape the drudgery of city life for introspection away from the distractions of the 'real' world. The simple scholarly figure and his assistant in this rustic setting head for the vast mountainous wilderness to find solace and calm.

According to Moss, Graham, and Tsang, *A Treasury of Chinese Snuff Bottles: The Mary and George Bloch Collection*, Vol. 5, Part 2, Glass, pp. 457-459, nos. 887 and 888, the rope twist border which surrounds both scenes is derived from decoration found on Han dynasty bronzes in the Imperial Collection. It is a common feature on Court works of art and appears on a range of Imperial jade carvings, including snuff bottles. A long rope can signify a long life.

Once again we have very good quality relief carving on this bottle, but the large size and flattened ovoid shape suggest a slightly later date of production than the previous bottle.

(CBL C 449)

190 (two views)

191 (two views)

192

Glass, appears to be a moulded iridescent glass of variegated creamy-beige colour, moulded over the entire body with irregular rows of dense flower heads each with a central raised boss surrounded by seven smaller petals, all in imitation of mother-of-pearl, with the exception of a row of small broken pearl fragments at the foot and neck rim, and a mother-of-pearl pierced circular disc forming the top of the neck and mouth

1760-1850

Height: 6.3 cm
Mouth: 0.7 cm
Neck: 1.75 cm mother-of-pearl disc; approx 3.2 cm across pearl fragments

This appears to be a unique bottle. At first glance it has the appearance of mother-of-pearl, particularly as the neck and foot rim are both encrusted with actual half pearls and the mouth is formed by a disc of mother-of-pearl. In fact the body is actually mould blown and made from an iridescent glass that very cleverly imitates mother-of-pearl. Each small flower head around the body is identically moulded with a central boss surrounded by seven small petals. The interior is plain.

Other bottles are recorded that have underlying glass bodies but the exterior surface is entirely covered by pearls, sometimes whole and sometimes cut, and appear rather lumpy as a rule. Ours appears to be the only one of the group that has moulded glass imitating the pearls.

For examples of the pearl group, see Hughes, *The Blair Bequest: Chinese Snuff Bottles from the Princeton University Art Museum*, p. 104, no. 112; White, *Snuff Bottles from China: The Victoria and Albert Museum Collection*, fig. 2; Kleiner, *The Bellis Collection: card catalogue*, no. 51; Hall, *Chinese Snuff Bottles XIII: The Boston Snuff Party*, no. 75; and another from the Ko Family Collection was sold at Christie's, London, 8 November 1976, lot 207.

See also the footnote to No. 171 in this publication regarding the possible location of workshops using mother-of-pearl or pearls as part of their decoration. It seems likely that a workshop producing mother-of-pearl would be located in a coastal region and if this was the case, it may well have been a southern port city like Guangzhou, where we know many handicraft workshops existed catering to the Imperial and export markets. It is also possible, of course that pearls were simply sent to another site for use in decoration though presumably to imitate a material would suggest that wherever it was made there was already a market for the real material.

One other small group of glass bottles has been recorded, which appear to imitate large baroque pearls and are made of transparent glass that is coated to the interior with a silvery-white paste or powder to give the appearance of pearl-like colouring. See Christie's, New York, 'Important Chinese Snuff Bottles from the J & J Collection', 22 March 2007, lot 84. The group usually has the neck dressed in gilt metal and embellished with various semi-precious stones or glass in a manner typical of Imperial production at Gaungzhou, which ties in rather neatly with the comments above regarding pearls.

(CBL C 455)

192 (two views)

193

Glass, of Guyue xuan type, painted in a continuous scene in various coloured enamels on an unusual opaque deep sky blue glass with Pekinese dogs on each side amongst scattered flower heads, autumn leaves, or stylized grassy clumps, one main face with a yellow enameled recumbent dog with bushy tail with a pink enameled cub clambering on to its back, the other side with a pink enameled dog with raised bushy tail striding along, each beneath clouds at the shoulder with a partially visible moon to one side, the very slightly waisted neck with scrolls and four-petalled flower heads in pink and yellow, the mouth quite wide, a flat oval foot ring and deeply hollowed base

Indistinct iron-red Qianlong seal mark in a line and probably late in the period, probably Yangzhou, 1770-1799

Stopper: jadeite on plain silver collar

Height: 6.2 cm
Mouth: 0.7 cm
Neck: 1.9 cm

The mystery of the elusive 'Guyue xuan' (Ancient Moon Pavilion) marked bottles has been ongoing for many years and is now perhaps partially solved by the recent exceedingly thorough and well argued article by Hugh Moss 'Mysteries of the Ancient Moon', *JICSBS*, Spring 2006, pp. 16-32. Despite some resistance to his ideas, Moss does argue quite convincingly for an eighteenth-century production date for many bottles in the group, if indeed the Guyue xuan mark on some of the bottles is connected to the Guyue xuan Pavilion built by Qianlong on the grounds of the Yuanmingyuan complex to the west of the Imperial City in Beijing, which now seems most likely knowing that the pavilion was completed in 1767 and the majority of dated Guyue xuan bottles date between 1767 and 1770. One common criticism of the group is the medium range quality of the painting itself and the unassuming nature of the bottles as a whole. Moss responds by suggesting that the group may have been made as gifts for the autumn hunt that took place annually north of Beijing. The Qianlong emperor would distribute gifts to successful hunters. Moss notes that there are records of bottles made as such gifts for a hunt in the autumn of 1755. He proposes that such gifts must surely have been plain ones without much workmanship when given to members of the Eight Banners, or Qing cavalry. Some of the inscriptions on the group include words like 'highest award' or 'first prize' so his theory may well be right.

Utilizing Moss's dating and production theories for the group this bottle would appear to fall into the group probably made in the 1770s or later when the Qianlong emperor, it seems, ordered a group of enameled glass snuff bottles from a distant facility, probably Yangzhou. They were produced in fairly large numbers until probably 1799 when the Emperor died. The style of painting is quite different from most of the Court wares and the enamels used in a thinner, more painterly, manner, than their Beijing counterparts. They often have neck borders of scrolls and multi-petalled flower heads. When marked, all except one, are in iron-red enamel. When the Qianlong reign mark was used in Yangzhou it was always as a four-character seal-script type, usually written in a single horizontal line as in our example.

The subject appears to be Pekinese dogs but might also represent Buddhist lions. According to Bartholomew, *Hidden Meanings in Chinese Art*, p. 116, no. 5.17.1 and 5 17.2, a large lion, *dashi*, and a small lion, *xiaoshi*, form the rebus 'May you and your descendants achieve high rank', *taishi shaoshi*.

The enamels on our bottle are painted in a quite unusual technique in which the clumps of hair on the dogs' bodies are actually delineated by leaving areas of the blue ground un-enameled to form outlines. What initially appear to be enameled blue outlines around the clumps of hair are actually the visible surface of the glass underneath. The yellow and pink enamels on each of the dogs have then been further highlighted with thin strokes of black enamel to form the individual strands. In contrast the larger areas of the noses and mouths of the dogs have in fact been lightly enameled in shades of blue when it might have been easier to expose the under surface. All in all it is a time consuming effort that points to a fairly costly production and therefore possibly imperial patronage.

The question of whether the moon or the sun is represented appears to be answered by the use of the unusual deep opaque blue glass, which forms a perfectly acceptable night backdrop.

(CBL C 460)

193 (mark)

193 (two views)

194

Glass, of Guyue xuan type, of flattened double-gourd shape, painted in various coloured enamels on an opaque white ground with ogival panels on each of the lower and upper gourds, one of the upper gourd panels painted with bees above peony, the other with butterflies above daisy or dandelion, one of the larger lower panels painted with a dragonfly and lotus, the other with a grasshopper and chrysanthemum, all on a ground of blue scrolls, yellow dots, and pink flower-heads, a waisted cylindrical neck and a slightly concave oval base

Iron-red three-character Guyue xuan mark in a line on the base, probably Yangzhou, 1770-1799

Stopper: rose quartz on gilt metal collar

Height: 6.4 cm
Mouth: 0.7 cm
Neck: 1.35 cm

The remarks regarding likely Yangzhou workmanship for the previous bottle also apply here and using Hugh Moss's dating and production theories for the group as outlined in his article, 'Mysteries of the Ancient Moon', *JICSBS*, Spring 2006, pp. 16-32, this bottle, like No. 193, would appear to fall into the group probably made in the 1770s or later when the Qianlong emperor appears to have ordered a group of enameled glass snuff bottles from a distant facility, probably Yangzhou. The enamels are used in a thinner, more painterly manner, than their Beijing counterparts, often have neck borders of scrolls and multi-petalled flower heads as here, and when the Guyue xuan mark was used it is always (with one exception) painted in an iron-red enamel in the distinctive simplified seal script unique in the middle character, *yue*, whereas at Beijing it was always in regular script.

The firing of this bottle was not of the finest quality, the upper gourd leans slightly to one side but the painting itself is delicate, wispy, and lively in subject. On one panel we have the combination of a dragonfly, *qingting*, and lotus. According to Bartholomew, *Hidden Meanings in Chinese Art*, p. 237, no. 8.11, the first character, *qing*, is a pun for pure, *qing*, and celebration, *qing*. As the lotus was also considered a pure flower rising as it does so beautifully from muddy waters, this amplified the symbolism. The grasshopper or cricket on another panel is the emblem of courage and the chrysanthemum, *juhua*, on which it sits, is an emblem for autumn and a symbol of longevity. On one smaller panel we have bees, *feng*, above peony, *shaoyao*, but also referred to as *fuguihua*, 'flower of wealth and honour'. In China the word *feng*, includes bees and wasps and is a pun for 'confer', *feng*, as well as 'harvest' *fengdeng*, see Bartholomew, ibid, p. 123, no. 5.26, and p. 130, no. 5.35.

The final panel has butterflies, *hudie*, which symbolizes blessings and happiness flying above what appears to be dandelion. Of course the gourd form of the bottle itself is highly auspicious, symbolizing fertility, abundance, and good luck.

(CBL C 463)

195

Glass, of Guyue xuan type, painted in various opaque coloured enamels on an opaque pale coffee ground with a continuous lotus pond scene, one main face with two egrets wading and feeding amidst lotus pods, pads, flowers, and grasses, and the other side with a similar scene with a pair of mandarin ducks, all below a waisted neck painted with scrolls and four-petalled flower heads in purple, blue, and yellow, shallow concave oval foot

Iron-red Qianlong four-character seal mark in a line on the foot and probably late in the period, probably Yangzhou, 1770-1799

Stopper: pink glass and green glass imitating rose quartz and jadeite or emerald

Height: 5.6 cm
Mouth: 0.6 cm
Neck: 1.6 cm

The remarks regarding likely dating and Yangzhou workmanship for the previous two bottles also apply here.

The spade shape of this particular bottle with waisted neck brings to mind the form used in the earliest of the Guyue xuan group dating from 1767 on which it is presumably based but uses designs that became popular in the 1770s and 1780s of birds and floral subjects, often lotus, which further ties the bottle back to the decorations, mostly of lotus, found on the early Guyue xuan group. It also utilizes a more rare café au lait coloured glass that seems to have been popularized at the Yangzhou workshops. The mark is also symptomatic of the workshop, like the example, No. 193, it has a Qianlong four-character seal-script mark written in a single horizontal line. It also bears the ubiquitous scroll and multi-petal flower head neck decoration.

The subject of two egrets feeding at a lotus pond on one side, was also one found on the earlier so-called Wu Yuchan bottles of the Guyue xuan group, see Hugh Moss 'Mysteries of the Ancient Moon', *JICSBS*, Spring 2006, p. 24, showing the development of the style to its conclusion on our bottle.

According to Bartholomew, *Hidden Meanings in Chinese Art*, p. 91, no. 4.10.2, pairs of egret, *lu*, lotus plant, *lian*, and reed, *lu*, form the rebus, 'May you pass your exams every way', *lulu lianke*.

Because of its clean white feathers the egret is often compared to an honest and incorruptible official. Because they mate for life, pairs of mandarin ducks symbolize a happy marriage. Depicted alongside lotus, *he*, it forms the rebus 'May you be paired for life', *yuanyang xihe* or 'May you give birth to illustrious sons', *yuanyang guizi*, see Bartholomew, ibid, p. 49, no. 2.16.5.

Another enamelled glass bottle formerly in the Ko Collection (purchased in Tianjin in 1943) and illustrated by Kleiner, *Treasures from the Sanctum of Enlightened Respect*, p. 28, no. 21, is also painted with egrets, which bear a remarkable similarity to the pair on our bottle as do the rather rigid short grasses or reeds that the birds wade through. Perhaps more importantly, the neck and foot rim have a red glass overlay extremely reminiscent of Yangzhou overlay bottles perhaps helping us to identify the place of manufacture for this particular type of Guyue xuan bottle.

(CBL C 458)

194 (mark)

195 (mark)

194 (two views)

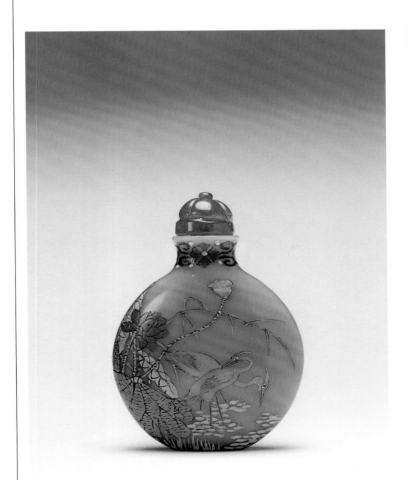

195 (two views)

Glass, of Guyue xuan type, painted in various coloured enamels on an opaque white ground in a continuous scene with two bushy-tailed Pekinese dogs on one main face, one blue enameled, the other pink, both with black fur highlights, their eyes picked out in yellow, seated on a grassy verge below clouds, the other side with three standing goats below a sun and further clouds, on one narrow side is an unusual circular iron-red seal mark, all below a cylindrical neck with quite large mouth, the slightly rounded oval foot ring with shallow base painted with either cloud and ribbon forms in blue and yellow, or possibly a stylized Pekinese dog

Unusual iron-red four-character Guyue xuan seal mark in a circle on one narrow side, probably Yangzhou, 1770-1799

Height: 6.5 cm
Mouth: 1.0 cm
Neck: 2.0 cm

The Guyue xuan mark is written in a highly unusual form. Rather than a common three-character inscription the artist has chosen a four-character inscription with the last character for *xuan* split in to two with the radical forming a separate character. This is probably an artistic conceit rather than meant to confuse. It also uses the distinctive simplified seal script unique in the middle character, *yue*, see No. 194 in this publication.

The bottle obviously bears comparison with No. 193 in this publication. Though painted in a very slightly different technique it appears to be from the same workshop and very likely the same hand. Despite the amusing depiction of dogs, which again may be Buddhist lions, we do have a rather cursorily depicted grassy verge and simply delineated clouds that could be described as lackidaisical. Pekinese dogs, because of their connection to the Buddhist lion, were popular at Court.

The subject of three goats (sheep) and a rising sun was a popular one in the decorative arts of the Ming dynasty but according to Bartholomew, *Hidden Meanings in Chinese Art*, p.146, 6.16.1, it did not gain prominence until the Qianlong period, particularly in jade carving. The Xuande Emperor (1426-1435) is known to have executed a painting of this subject showing an ewe and two lambs under a rock and a flowering bush. No distinction is made in Chinese between sheep and goats, *yang*, the collective name for sheep, rams, lambs, ewes, and goats is a homophone of *yang*, the male principle or positive force. Therefore, the depiction of three goats or sheep, *sanyang*, along with a rising sun, *taiyang*, form the rebus' the new year brings a change of fortune', *sanyang kaitai*.

For another Guyue xuan opaque white glass bottle enameled with three goats on one side but with two monkeys on the other, see Christie's Hong Kong, 1-3 May 1994, lot 1011, from the Joseph Baruch Silver Collection.

(CBL C 464)

Glass, of Guyue xuan type, painted in various coloured enamels on an opaque white ground with a continuous bucolic scene, one side with a cowherd seated under a willow, another tree in the background with pink flowers, a buffalo and her calf nearby, the other side with another buffalo with a rope tied through its nose raising its head as if to bellow and watched by the cowherd and presumably the buffalo's mate and offspring, all below a waisted cylindrical neck, the narrow sides beveled flat and with a flat oval foot

Iron-red four-character Qianlong mark in a line on the base and probably late in the period, probably Yangzhou, 1770-1799

Stopper: jadeite and gold collar

Height: 6.1 cm
Mouth: 0.7 cm
Neck: 1.8 cm

The remarks regarding likely dating and Yangzhou workmanship for the previous three bottles also apply here.

The spade shape of this particular bottle, like the No. 195 in this publication, with its tall waisted neck and beveled narrow edge, brings to mind the form used in the earliest of the Guyue xuan group dating from 1767 in Beijing. However the depiction is far more in keeping with the later group produced in Yangzhou and can be favorably compared with another with a scene of water buffalos on one side illustrated by Moss, Graham, and Tsang, *A Treasury of Chinese Snuff Bottles: The Mary and George Bloch Collection*, Vol. 6, Part 1, Arts of the Fire, pp. 321-322, no. 1143. Significantly it has a scene on the opposite face of an equestrian hunter and attendant, which appears to have been taken directly from a famous painting by the Yangzhou artist Hua Yan dated 1755, further cementing the likely Yangzhou origins of this particular group of Guyue xuan wares. Interestingly, the subject of buffalos was also a popular one on the Yangzhou seal-school glass overlay bottles attributed to Li Junting.

For another example of a Guyu xuan enamelled glass bottle with a similar subject, though the herdboy is riding on the back of his buffalo alongside a willow tree rather than sitting under its shade, as in our example, see an article by Tsang, 'Decoding Ox/Water Buffalo Designs on Chinese Snuff Bottles' ICSBS *Journal*, Spring 1998, pp. 11-27, fig. 24. The lengthy article discusses the numerous meanings implicit in the subject.

Once again like Nos. 193 and 195, it has a Qianlong four-character seal-script mark written in a single horizontal line.

(CBL C 466)

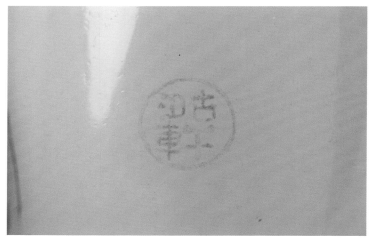

196 (mark)

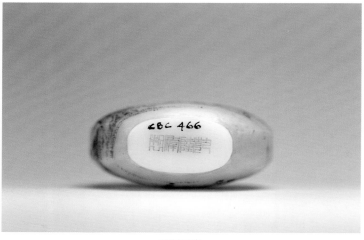

197 (mark)

196 (two views)

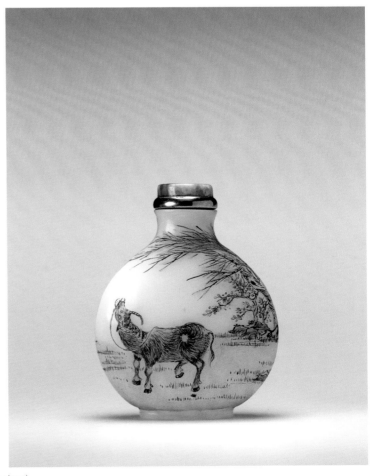

197 (two views)

INSIDE-PAINTED

198

Glass, painted in muted colours, primarily grisaille with a continuous river landscape, one side with a weary figure on a mule both with heads held low crossing a bridge towards a building with seated figures in the interior set against a massive mountainous river landscape with men in boats, the other side with two figures nestled under a simple straw-roofed canopy with another approaching on a promontory with trees, fishermen in a boat beyond, a short inscription, signature, and seals, a short neck, a slightly concave rim, a shallow concave oval base

Signed Zhou Leyuan and dated Jiashen year, corresponding to 1884

Stopper: bone or ivory stained red to imitate coral and bone finial

Height: 5.7 cm
Mouth: 0.7 cm
Neck: 2.0 cm

The inscription can be read as:
Shi zhai jia shen dong yue jing shi Zhou Leyuan

This can be translated as:
The date is Jiashen year [corresponding to 1884], winter month in the capital, by Zhou Leyuan

The inscription is preceded by a small iron-red seal possibly reading *Yuan* (as in Zhou Leyuan) and is followed by a seal which possibly reads *Yin* (seal).

Much has been written about Zhou Leyuan who is widely acknowledged as the single most influential artist working in the inside-painted medium. Zhou founded the popular Beijing School of painting. Every artist of the first phase of the school owes a debt to him and they include Ding Erzhong, Ma Shaoxuan, Ye Zhongsan, Ziyizi, Sun Xingwu, and Yan Yutian amongst others.

There are some unresolved questions about his exact working period which spanned the early 1880s and into the 1890s. According to Moss, Graham, and Tsang, *A Treasury of Chinese Snuff Bottles: The Mary and George Bloch Collection*, Vol. 4, Part 1, Inside Painted, p. 93, no. 465, his earliest dated bottle, with calligraphy only rather than a painting, is dated 1879. The majority of his dated bottles, however, seem to span the years 1881 until 1893.

For further reading on the various inside-painted schools and artists, see Hui, Yee, and Lam, *Inkplay in Microcosm: Inside-Painted Chinese Snuff Bottles, The Humphrey K. F. Hui Collection* Art Museum, The Chinese University of Hong Kong, 2002 and Moss, Graham, and Tsang, *A Treasury of Chinese Snuff Bottles: The Mary and George Bloch Collection*, Vol. 4, Parts 1 and 2, Inside Painted.

The shape of this bottle is quite unusual for one made of glass. In general, glass forms tend to be of rounded rectangular shape. The bottles that do seem to buck this general trend are those made from crystal (and possibly why this bottle had for years been listed as such), and interestingly one of the few bottles by Zhou of similar shape is a crystal bottle dated 1891, see Moss et al, op cit, Vol. 1, pp. 181-182, no. 500.

It is generally agreed that by 1884, the year this bottle was painted, Zhou had hit full stride in his mature style. There is a certain formal elegance in this composition and a rich interplay of ink tones and colour. There is also a delicacy in the depiction of the human figures in the scene. On one side the hunched rider is cleverly portrayed with head hanging down. This is mirrored in the head of the mule. This simple device satisfactorily portrays the feeling of weariness after an exhausting journey. The landscape in which the scenes are set are immense and spectacular and the use of negative space to highlight the tree branches and also the various mounds in the mountains is a highly successful and often used signature technique by this artist. However, compared to other Zhou bottles, this one would be more appropriately labeled competent rather than majestic.

(CBL C 914)

199

Glass, painted in muted colours, primarily grisaille, one main face with a figure below willow on a riverbank, the other side with a tall vessel issuing prunus and bamboo, another vessel with *lingzhi*, an iron pot with trigrams, a kettle or wine ewer, grasses in a tray and rockwork, all below the inscription and two seals, the cylindrical neck tapering slightly to the shoulders, flat oval foot ring and slightly convex shallowly-cut base

Signed [Zhou] Leyuan and dated Wuzi year, corresponding to 1888

Stopper: Jadeite

Height: 6.2 cm
Mouth: 0.6 cm
Neck: 1.5 cm

The inscription reads:
Wu zi shou an ren xiong da ren zheng Leyuan zou

This can be translated as:
'Wuzi year [corresponding to 1888], dedicated to the Shou An brothers for the approval (?) of great person/superior/elder brother Da Ren' [not related], followed by 'Leyuan made'

The inscription is followed by a two small iron-red square seals, which read *Wang Tian*, which can be read as 'king field'.

The subject of this bottle was an extremely popular one in Zhou's oeuvre and we often find the same juxtaposition of themes to each side usually dated between the years 1887 and 1891, though occasionally earlier. For other examples see Hui, Yee, and Lam, *Inkplay in Microcosm: Inside-Painted Chinese Snuff Bottles, The Humphrey K. F. Hui Collection*, nos. 9-12 and Moss, Graham, and Tsang, *A Treasury of Chinese Snuff Bottles: The Mary and George Bloch Collection*, Vol. 4, Parts 1 & 2, Inside Painted, pp. 123-131, nos. 477-479, and Moss et al, *The Arts of the Chinese Snuff Bottle: The J & J Collection*, Vol. II, pp. 670-671, no. 410.

Interestingly, a bottle illustrated by Hui et al, op cit, no. 19 which is dated to 1891 shows a similar scene (though in brighter colours) of a fisherman in a straw coat and hat rushing to his warm and dry home and out of turbulent windy and rainy conditions illustrated by the bending willow branches. From the inscription on the bottle it is clear that the painting is based on the style of Shitian, also known as Shen Zhou (1472-1509), a Ming artist of the Wu School, who is recognized as one of the four great masters of the period. The authors also make note of the fishing pole resting on the weary shoulders of the fisherman which, like ours, appears to have bolts of cloth or rags attached to it. Yet again the feeling of weariness experienced by the figure buffeted by high winds and holding a heavy weight over his shoulders is simply shown by a single stroke that curves from the figure's shoulders, down his back and through his left leg to his feet. As in the previous bottle, though to a lesser extent, we see the use of negative space to highlight the willow branches.

The subject of ornamental rocks, archaic vessels, and flowers is replete with auspicious meaning, and one of Zhou's favorite subjects. He returned to it again and again, though always with a slightly different interpretation, from around 1885 until the end of his career in the mid 1890s. Such items would probably have been a fixture in most painting studios. The rock, which sits in the foreground of this scene, would be instantly recognized as symbol of longevity as would the fungus, *lingzhi*, bamboo, *zhu*, and plum, *meihua*, in the vases beyond. According to Moss, et al, op cit, Vol. 4, Parts 1, Inside Painted, pp. 95-96, no. 466, the calamus grass, usually shown growing densely and bending little, stands for youthful energy. A vase, *ping*, suggests peace, *ping'an*, while a crackled vase *suiping*, represents continuous peace, *suisui ping'an*. The tripod vessel, *ding*, symbolizes prosperity and high achievement. The yixing teapot represents good fortune or happiness.

The interior appears to be painted with a beige backdrop that at first was believed to be caused by the accrued remnants of snuff powder. Moss et al, ibid, pp. 123-124, however, suggest that it was intended to imitate painting on gold paper or gold-speckled paper for which there is a long literati tradition. The scenes on this bottle are actually extremely well painted in a controlled thoughtful style and amongst the finest produced by this experienced artist.

(CBL C 915)

198 (two views)

199 (two views)

200

Glass, painted primarily in grisaille and blue with touches of red, with a continuous scene with a crane on rockwork at the base of a pine tree on one side along with a vertical inscription, signature, and seal, the pine continues to the other side with further branches hanging over mossy rockwork and grasses, a single bird in flight above, the cylindrical neck tapering slightly to the shoulders, slightly rounded oval foot ring and slightly convex shallowly-cut base

Signed Zhou Leyuan and dated Xinmao year, corresponding to 1891

Stopper: glass imitating coral

Height: 6.3 cm
Mouth: 0.5 cm
Neck: 1.9 cm

The inscription reads:
Xin mao zhong xia zuo yu san shi liu xu zhai Zhou Leyuan xia

This can be translated as:
Xinmao year [corresponding to 1891], midsummer, Sanshiliuxu Zhai [Studio of 36 Documents] by Zhou Leyuan

The inscription is followed by two small iron-red square seals which appear to read Yuan Hua (Yuan painting)

This bottle can be closely compared with two others also dated 1891, illustrated by Moss, Graham, and Tsang, *A Treasury of Chinese Snuff Bottles: The Mary and George Bloch Collection*, Vol. 4, Part 1, Inside Painted, pp. 162-165, nos. 492 and 493. Both, like ours, bear the unusual studio name Sanshiliuxu Zhai (Studio of 36 Documents) that according to Moss et al was only used from the fourth month of 1891 until the autumn of that year. For the rest of his career Zhou used the studio name Ouxiang zhai (Studio of Lotus Fragrance), identified as being at Xuannan, in southwest Beijing, where Zhou lived and painted throughout his career. Moss et al suggest that this probably meant that for some unknown reason Zhou renamed his studio for this short period rather than opening a second studio under a different name. The first bottle they illustrate is painted in a similar fashion to ours, though a cockerel replaces the crane of our example. The second has a crane and pine to one side but there is a fisherman seeking shelter from the storm on the other, as in No. 199 in this publication. The crane, pine, and rocks are all common symbols of longevity. The generic long-tailed bird on the other side appears in numerous bottles by Zhou with slight variance of colour but may very well depict the red-billed blue magpie, *Urocissa erythrorhyncha*. Because of its ribbon-like tail it is also named the 'longevity-tailed bird', *shoudainiao*, see Bartholomew, *Hidden Meanings in Chinese Art*, p. 215, no. 7.51. This would fit very neatly with the overall theme of the bottle.

Moss et al, ibid, p. 163, no. 492, also points out the odd fact that Zhou really only made full use of continuous scenes to the interiors of his bottles in the last two years of his career, and that he painted considerably more pieces with a different subject on each side.

(CBL C 916)

201

Glass, painted in muted colours, primarily in shades of greenish-brown and orange-red with touches of blue with a continuous river landscape, one main face with a figure of a standing man punting his craft under a tree at the shore line, another seated in his vessel in the middle distance before a mountainous backdrop below an inscription, signature, and seal, the other side with a single figure seated in a stone building under willow and other trees, vessels sailing in the middle distance before further mountains, the cylindrical neck tapering very slightly to the rounded shoulders, a slightly concave rim and a slightly spreading flat oval foot ring and shallow base

Signed Ye Zhongsan and dated Wuxu year, corresponding to 1898

Stopper: glass imitating coral with glass finial imitating a pearl

Height: 6.4 cm
Mouth: 0.6 cm-0.8 cm (beveled)
Neck: 1.5 cm

The inscription reads:
Wu xu lou yue zuo yu jing shi Ye Zhongsan followed by the seal *Hua Yin*

This can be translated as:
Wuxu year [1898], fifth month, in the capital by Ye Zhongsan, [followed by the seal] Hua Yin (painting seal)

Ye Zhongsan was perhaps the most important follower of Zhou Leyuan. He was heavily influenced by Zhou's style, palette, and subject matter. His earliest bottles according to Moss, Graham, and Tsang, *A Treasury of Chinese Snuff Bottles: The Mary and George Bloch Collection*, Vol. 4, Part 1, Inside Painted, pp. 199-200, no. 507, are dated to the spring of 1892 and are of an idiosyncratic crude style. By the end of the year he had shifted to the style of Zhou Leyuan and over the next three years perfected his techniques. From 1895 onwards we see Ye's mature style in full force.

For another landscape bottle by Ye Zhongsan, dated to the same year see Hui, Yee, and Lam, *Inkplay in Microcosm: Inside-Painted Chinese Snuff Bottles, The Humphrey K. F. Hui Collection*, no. 68. Though there is a similar subject (a fisherman in a boat and a lone pavilion set in an immense landscape), we see that Ye was not adverse to utilizing a quite different palette. On the Hui bottle he is clearly imitating the green-blue style that can be traced back to the Tang dynasty and also follows very closely Zhou Leyuan's characteristic technique for depicting mountains using paler blotches, but he doesn't use that technique in our example. However, in our bottle he does borrow many other elements to be found in Zhou's oeuvre, which include the ferryman punting his craft on one side, and the elaborate open pavilion set on a sloping stone foundation on the other. This idiosyncratic building can be found on a bottle dated 1891 by Zhou Leyuan, see Moss et al, ibid, pp. 166-168, no. 494.

(CBL C 912)

200 (two views)

201 (two views)

202

Glass, painted in muted colours, primarily in grisaille and sepia, but with touches of blue, salmon, and white, one side with two long-tailed pheasants on rockwork amidst pine and *wutong* (pawlonia) branches and with an inscription and seal, the other side painted with two five-clawed dragons amidst clouds contesting a flaming pearl, the cylindrical neck tapering very slightly to the rounded shoulders, a concave rim, slightly rounded oval foot ring and shallow base

Signed Zhou Leyuan and dated Bingwu year, corresponding to 1906, but by another anonymous artist

Stopper: jadeite

Height: 6.5 cm
Mouth: 0.55 cm
Neck: 1.8 cm

The inscription reads:
Shi zhai bing wu zhong dong liu ri hua yu jing shi Zhou Leyuan zuo

This can be translated as:
The date is Bingwu year [corresponding to 1906], midwinter month, sixth day, painted at the capital, by Zhou Leyuan.

An indecipherable iron-red oval seal follows the inscription.
The ivory spoon has an added ink character, *Cheng*.

If the cyclical date does indeed read *bingwu*, which corresponds to 1906, then this bottle is dated thirteen years after Zhou was believed to have stopped painting. Stylistically it is close, though with many marked differences, to the earliest works of Zhou. So if we allow ourselves, to read the cyclical date as *bingzi* rather than *bingwu* (the *zi* and the *wu* characters are not dissimilar), then we would have a date corresponding to 1876, three years prior to the earliest known dated bottle by Zhou. Moreover, the quality of painting of the twin pheasants and the calligraphy veers to the poor side even though the side with the dragons is quite powerful. It is extremely unlikely that this is Zhou's earliest known dated bottle when his style was still maturing. The most likely scenario is that this bottle was painted by a follower of Zhou Leyuan who acknowledged his debt by working in his style and even signing Zhou's name to his own work. If this is the case then the *bingwu* date (1906) would be the correct reading. The artist is probably not proficient enough to be Yan Yutian, one possible candidate working at this period, but might be by one of his followers. According to Moss, Graham, and Tsang, *A Treasury of Chinese Snuff Bottles: The Mary and George Bloch Collection*, Vol. 4, Part 2, Inside Painted, pp. 458-459, no. 612, he was a sporadic artist who left behind only dated bottles for the years 1894 (one only), 1895, 1898, 1907, 1918 (one only) and 1919 (one only).

The subject of paired birds symbolizes both conjugal bliss and a wish for progeny. Pheasants, *zhi*, can also symbolize 'order', *zhi*.

Among the rank badges of the civil officials of the Qing dynasty, the pheasant represents the second rank, *daotai*, and this would be an appropriate gift for a second-rank official, though a little daring with the use of an imperial five-clawed dragon on the other side. This is a subject that we know was painted by Zhou Leyuan's nephew Zhou Shaoyuan, see Moss, Graham, and Tsang, *The Arts of the Chinese Snuff Bottle: The J & J Collection*, Vol. 2, pp. 721-722, no. 442, but again the style is not consistent with his work nor as accomplished.

(CBL C 917)

203

Amber, one side plain, the other inside-painted with a 20-character poem in four lines of five characters each above a partially indistinct rectangular panel with paintings and calligraphy, the amber of semi-translucent orange-red colour, rounded shoulders, and a cylindrical neck, slightly concave rim, the foot spreading very slightly, a flat oval foot ring and shallow base

Unsigned but probably by Ma Shaoxuan, 1895-1905

Stopper: jadeite

Height: 6.5 cm
Mouth: 0.55 cm
Neck: 1.5 cm

The inscription reads:
Ci luo san qiu ye
Neng kai er yue hua
Guo jiang qian chi lang
Ru zhu wan (huang?) xie

This can be translated as:
Falling away three autumn leaves
Flowers may open in the second month
Pass down the river, One-thousand-foot waves
Entering the bamboo, ten thousand swaying stalks on stems

The rectangular panel below the inscription has two halves, the left side though indistinct appears to be an ink rubbing of Tang calligraphy, whilst the right half has a landscape or floral painting within an oval which appears to bear the signature of Bada Shanren, the *hao* of Zhu Da (1626-1705).

Though it is extremely difficult to read the decoration within this bottle, the combination of calligraphy and paintings in this fashion known as *Jiu hui duei* which can be translated as 'an assembly of old things' is idiosyncratic of Ma Shaoxuan's work.

He often painted scenes depicting groups of documents which are damaged or fragmented, or represent antiquity in general, *Baishui tu* (Picture of Longevity) and sometimes groups of orderly undamaged documents, *Bogu tu*, (Picture of Antiquity), as here and bottle No. 206 in this publication, see Ma Zhengsan, *Inside-Painted Snuff Bottle Artist Ma Shaoxuan*, p. 33. We also know that he copied paintings by Bada Shanren, as his signature appears on other paintings in Ma's bottle oeuvre, see Moss, Graham, and Tsang, *A Treasury of Chinese Snuff Bottles: The Mary and George Bloch Collection*, Vol. 4, Part 2, Inside Painted, pp. 378-380, no. 580.

There do not appear to be many inside-painted amber bottles recorded by Ma Shaoxuan. Presumably the difficulty of reading either a script or a painting through the semi-opaque amber made them difficult to sell.

(CBL C 910)

202 (two views)

204

Smoky crystal, brightly painted with a continuous scene around the bottle with the eight horses of Muwang, each painted in a different colour in a hilly landscape with willow and a mountainous backdrop, seven of the horses in profile and shown running, standing, bending down or walking, one painted directly from behind on one narrow edge, a short cylindrical neck with slightly concave rim, regular mouth and quite well hollowed and lightly 'frosted', a rounded oval foot ring and shallowly-cut base

Signed Ye Zhongsan and dated Dingwei year, corresponding to 1907

Stopper: coral stopper on metal collar
Height: 5.8 cm
Mouth: 0.7 cm
Neck: 1.9 cm

The inscription reads:
Ding wei xin yue Ye Zhongsan zuo followed by the seal *Yin*

This can be translated as:
Dingwei year (corresponding to 1907), apricot month (second month), by Ye Zhongsan and a red seal 'yin' which reads 'seal'

The subject of eight horses derives from the legend of Muwang (King Mu) the fifth sovereign of the Zhou dynasty who reigned from 1001 to 946 BCE and was famed for his eight spirited steeds, which he put to purposeful use on his royal inspection tours around his kingdom.

Williams, in *Outlines of Chinese Symbolism and Art Motives*, pp. 224-225, notes that the horse is an emblem of speed and perseverance and that the sleeve of the Manchu official costume was shaped like the hoof of a horse as a grateful tribute to the animal to which they owed so much. Moss, Graham, and Tsang, *A Treasury of Chinese Snuff Bottles: The Mary and George Bloch Collection*, Vol. 4, Part 1, Inside Painted, pp. 231-232, no. 521, illustrate another Ye bottle depicting the same subject but dated seven years earlier and note that over the years the eight horses have come to symbolize men of talent because the character for 'steed', *jun*, is homophonous with the character meaning 'a talented man' and that the message implied by a gift with this subject is 'May you be one of the talented people'.

The authors also note that Ye Zhongsan began to paint horses and ponies in 1895 and that in the following year the eight horses' theme makes its first appearance. In every bottle produced from 1896 to 1900, whilst the subject was repeated, this particular composition was not.

By the time of our bottle, however, rank commercialism had definitely crept into his studio and we have a rather poorly executed echo of the subject. However, the slightly smoky quality of the crystal coupled with cloudy inclusions within its matrix actually add a little drama to the subject suggesting a misty early morning setting. Certain passages in the painting, such as the head and mane of the grey horse in the foreground on one side and the white horse with black mane and tail viewed from behind on one narrow side of the bottle, give an extremely convincing three-dimensional quality to the painting.

The painting is loosely modeled after the Yuan dynasty painter Zhao Mengfu (1254-1322), famous for his paintings of groups of horses cavorting in fields.

(CBL C 913)

205

Crystal, the exterior of the bottle carved in low relief with a dragon amidst clouds and fire scrolls above waves on one main face and a seven-character inscription on the other, the interior of the bottle painted in bright colours but primarily green, red, and black with a continuous scene of a large carp and other bug-eyed fan-tailed fish swimming amidst water vegetation, each side with a short inscription, preceded or followed by a seal, the neck tapering slightly towards the mouth, a concave rim, flat oval base with shallowly-cut concave base

Signed Zhou Shaoyuan and dated Wushen year, corresponding to 1908

Stopper: coral on stained bone collar

Height: 7.2 cm
Mouth: 0.7 cm
Neck: 1.9 cm

The seven-character inscription carved on the exterior reads: *Yao long tou tao jiang hong lang*

This can be translated as: Leaping dragon emerges through red waves on Peach River

There is a four-character inscription inside-painted in a line on one side, preceded by a seal, that reads: *Fang yuan ren fa*
This can be translated as: After the methods of the Yuan artists.
The seal is indecipherable.

The eight-character inscription inside-painted to the other side and followed by a seal reads: *Wu shen xia ri Zhou Shaoyuan zuo*

This can be translated as: Wushen year (1908), summer day, by Zhou Shaoyuan
The seal possibly reads: *Shan* (mountain)

Zhou Shaoyuan is recorded to have been a nephew of Zhou Leyuan as discussed in Hugh Moss's interview of Ye Bengqi in 1974, see Moss, Graham, and Tsang, *The Arts of the Chinese Snuff Bottle: The J & J Collection*, Vol. II, pp. 721-722, no. 442. He was generally not considered a good painter and subsequently had a short career.

His works are dated between 1901 and 1909, so this should be considered a late mature work. He began by following the style of his illustrious uncle but it appears he spent most of his career working the in style of Ye Zhongsan, as is the case with this bottle.

The carp is associated with motifs for passing the civil service examinations. The large carved inscription on one exterior side appears to refer to the story of carp swimming upstream, fighting against the opposing current and leaping the rapids of Dragon's-Gate (Longmen) falls; the first to ascend the rapids transforms itself into a dragon. This story is a metaphor for a poor scholar who, by passing the civil services exams, raises himself to the status of high official, see Bartholomew, *Hidden Meanings in Chinese Art*, p. 92, 4.11.2. It is a clever illusionistic ruse to place the fish in the interior of the bottle and then its transformation to a dragon on the exterior of the crystal. There is little doubt therefore, that whilst the crystal bottle itself is probably earlier than the painting, the carving is contemporary with the painting.

(CBL C 918)

204 (two views)

205 (two views)

206

Clear crystal, painted in quite bright colours with a scene of Ouyang Xiu reading by candlelight in a small pavilion, his assistant nearby, the scene set under a gnarled pine and further trees and bamboo under a moonlit sky, an inscription and seal to one corner of the vignette on one main face, the other side with calligraphy rubbings and paintings, *Jiu hui duei*, the neck slightly waisted and slightly oval, the rim flat, the mouth regular and the interior well hollowed, a flat oval foot ring and shallow base

Signed Ma Shaoxuan and negative iron-red artist seal Shao, 1895-1903

Stopper: stained ivory on bone collar

Height: 6.3 cm
Mouth: 0.6 cm
Neck: 1.6-1.8 cm (oval neck)

Ma Shaoxuan was born in 1867, in the sixth year of the reign of the Tongzhi emperor, and died in 1939, just after the outbreak of World War II. He lived a long and productive life. According to Ma Zengshan *Inside-Painted Snuff Bottle Artist Ma Shaoxuan*, p. 18, he was born in the Niujie (Ox Street) district of Beijing and lived his entire life there. He and his ancestors, who hailed from eastern Turkistan, were Muslims. In Ma Zengshan's words 'He was shaped simultaneously by Confucian thought, exemplified by the *Four Books* and *Five Classics*, and the rules and doctrines of Islam.'

It appears that his first forays into the inside-painting techniques were in the early 1890s; perhaps as early as 1891 (by family tradition) or 1892, but certainly by the spring of 1894 as attested to by a bottle illustrated by Moss, Graham, and Tsang, *A Treasury of Chinese Snuff Bottles: The Mary and George Bloch Collection*, Vol. 4, Part 2, Inside Painted, pp. 363-366, no. 576. Certainly by 1895, he has full mastery of the techniques involved in inside-painting and begins to follow his path with growing confidence.

On one side of our undated bottle is a scene of the scholar Ouyang Xiu seated reading by candlelight. For an identical depiction of the subject see Hui, Yee, and Lam, *Inkplay in Microcosm: Inside-Painted Chinese Snuff Bottles, The Humphrey K. F. Hui Collection*, no. 28, where the theme is fully discussed. The Hui bottle is dated 1895 and the reverse side has an inscription partially taken from the essay *Qiusheng fu*, 'Ode to the Autumn Sounds', written by the Northern Song dynasty writer Ouyang Xiu (1007-1072). In order to make more sense of the depiction on our bottle, I have taken the liberty of copying here a translation of the entire passage written on the reverse side of the Hui bottle because it is such a perfect description of the scene depicted:

'"The moon and the stars are perceptively seen in the clear sky,"
so said the boy.
In the expanse of the vast land, total dead silence prevails,
But the chirping sound of the late crickets is audible,
That announces the autumn is coming around,
To whom the advent of the season is intended for?'

We know then from the Hui bottle that this subject was painted at least as early as 1895. Another bottle from the Rachelle R. Holden Collection illustrated by Ma Zengshan, *Inside-Painted Snuff Bottle Artist Ma Shaoxuan*, p. 39, fig. 13, is dated to 1903. It seems likely then that our undated bottle was probably produced within this date frame.

The subject of calligraphy and paintings on the other side is called *Jiu hui duei* which can be translated as 'an assembly of old things'. The ink rubbings are of Tang calligraphy, one is part of the *Yanta shengjiaoxu* written by Chu Suiliang (596-658) and the other is from *Jiuchenggong* by Ouyang Xun (587-641). The two fan-shaped paintings, one circular and one concertina (or folding), are unsigned, and finally there is a printed book entitled *Shi Yin San Guo* or 'Stone Seal of The Three Kingdoms'. Another Ma bottle with the identical depiction of paintings and rubbings on one side but a partial text from the famous 'Lanting Preface' by Wang Xizhi on the other side dated to 1897 is illustrated by Holden, *Rivers and Mountains Far From the World: The Rachelle R. Holden Collection*, pp. 322-323, no. 143. Another Ma bottle, also dated 1897, depicts the identical folding fan painting but in conjunction with different

rubbings and paintings, see Moss, Graham, and Tsang, *A Treasury of Chinese Snuff Bottles: The Mary and George Bloch Collection*, Vol. 4, Part 2, Inside Painted, pp. 378-380, no. 580. This would seem to support the suggested date frame for our bottle.

Another un-dated bottle from the Tuyet Nguyet Collection with an identical scene of Ouyang Xiu reading by candlelight and dated to circa 1895, is illustrated by Hui, Kwong and Sin, eds., *A Congregation of Snuff Bottle Connoisseurs*, pp. 242-243, no. 298.

The negative iron-red seal under the signature on our bottle appears to be a poorly executed *Shao* seal used regularly by the artist and sometimes seen in this slightly truncated format.

The neck on our bottle is most unusual in that it is actually deeper than it is wide.

(CBL C 909)

206 (two views)

207

Glass, superbly painted with a continuous scene of a variety of fish including large carp, bug-eyed fan-tailed fish, a catfish, a spotted rock cod, and numerous smaller fish swimming amidst water vegetation, a 16-character inscription, preceded and followed by a seal on one main face, rounded shoulders and a cylindrical neck, an uneven flat oval foot ring and slightly convex shallow base

Signed Meng Zhishou and dated Jiyou year, corresponding to 1909

Height: 6.9 cm
Mouth: 0.6 cm
Neck: 1.85 cm

The inscription reads:
Ji you chun ri xie yu jing shi xi gu shan fang Meng Zhishou zuo

This can be translated as:
'Jiyou year (1909), spring day, painted at the capital in the Mountain Hut (Studio) of Practising the Ancient', followed by 'Meng Zhishou made'

The seal that precedes the inscription reads: *gu* (ancient), and the seal that follows is indistinct, but in keeping with most of his works, it is almost certainly the seal *Zishou,* in negative script.

Meng Zishou was another follower of Zhou Leyuan and numbered amongst the Beijing School artists. His dated works span 16 years between 1904 and 1919. His career starts at the height of the craze, if you will, for inside-painted bottles and he entered a marketplace bustling with competent artists. As a result it appears his art suffered. Commercialism, it seems, drew his attention from the real task at hand for a 'true' artist, that of creating masterpieces and he was instead focused on the quantity of pieces he produced. However he did on occasions manage to create some extraordinary pieces, particularly with some of his portrait bottles (see Kleiner, *Chinese Snuff Bottles from the Collection of Mary and George Bloch*, p. 232, no. 304, dated 1914; and Hall, *Chinese Snuff Bottles*, pp. 154-155, no. 76, dated 1908). This bottle should also be counted amongst his great achievements. Whilst it owes its choice of subject to Zhou Leyuan via Ye Zhongsan, Meng imbues it with an impressionistic touch seldom seen in this popular, if arguably overused, theme. According to Moss, Graham, and Tsang, *A Treasury of Chinese Snuff Bottles: The Mary and George Bloch Collection*, Vol. 4, Part 2, Inside Painted, pp. 510-511, no. 635, Ye Zhongsan had established what would become the standard 'fish painting' by 1903, in which at least one large carp, invariably turning to race upwards, as in our example, is surrounded by a variety of fan-tailed fish and sometimes other species all set amidst weeds. What Meng achieved in our example is a much more graceful and delicate vision in which the fish glide smoothly in untroubled waters, with less need for vigorous motion. They are more lightly delineated unlike Ye's rather strong outlines and deeper colour palette. Ye's fish often look contrived in their placements as did his aquatic plants, whilst in this bottle they are endowed with a naturalism that pervades the entire scene; the vegetation gently recedes and does not invade the subject. The tails of our fan-tailed fish, whilst sharing Ye's quadfurcation (four-branch tails), are treated in thinner, more shaded, and 'wispy elongated' format. The Bloch bottle, like ours, is dated 1909; has the identical studio name; and is of a similar unusual shape, being much closer to a bulbous crystal type than the more usual standard glass version. However it is much closer in colour palette and technique to Ye than ours.

See Moss et al, ibid, pp. 501-502, for a discussion of the inherent instability of the material of some of Meng's glass bottles and the subsequent loss of an unknown number of them.

For a glass bottle of the same subject dated to the following year 1910, see Hall, *Chinese Snuff Bottles XI: The Snowy Peaks Collection*, no. 103. For a crystal bottle of the same subject dated like our bottle to 1909 from the Carl F. Barron collection, see Moss, *The Barron Collection: Illustrated Handlist*, ICSBS Convention, Boston, 2008, p.14, no. 2946.

(CBL C 911)

207 (two views)

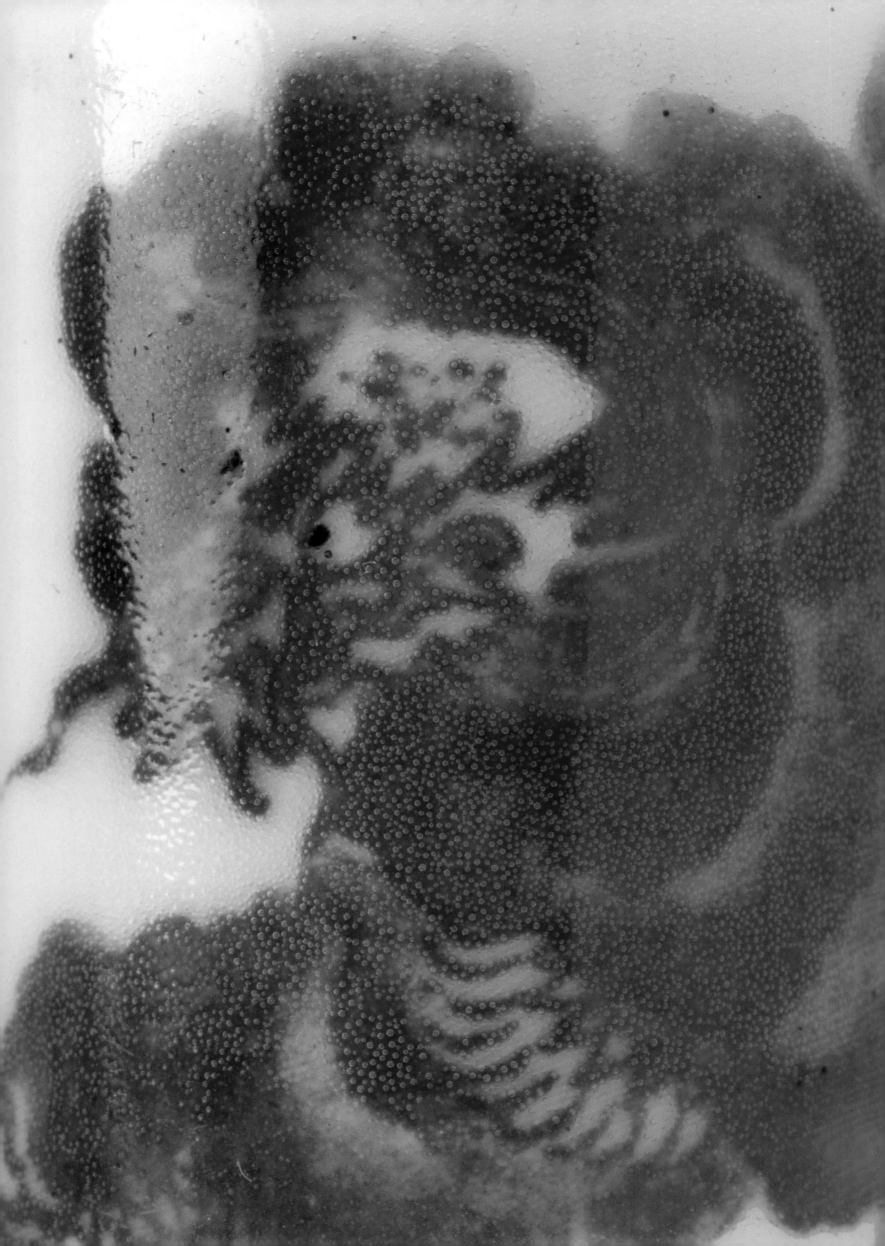

PORCELAIN

208

Porcelain, painted in underglaze blue with a more or less continuous land-scape scene depicting figures at different pursuits, including a woodcutter carrying bundles on a pole, two fishermen, one on a promontory, the other on a bridge, a farmer leading a buffalo with a hoe over his shoulder, and a scholar seated in a small building, all within a rocky landscape with pine trees, below rounded shoulders and a cylindrical neck painted with four bats, the neck interior glazed, biscuit foot rim and glazed base

Yongzheng four-character seal mark in underglaze blue to the base, Jingdezhen, 1790-1860

Height: 8.7 cm
Mouth: 0.7 cm
Neck: 1.3 cm

Provenance: Possibly Thomas B. Clarke, New York, January 1911.

The subject on this bottle depicts the *Yu Qiao Geng Du* or 'Four Noble Pro-fessions or Occupations', the fisherman, farmer, woodcutter, and scholar. It is a popular decorative theme on snuff bottles in a variety of media. Here the figures are spaced around the bottle to give a lyrical rhythm to the illustration. Cleverly, an unnecessary additional fisherman has been slotted into the im-agery to help balance out the composition. According to Confucian princi-ples when all four professions are in harmony the country is sustained. The farmer, fisherman, and woodcutter provide sustenance and fire and the scholar provides philosophic vigour. Whilst there is meant to be equality in the roles clearly the scholar here rises above the manual drudgeries experi-enced by his fellow 'companions'. The scene is almost a continuous one but with some areas not transitioning perfectly into the next panel. The neck is cleverly cylindrical despite rising from a square platform. The bats at the neck are obvious symbols of longevity and coupled with the other longevity sym-bols, the rocks and the pine depicted below, further create another layer of meaning to this bottle. The high-quality painting style and elegant violet blue set against a brilliant creamy white ground could quite easily date to the Ji-aqing period but the shape and large size and perpendicular format suggest a possible later date, as do the uneven lines at the neck. The four-character Yongzheng mark is neatly written but, sadly, inauthentic. Whilst many blue-and-white vases and vessels, including miniatures, exist from the reign of the Yongzheng emperor, as yet we know of no definite proof of blue-and-white snuff bottles having been made during that period.

This unusually tall bottle with its unusual flat facetted sides yet cylindrical neck can be compared with a hexagonal faceted bottle illustrated by Moss, Graham, and Tsang, *A Treasury of Chinese Snuff Bottles: The Mary and George Bloch Collection*, Vol. 6, Part 3, Arts of the Fire, pp. 806-807, no. 1376, which is dated to between 1810-1870. In the same publication, Vol. 6, Part 1, Arts of the Fire, pp. 49-51, the authors note two intriguing technical changes in mid-Qing ceramic snuff bottle production worthy of attention. The first is the in-troduction of different porcelain, which is outlined in the following entry (No. 209 in this publication). The second is an alternation between unglazed and glazed interiors. To summarise, whilst there are some early Qianlong bottles with glazed interiors, by the end of the reign they were habitually left unglazed. At some time during the Jiaqing reign the practise was re-intro-duced and with some exceptions was standard by the Daoguang reign. The reasons for the return to internal glazing include the use of a wider mouth, which revealed the interiors that were unsightly if unglazed; changes in con-struction methods that left joint lines that needed to be sealed; and, finally, a renewed appreciation of the fact that internal glazing might keep snuff more fresh.

For another bottle of rectangular shape with a flat shoulder depicting land-scape scenes and bearing a Tongzhi four-character mark on the base, see Kleiner, *Chinese Snuff Bottles from the Collection of John Ault*, pp. 106-107, no. 188.

(CBL C 101)

208 (two views)

209

Porcelain, painted in underglaze blue in a continuous scene with a scholar gentleman and attendant on a rocky promontory with trees, overlooking a scene of five or possibly more islands or mountain peaks surrounded by waves or clouds, the short waisted neck painted with a chevron band, the interior glazed, a biscuit foot-ring and glazed base, an overall very pale beige crackle to the glaze

Unusual Gu Jin Pu three-character seal mark, Jingdezhen, 1800-1880

Height: 6.2 cm
Mouth: 1.5 cm
Neck: 2.1 cm

The mark on this jarlet, which is not written in typical script and is missing a few strokes probably reads *Gu Jin Pu*, or 'Ancient-Modern Story'. The seal characters for *gu* and *jin* form the top two characters and the lower part of the seal is a single character with the radical below the *jin* character and the rest below the *gu* character. Presumably the seal mark refers to the story depicted. Whilst there are large massings of rocks around the promontory on which the scholar and his assistant stand, there appear to be another five islands or mountains set in the waves or clouds beyond them. This may refer to the Five Sacred Mountains of China. Alternatively, the peaks might represent the five distinguished sons of the scholar Dou Yujin (907-960 CE), each of whom famously achieved exceptional success at the civil service examinations to become high officials. Dou was revered as the ideal parent. (See Bartholomew, *Hidden Meanings in Chinese Art*, p. 68, no. 3.11). As a gift this bottle could then express the wish for raising successful sons. This reading would certainly explain the unusual mark. The possibility that it depicts no more than the top of a mountain range covered in mist or clouds or as figures rising above the natural world to find meaning in the heavens cannot be fully discounted though less likely.

This is an extremely well painted bottle. Until the recent publication by Moss, Graham, and Tsang, *A Treasury of Chinese Snuff Bottles: The Mary and George Bloch Collection*, Vol. 6, Part 1, Arts of the Fire, pp. 49-50, this type of exquisitely penciled blue-and-white bottle with a soft overall crackle was called 'soft-paste', a useful term of reference to differentiate it from the high gloss uncrackled surface of pure kaolin. The authors now suggest that this particular ware or paste should be referred to as *huashi*, or 'slippery stone' in Chinese. They lay out their argument by drawing on letters written by the Jesuit Père Francois Xavier d'Entrecolles in 1722 describing a new paste that he refers to as *huashi* with a fine grain which 'is to ordinary porcelain what vellum is to paper' and 'the lightness of this porcelain surprises the hand used to other porcelains'. Certainly the control of the underglaze blue on these crackled wares does seem to be greater than on the high-gloss products and they are often of light weight. However, we still do not have positive proof that *huashi* was used on snuff bottles, though it is certainly possible. We also cannot be totally sure what exactly was being described in the letters and if indeed this refers to the material we once erroneously called 'soft paste'.

(CBL C 104)

210

Porcelain, painted in underglaze blue in an almost continuous scene around the body with a groom leading two caparisoned Bactrian camels on a grassy path amidst rockwork and vegetation with a mountainous backdrop, a faint wide crackle throughout the glaze, a shallow shoulder, a slender neck and rounded rim, the neck interior glazed, biscuit foot ring, glazed base

Yongzheng six-character mark in underglaze blue in two vertical lines, Jingdezhen, 1850-1900

Height: 6.8 cm
Mouth: 0.5 cm
Neck: 1.25 cm

The depiction of camels on porcelain snuff bottles is, with a few exceptions, usually confined to a well recorded though small group of enameled porcelain bottles that are mostly Daoguang-marked. These more often than not depict a camel, with our without an armed rider on one side, and a gentleman with or without his horse, carrying a rifle and walking a dog, on the other. It is uncertain what the exact subject of this small group depicts but a plausible explanation is offered by Hui and Lam, *The Imperial Connection: Court Related Chinese Snuff Bottles*, no. 115, where the authors suggest that it is an historical rendering of the annual *Quili* or 'Autumn Hunting Trip'. From records we know that the Qianlong emperor ordered paintings of the event and the Daoguang enameled group may well represent this.

However our bottle depicts a far more pedestrian scene, even though it may actually be more rare than the enamel group. The crudely shaped 'mallet' from of our bottle suggests a quite late production date, as does the rather cursory and comical rendering of the subject itself in a low-grade cobalt blue. Our bottle must be later than the Daoguang group. The absence of armed hunters or dogs on our scene and the simple portrayal of a rather begrudging groom leading two lightly-laden camels suggests that it is no more than a contemporary rendering of an everyday scene. For a turn-of-the-century photograph of such a scene, see an article by Phyllis Boots Fast, 'History in a Bottle', ICSBS *Journal*, Spring 2002, p. 7.

For an example of almost identical shape painted with a figure of a groom leading a single camel towards a city wall, see Kleiner, *Chinese Snuff Bottles from the Collection of Denys and Eithne Cowell*, pp. 20-21, no. 45. For another rare example of a squat cylindrical bottle painted in underglaze blue and copper-red with a Manchu official on a camel led by a groom, see Hui, Kwong and Sin, eds., *A Congregation of Snuff Bottle Connoisseurs*, no. 109.

The Bactrian camel, which is now so closely associated with the ancient 'Silk Route', was in fact not indigenous to China. According to Schloss, *Ancient Chinese Ceramic Sculpture*, Vol. 1, pp. 220-221, tens of thousands of these camels were imported to China from the Tarim Basin, Eastern Turkistan, and Mongolia during the Tang dynasty and the state even created a special office to supervise the herds. By the nineteenth century, however, they were an ubiquitous feature of the Chinese landscape and used by the Court and merchants for local transportation.

Due to a blocked cork at the neck it is impossible to know if the bottle's interior is glazed.

(CBL C 105)

209 (mark)

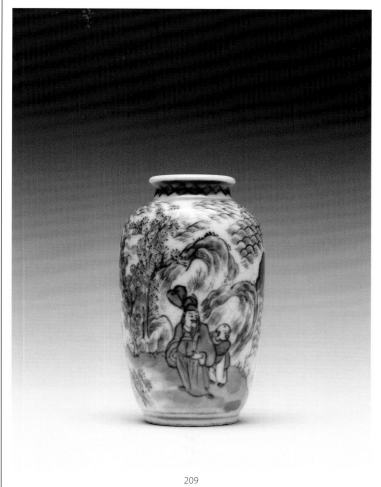

209

209 (detail)

210

211

Porcelain, painted in underglaze copper-red in differing shades with a five-clawed Imperial dragon in a penciled vivid copper-red with its eyes picked out in underglaze blue chasing a flaming magical pearl, the surrounding clouds and fire scrolls from which the dragon appears are painted in slightly muddier shades of copper-red with some areas firing to a pale green, the sloping shoulder and slightly waisted cylindrical neck painted with further fire-scrolls and clouds, a single cursory underglaze blue line below the rim and double lines above the foot, the interior glazed, a biscuit foot ring, glazed base

Chenghua four-character mark in underglaze blue in two vertical lines, probably Imperial, Jingdezhen, 1800-1880

Height: 7.7 cm
Mouth: 0.5 cm
Neck: 1.0 cm

The exquisite painting and the extraordinary fine-tuned firing of the notoriously difficult copper-red underglaze in various shades, renders this bottle masterful. Firing the copper-red with such precision takes a kiln master of great skill and judgement. The quality is so high, that it would be easy to believe that the painting dates from earlier than it probably is. The delicate use of a bright and clean copper-red penciled outline for the dragon's face, portions of his body, and the claws is superb, and made extraordinary, in combination with the slightly muddier copper-red of the murky darker clouds and fire scrolls which act as a perfect foil to the precision of the dragon. This depiction would not be out of place on an Imperial Qianlong bottle. However, the poor quality of the cursorily applied underglaze blue lines which frame the subject has the appearance of an afterthought and the tall mallet shape with flaring foot and long slightly everted rim are purely nineteenth century in concept. The use of a Chenghua mark appears to mirror that found on late Kangxi porcelains, often copper-red decorated, but also apocryphal.

The depiction of a dragon set amongst clouds chasing a flaming pearl can be traced back in Chinese painting to at least the ninth century, see Wu Tung, *Tales from the Land of Dragons: 1000 Years of Chinese Painting*, pp. 197-200, no. 92. The author illustrates a hand scroll in ink with touches of red by Chen Rong, dated 1244, which is unquestionably the type of depiction that inspired later artists and artisans of the Ming and Qing dynasties and was certainly a forerunner of our bottle. Chen Rong painted the dragon scroll when he was in an intoxicated state of mind, as he described in a companion text to the painting. The process reflected certain mind-altering experiences and insights long associated with Daoist transcendental practices.

The five-clawed dragon is symbolic of the Emperor and his sons of the first and second rank and by extension royalty, authority, and power. It also came to stand for vigilance, the spirit of change, beneficence, and protection.

Moss, Graham, and Tsang, *A Treasury of Chinese Snuff Bottles: The Mary and George Bloch Collection*, Vol. 6, Part 2, Arts of the Fire, pp. 416-419, no. 1186, illustrate a blue-and-white tall cylindrical bottle with a single five-clawed dragon chasing a flaming pearl that is strictly more formalized than ours, which he attributes to the nineteenth century (in an addendum) and suggests that the source of the bottle's decoration is the pillar carpets commonly used at Court. Our bottle may represent a link with this group.

(CBL C 115)

212

Porcelain, painted in underglaze copper-red and underglaze blue in a continuous scene with the eight horses of Muwang frolicking near a willow tree and bushes, the copper-red horses depicted as piebalds with their eyes picked out in underglaze blue, the horses variously dispersed some pawing at the ground and one rolling on its back, the lightly sloping shoulder painted in underglaze copper-red with a band of *ruyi* lappets below a further band in underglaze blue to the cylindrical neck with a slightly rounded mouth, the interior glazed, a double line above the foot, biscuit foot ring, glazed base

Jingdezhen, 1820-1880

Height: 7.6 cm
Mouth: 0.85 cm
Neck: 1.3 cm

The subject of eight horses derives from the legend of Muwang (King Mu, the fifth sovereign of the Zhou dynasty who reigned from 1001to 946 BCE) who was famed for his spirited steeds, which he used on his royal inspection tours around his kingdom.

Williams in *Outlines of Chinese Symbolism and Art Motives*, pp. 224-225, notes that the horse is an emblem of speed and perseverance and that the sleeve of the Manchu official costume was shaped like the hoof of a horse as a grateful tribute to the animal to which they owed so much. Moss, Graham, and Tsang, *A Treasury of Chinese Snuff Bottles: The Mary and George Bloch Collection*, Vol. 4, Part 1, Inside Painted, pp. 231-232, no. 521, illustrate a bottle by Ye Zhongsan depicting the same subject and note that over the years the eight horses have come to symbolize men of talent because the character for 'steed', *jun*, is homophonous with the character meaning 'a talented man' and that the message implied by a gift with this subject is 'May you be one of the talented people'.

For another porcelain example also painted with the eight horses of Muwang, but with the horses variously underglaze blue and underglaze copper-red, see Nicollier, *The Baur Collection*, pp. 182-183, no. H 70. Another in blue and white only is illustrated by Hughes, *The Blair Bequest: Chinese Snuff Bottles from the Princeton University Art Museum*, p. 228, no. 315.

The kiln control of the underglaze copper-red on this bottle is plainly not as consistent as the previous bottle and a lack of oxygen within the kiln at some point in the firing has left us with mottled areas of green on many of the horses. Whilst presumably not intentional it is certainly not unsightly. The more stable underglaze blue shows none of the faults associated with the copper-red firing. Like the previous bottle where the eyes of the dragons are cleverly picked out in underglaze blue, the eyes of each horse here are also painted in an identical fashion.

The use of a loosely painted *ruyi* band at the neck is fairly indicative of a nineteenth-century date. Whilst some are earlier, the majority tend to date from between 1820 and 1900.

(CBL C 117)

211

212

213

Porcelain, painted in underglaze copper-red and underglaze blue with twelve neatly outlined scenes of dutiful filial piety, each scene with accompanying text below a band of pendant *ruyi* at the short waisted neck, glazed interior, biscuit foot ring, glazed base

Jingdezhen, 1820-1900

Height: 8.8 cm
Mouth: 0.85 cm
Neck: 1.7 cm

The subject of dutiful filial piety was a popular one and is normally depicted in 24 separate scenes. There is a strong likelihood that this bottle, which only depicts 12 scenes, was paired with another now missing. The surface of our bottle has been neatly divided into 12 compartments of equal size and then painted in underglaze blue and copper-red with these scenes. The firing is of a competent fairly even type with just the lower third of the bottle showing signs of oxygen deprivation in the kiln and the concomitant paling of the copper-red.

The various figures depicted include Ye Guan, Guo Ju, Huang Lu Zhi, Cai Shun, Yang Xiang, Zi Lu, and Wang Xiang. The story of Wang Xiang (184-268) will suffice to describe the kind of filial duties or pieties celebrated by the painter of this bottle. His stepmother fell gravely ill one winter and had taken to bed where she refused to eat. However, one winter day she awoke with a craving for fresh fish. Wang Xiang not wishing to disappoint (nor starve) her set out in the bitter cold in search of fish. He came to a lake with a frozen surface and discarded all but his lower undergarments and lay on the ice. Slowly the warmth of his body melted the ice and Wang Xiang was able to catch a fish for his hungry stepmother. The scene depicted on our bottle shows the moment a fish surfaces from under the melted ice.

For a bottle with a similar shape, height, and neck decoration as well as identical horizontal band demarcations at the shoulder and neck and also painted in the same colours in two horizontal registers but depicting a scene of tribute bearers which is dated to between 1840 and 1870, see Moss, Graham, and Tsang, *A Treasury of Chinese Snuff Bottles: The Mary and George Bloch Collection*, Vol. 6, Part 3, Arts of the Fire, pp. 820-821, no. 1186.

(CBL C 119)

214

Porcelain, painted in vibrant rich underglaze copper-red background with an underglaze blue penciled five-clawed Imperial dragon chasing the elusive flaming pearl around the body, a single blue line above the foot and a very faintly outlined line at the shoulder edge below a cloud design on the shoulder and a pendant *ruyi* band on the cylindrical neck, a wide mouth, glazed interior, biscuit foot ring, glazed base

Probably Imperial, Jingdezhen, 1820-1880

Height: 8.1 cm
Mouth: 1.05 cm
Neck: 1.5 cm

Once again we have an extremely well fired bottle. The copper-red ground is of incredibly even tone throughout the body but also, as importantly, on the shoulder and neck decoration. Whilst there are some errors in the copper-red running across various blue outlines, for the most part it is confined to subsidiary areas. Perhaps the only significant area of concern is just above the foot where the copper-red is left well short of the blue line border. The dragon is painted quite satisfactorily, though the crisscross pattern that covers the dragon's body and legs has the unfortunate appearance of a fishnet rather than scales. However, the design sits well around the body and the rich strawberry-red and dark cobalt blue play off well against the extremely white body of the porcelain. There is also a quiet dignity and integrity to the shape of this delightful bottle with its very minutely waisted cylindrical shape, gently sloping shoulders and perfect cylindrical neck.

For another bottle painted in underglaze blue with a dragon chasing a flaming pearl set amongst copper-red clouds see Moss, Graham, and Tsang, *A Treasury of Chinese Snuff Bottles: The Mary and George Bloch Collection*, Vol. 6, Part 3, Arts of the Fire, p. 839, no. 1396. In some ways it is painted with more freedom than ours, but certainly with less precision and formality. Even the shape of our bottle with its crisp profile and perfectly simple cylindrical neck conveys a feeling of exacting precision. It is this very fastidious rigour that gives this bottle its brilliant touch of authority.

It is also worth noting the comments of Moss et al, ibid, p. 839, regarding the meaning of the five-clawed dragon in the dying years of the Qing dynasty when the government was in disarray and corruption was rife, and honours, presumably including the use of the five-clawed dragon, were apparently bartered freely. They also suggest that private kilns may have freely used the forbidden five-clawed dragon subject to fool foreign collectors into purchasing so-called 'Imperial' bottles.

(CBL C 121)

213

214

215

Porcelain, painted in underglaze copper-red and underglaze cobalt-blue with an unusual seemingly abstract swirling design possibly suggestive of grasses, with primarily blue on one side of the double gourd and copper-red on the other, with a small area left white between them mostly on one side, the rim and interior white-glazed and the glaze stopping just above the biscuit foot, glazed base

Qianlong four-character mark in underglaze blue to the base, Jingdezhen, 1800-1880

Height: 5.4 cm
Mouth: 0.55 cm
Neck: 0.9 cm

This is quite an unusual bottle. The painting appears to be non-representational, though it may perhaps depict wind-swept grasses. It appears to display two or three separate glazing techniques: the applied brush, the bamboo reed, and 'flicking'. It is difficult to be totally sure how the glaze was applied on certain areas of the bottle, but certainly where the two colours of underglaze copper-red and cobalt blue are divided by the transparent white porcelain, we can clearly see some splashing from the 'blown' technique, where a bamboo reed is used as the vehicle for applying the glaze by blowing or where the brush is literally 'flicked' over the surface to produce an uneven dappled effect. Other areas, however, appear to show the use of a brush with visible deft strokes. Interestingly the bottle, when viewed from four different viewpoints, can give four quite different readings. It can be turned so that only cobalt blue as a monochrome is visible and likewise so that only copper-red is visible, albeit both with blotches. On the reverse side of the bottle the copper-red and cobalt blue glazes converge into one of almost purple-pink colour and the other view, as illustrated, shows the transparent white glaze dividing the two, to give the appearance of blue and red grasses converging. A second bottle of shorter squat jarlet shape with a very similar glaze and also bearing a Qianlong four-character regular script mark does form part of the Beatty collection, though it has not been included in this publication.

Both underglaze blue, derived from cobalt and initially imported from the Near East, and underglaze red, derived from copper-oxide apparently mixed with an iron oxide, have been popular colourants in porcelain produced at Jingdezhen since the fourteenth century. By the Qing dynasty local deposits of cobalt were used and the red was composed of a copper-lime mix, without iron. The blue matured at a very slightly higher temperature than red (in excess of 1250 degrees centigrade). Copper red is much more difficult to fire due to the volatility of copper. For a further detailed explanation of porcelain glazes, see Kerr, *Chinese Ceramics: Porcelains of the Qing Dynasty, 1644-1911*, pp. 55-81.

See Bartholomew, *Hidden Meaning in Chinese Art*, p. 61, no. 3.3 for an explanation of the gourd as an important auspicious symbol.

The mark on this bottle, though quite neatly written, is once again inauthentic.

(CBL C 222)

216

Porcelain, painted in so-called robin's-egg glaze with shaped blue cell-like pattern on a bright turquoise ground over a white porcelain, with rounded shoulders, tall neck and with rounded lip rim, the interior unglazed, the base glazed but the foot rim exposing the white porcelain underneath

Jingdezhen, 1780-1880

Height: 7.2 cm
Mouth: 0.8 cm
Neck: 1.2 cm

According to Kerr, *Chinese Ceramics: Porcelains of the Qing Dynasty, 1644-1911*, pp. 87-88, in contrast to the underglaze copper-reds and cobalt blues, turquoise glazes were fired at a lower temperature in a second firing which fused the 'overglaze enamel' to the previously higher-fired and clear-glazed porcelain. It was first used at Jingdezhen in the fifteenth century but due to its relative instability was infrequently employed. Improvements in the glaze (a mixture of copper fluxed with potash) in the Qing dynasty reestablished its popularity and invigorated potters to produce a variety of types that included 'robin's egg' glaze which is opacified with arsenic. Kerr suggests that the glaze was likely reintroduced to Jingdezhen under the pioneering direction of Tang Ying and that at least two distinct types, one streaked with copper-red and another stippled with blotches of turquoise and dark blue (as in our example), were employed but that further chemical analysis is required to clarify the exact ingredients.

The glaze on our example actually appears as blue cells of variant size covering the entire surface, which appears to be a turquoise glaze over transparent white porcelain that is clearly apparent at the foot ring.

Just as the glaze has a long tradition in Chinese ceramic production, so too has the *meiping* form of our bottle. It was extremely popular during Song dynasty ceramic output, appearing in a wide variety of kiln production from the north and south. Its popularity continued during the early part of the Ming dynasty and was revived during the reigns of the Yonzheng and Qianlong emperors in the eighteenth century. Our form is loosely based on the more rounded-shouldered form.

The word *meiping* literally denotes a vase made to hold a single spray of plum blossom.

For another example of baluster shape from the Edmund F. Dwyer Collection see Christie's London, 12 October 1987, lot 125.

(CBL C 147)

215

216

217

Porcelain, the body very delicately moulded with three goats under the sun with a pine branch nearby, all under a pure white glaze with a light crackle in places, sloping shoulder and cylindrical neck, rounded at the rim, the interior glazed, the foot ring unglazed, the base glazed

Jingdezhen, 1790-1860

Height: 8.1 cm
Mouth: 0.7 cm
Neck: 1.35 cm

The subject of three goats (sheep) and a rising sun was a popular one in the decorative arts of the Ming dynasty but according to Bartholomew, *Hidden Meanings in Chinese Art*, p.146, 6.16.1, it did not gain prominence until the Qianlong period, particularly in jade carving. The Xuande Emperor (reigned 1426-1435) is known to have executed a painting of this subject showing an ewe and two lambs under a rock and a flowering bush. No distinction is made in Chinese between sheep and goats, *yang*, the collective name for sheep, rams, lambs, ewes, and goats is homophone of *yang*, the male principle or positive force. Therefore, the depiction of three goats or sheep, *sanyang*, along with a rising sun, *taiyang*, form the rebus' the new year brings a change of fortune', *sanyang kaitai*.

The addition of a pine tree to this depiction can be read as both a symbol of longevity symbol as well as the new year.

White glazed wares existed as early as the Tang dynasty but true porcelain was not manufactured until the Ding wares of the Song dynasty (from the tenth to thirteenth centuries). By the eighteenth century the white porcelains were of the finest quality and lightness due to refined clays and superior kiln technology. According to Kerr, *Chinese Ceramics: Porcelains of the Qing Dynasty, 1644-1911*, pp. 52-53, these qualities were enhanced by the addition of powdered white clay called *huashi*, 'slippery stone' to the porcelain body rendering it a slightly creamy white colour and usually slightly crackled. This material had, in the past, been misleadingly termed 'soft paste'. See No. 209 in this publication. White wares were often enhanced by raised decoration that was usually moulded as in our snuff bottle or carved as are the two lines which have been incised above the foot. The detailing of the three goats in our bottle is meticulous and miraculous. After moulding they may well have been enhanced by further carving.

(CBL C 207)

218

Porcelain, with steeply rising shoulders and cylindrical neck, very delicately incised with a group of floating cymbidium (orchid) with faintly visible roots to the upper half of the body, all under a pure white glaze, the interior glazed, the foot ring unglazed, the base glazed white

Jingdezhen, 1790-1850

Height: 7.7 cm
Mouth: 0.7 cm
Neck: 1.15 cm

A most unusual design that is, in effect, a miniature version of an eighteenth-century porcelain vase. This is probably about as close as a snuff bottle gets to being a pure ceramic vase form, not at all compressed and clearly following the popular baluster shape. Here there is a particularly elegant transition between the slender ovoid body and the delicate cylindrical neck. The detailing is superb and the cymbidium (orchid) is lyrically incised with the roots floating below and giving it a wonderful freedom.

The depiction here is of a type of orchid called cymbidium, *lanhua*, which is one of China's most ancient and best-known ornamental flowering plants. It is considered a symbol of spring. See Bartholomew, *Hidden Meanings in Chinese Art*, pp. 68-69, no. 3.8 and 3.8.1. It is always depicted with graceful grass-like foliage and with the flower petals surrounded by four, or more often five, larger ovate sepals (calyx). It is often mistaken by collectors for narcissus. According to Bartholomew, Confucius found the fragrance so enchanting that he called it 'the scent of kings'. When grouped with plum, bamboo, and chrysanthemum they are known as 'the four gentlemen among flowers'. For further discussion of this subject see the entry for No. 103 in this publication.

For a small bottle vase of almost identical size with incised decoration of a heron in a lotus pond, see 'The Collections of the National Gallery of Art', *Decorative Arts, Part II, Far Eastern Ceramics and Paintings*, Washington D.C., p. 146, No. 1972.43.36, where it is suggested by Stephen Little that the vessel was used as a snuff bottle but that due to its attenuated profile and thick potting he proposes a late nineteenth-century dating. Whilst this may be the case, the quality and freedom of the incised decoration suggests an earlier production date. The same publication also illustrates a green glazed vase of larger size but similar profile which is dated as late eighteenth century by Virginia Bower, see ibid, pp. 118-119, no. 1942.9.541.

For an enameled vase of similar shape that would have been the model for our bottle, see *Mayuyama, Seventy Years, Vol. 1*, p. 356, no. 1069.

(CBL C 211)

217

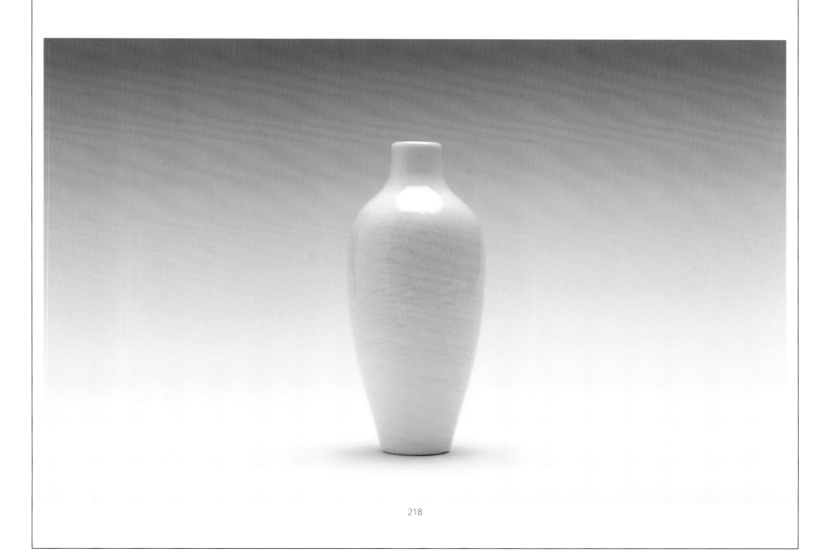

218

219

Porcelain, very delicately moulded and possibly incised with a coiling five-clawed dragon amongst cloud and fire scrolls, grasping at a flaming pearl, the eyes of the dragon very cleverly picked out in underglaze blue, the entire glaze with a widely-spaced pale-brown crackle and a less obvious more tightly-spaced clear crackle, with a short flattened shoulder and waisted and widely everted neck, the interior glazed, the slightly concave base unglazed and cut with concentric rings

Probably Imperial, Jingdezhen, 1800-1880

Height: 9.5 cm
Mouth: 0.8 cm
Neck: 2.1 cm

Moss, Graham, and Tsang, *A Treasury of Chinese Snuff Bottles: The Mary and George Bloch Collection*, Vol. 6, Part 2, Arts of the Fire, pp. 416-419, no. 1186, illustrate a blue-and-white tall cylindrical bottle with a single five-clawed dragon chasing a flaming pearl that can be favourably compared to ours in shape and also in decoration, although our encircling dragon is moulded rather than painted (with the exception of the eyes). They date the bottle, in an addendum, as most likely having been produced in the nineteenth century and suggests that the source of the decoration are the pillar carpets commonly used at Court. Columns or pillars would be decorated by wrapping them in carpets woven with a dragon design. It seems fairly certain that our bottle was produced at the same kiln and at a similar period of time as the Bloch bottle. The group appears in a variety of glazes that include clear white porcelain likes ours, underglaze blue and copper-red, and even iron-red.

As Moss et al, ibid, p. 419, point out, a very similar bottle with colourless glaze (appearing white) with engraved dragons (they may be moulded) where only the eyes are picked out in underglaze blue was already in the famous Bragge Collection prior to 1876, see Bragge, *Bibliotheca Nicotiana*, no. 159, where it is listed as 'Cylindrical, tall, white; five-clawed dragon and clouds, incised under glaze… 13 rings on bottom.'

Our bottle appears to have 12 concentric rings but these could be easily counted as 13 if the central concave depression is included. There seems little doubt from the remaining description that Bragge was handling a very similar bottle. However he does not make mention of a pale brown widely-spaced crackle which is clearly visible on our bottle and also in the blue-and-white Bloch example noted above, which is a feature of this particular *huashi*, or 'slippery stone', paste (see No. 209 in this publication).

This particular shape, though occasionally found in slightly different proportions during the eighteenth century, was unquestionably a popular one in the nineteenth. The subtle tapering shape is achieved with only a remarkable .05 cm difference between the circumference of the base and the shoulders. A very slight waisting of the centre of the body is also used to enhance the subtle difference.

For another similar example see Sotheby's, New York, 17 March 1997, lot 371, listed as 9.7 cm high and as having carved decoration rather than moulded and which is dated to the Daoguang period (1821-1850).

(CBL C 205)

220

Porcelain, painted in a rich emerald pea-green glaze outlined in black with 12 stylized lotus flower heads in three horizontal bands running from vertical scrolling tendrils and leafy foliage bordered by a thin band below, an unusual wavy band at the neck, and a single band above the foot, with a sloping shoulder and waisted cylindrical neck with wide mouth, the interior glazed, an unglazed circular foot ring, the base glazed and painted in iron-red with a square iron-red seal mark

Daoguang six-character seal mark in iron-red in a square and of the period, Imperial kilns, Jingdezhen,1820-1850

Stopper: matching porcelain, with nine-petal lotus flower head painted on the slightly domed top

Height: 6.6 cm
Mouth: 1.6 cm
Neck: 2.1 cm

The stylized lotuses on this snuff jarlet are even more formalized than those on the previous bottle with tendrils forming framing cartouches for some of the flower heads, either pointed ovals or figure-eight surrounds. Clearly the stopper, with its single green-glazed lotus flower head outlined in black, mirrors the method used on the body of the vessel and must surely be the original.

For a discussion of the jar or jarlet form see Moss, Graham, and Tsang, *A Treasury of Chinese Snuff Bottles: The Mary and George Bloch Collection*, Vol. 6, Part 2, Arts of the Fire, pp. 664-665, no. 1305. The authors prefer the term 'snuff pot' for this particular shape, however given the fact that a pot can also be a rounded vessel for cooking and other uses, the term jar or jarlet seems less confusing. According to the authors this type of wide-mouthed bottle was designed, apparently, to accommodate a mid-Qing fashion for adding sweet-smelling petals to the snuff overnight in order to scent and freshen it and they would be removed the next day. They quote an 1893 preface by Zhou Jixu to his *Yonglu Xianjie pingyu* as a reference. The bottle that the authors illustrate, like ours, bears a six-character seal mark of the Daoguang emperor, though it is painted with two dragons chasing a flaming pearl. They note that the preference for wide-mouthed snuff vessels seems to have begun only in the early nineteenth century. Our marked bottle seems to bear out this suggestion.

According to Kerr, *Chinese Ceramics: Porcelains of the Qing Dynasty, 1644-1911*, pp. 88-91, green was another colour derived from copper in the medium of a full lead glaze. When used as a monochrome at Jingdezhen it was applied over a transparent high-fired glaze (as is the case with our painted jarlet). In its earlier Kangxi manifestation the green had a tendency to run slightly unevenly but by the eighteenth century these problems had been resolved. A feature of some green glazes is a faint iridescence, like oily water, when turned to the light. Lead glazes of this type are actually very slightly poisonous and hence the plain, unglazed interiors.

The use of a green, *qing*, enamel for this particular lotus design may well be used to enrich the symbolism forming the rebus *qinglian* (pure and honest), which would be wholly appropriate to the decorative motif. For a blue-and-white snuff jarlet in the Imperial collections painted in a similar fashion though with differing borders but also bearing a Daoguang six-character seal mark, see *Gugong Complete Snuff Bottles*, p. 219, no. 332. A compressed spade-shaped bottle in blue and white bearing a Tongzhi cyclical date of 1864 and painted with a similar design is illustrated by Moss et al, ibid, Part 3, p. 882-883, no. 1419 and clearly of later manufacture.

(CBL C 212)

220 (mark)

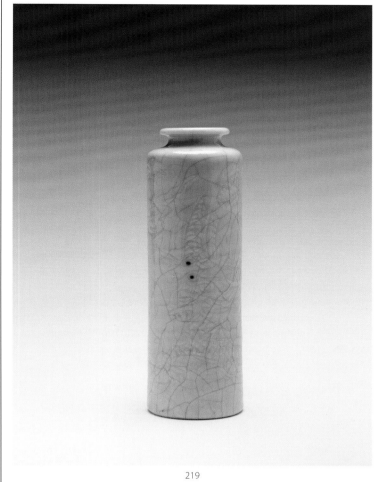

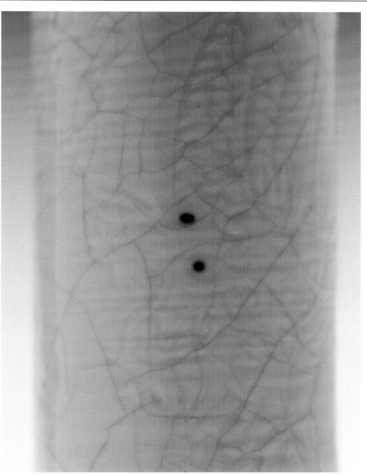

219   219 (detail)

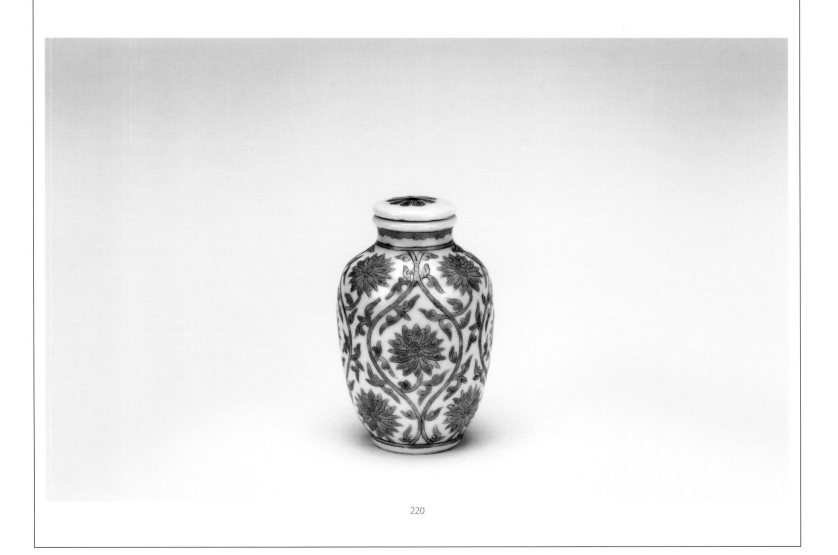

220

221

Porcelain, painted in various shades of iron-red with a beautiful five-clawed dragon chasing a flaming pearl amidst clouds and fire scrolls, the claws and teeth of the dragon picked out in white enamel, whilst the eyes are picked out in black, with flattened rounded shoulder and cylindrical neck with wide mouth, partially glazed interior neck, all on a pure white glaze that stops at the unglazed cylindrical foot ring, the base glazed white and painted in iron-red with a six-character seal mark

Daoguang six-character rectangular seal mark in iron-red and of the period, Imperial kilns, Jingdezhen, 1820-1850

Height: 6.2 cm
Mouth: 0.7 cm
Neck: 1.15 cm

Whilst the painting of the dragon itself is of a very high quality it is rather unusual that as the craftsman was finishing the last touches, crossing the t's and dotting the 'eyes', literally, made such simple, albeit amusing, mistakes in his draughtsmanship. It appears as if the artist accidentally painted a black dot on the large upper incisor, mistaking it for one of the eyes, where he did paint black enamel dots. It gives the appearance of a three-eyed dragon. Similarly, each of the five claws on the two rear legs have also been highlighted with the same black dot whilst it has been omitted from the claws on the front two legs.

See entry No. 211 in this publication for a history of dragon depictions of this kind. The five-clawed dragon is symbolic of the Emperor and his sons of the first and second rank, and by extension royalty, authority, and power. It also came to stand for vigilance, the spirit of change, beneficence, and protection. The flaming or wish-granting pearl, *baozhu*, of which only the flames are visible before the outstretched leg of the dragon in our illustration, appears in a variety of subjects in Buddhist legends according to Williams, *Outlines of Chinese Symbolism and Art Motives*, p. 318, but most usually it appears in association with the dragon. It is found amongst the Hundred Treasures of Buddhism, *baibao*, and is a symbol of wealth.

Once again the form of this bottle is closer to a ceramic vase shape than is typical. It is not compressed and loosely derives its shape from popular seventeenth-century monochrome vases. According to Kerr, *Chinese Ceramics: Porcelains of the Qing Dynasty, 1644-1911*, pp. 91-92, iron-red overglaze enamels made their appearance on porcelain at Jingdezhen in the fourteenth century, but because the colourant is only suspended in the glaze rather than fully dissolved in it, the colour has a tendency to rub off over time. The original rather dull tomato red was improved upon in the Qing era by using a high alkaline glaze with less lead, which resulted in a soft luminous tone.

(CBL C 217)

221 (mark)

222

Porcelain, of twin cylindrical shape, conjoined along one vertical side, one painted in underglaze blue, the other in overglaze iron-red, each with three horizontal rows of stylized lotus flower heads running from vertical scrolling tendrils, a single line above the foot and a band of *ruyi* at the cylindrical neck, the interior glazed, the foot ring unglazed, the base glazed white

Possibly Imperial, Jingdezhen, 1790-1850

Stopper: glass imitating coral on green glass collar; possibly rose quartz on metal collar

Height: 6.0 cm
Mouth: 0.8 cm
Neck: 1.4 cm

For four bottles of identical design, see Kleiner, *Treasures from the Sanctum of Enlightened Respect*, pp. 188-189, no. 162 from the Denis S.K.Low Collection; *Snuff Bottles: Little Gems of Delight*, p. 81, no. M 273 from the Joseph Grimberg Collection; and two illustrated by Moss, Graham, and Tsang, *A Treasury of Chinese Snuff Bottles: The Mary and George Bloch Collection*, Vol. 6, Part 2, Arts of the Fire, pp. 420-421, no. 1187, and pp. 594-595, no. 1268. The latter, which the authors believe to date to between 1790 and 1840 and to be of slightly later manufacture than the first, which they date to between 1785 and 1830, appears to draw the closest parallels with this example, in particular in the manner in which the lotus design at the junction of the conjoined bottles fails to join precisely, leaving an imprecise blank area between the underglaze blue and iron red decoration. The lotus on both the Bloch examples is called 'Indian lotus' on account of its formalized design with a central stamen element so beloved of Hindustan workmanship. On our bottle the overglaze iron-red is rubbed quite heavily and displays well the fugitive nature of an overglaze compared to the underglaze blue on the conjoined bottle, see the entry for the previous bottle for a discussion of this phenomenon.

Moss, et al, ibid, p.595, are uncertain of the exact nature of the construction of the conjoined bottles but suggest that whilst there are no obvious signs that moulds were commonly used, such as vertical join lines on the interior or exterior of the bottle, there do appear to be join lines between the foot and the body. This favours the theory that sheets of porcelain were pressed against the interior of a pre-joined two-piece mould by use of a hand-held tool and that the foot was made separately and luted when the porcelain was at a leather-hard consistency prior to firing.

A conjoined bottle painted entirely in iron-red enamels of similar design but with two rather than three rows of stylized lotus entered the Walters Collection in Baltimore some time prior to 1894, the date of William Thompson Walters' death, see Bushell, *Oriental Ceramic Art*, p. 238, fig. 293. It appears to be more crudely painted (based on the black-and-white illustration) and certainly the design is neither as well spaced nor as formalized as the painting in our example suggesting that our bottle was an earlier production.

The lotus has many varied meanings but was particularly sacred to Buddhists. It is a symbol of purity and perfection, growing as it does from muddy waters yet remaining undefiled. According to Williams, *Outlines of Chinese Symbolism and Art Motives*, p. 257, its constant use as an emblem seems to have been inspired by the wheel-like form of the flower, the petals replacing the spokes and thus representing the doctrine of perpetual cycles of existence. The flower is also venerated by Daoists and the immortal He Xiangu holds one as an attribute.

(CBL C 122)

221

222

223

Porcelain, painted on each main face in bright enamels within a truncated spade-shaped panel with an identical floral scene including, cockscomb, peony, chrysanthemum, and sweet olive, and possibly hibiscus, mallow, aster, and amaranth; and other flowers, the narrow sides painted in iron-red with stylized floral scrolling, the everted neck (reduced and re-gilt) has a partial *shou* (long-life) character in gilt and iron-red, the slightly rounded flat base has an iron-red four-character mark

Qianlong four-character iron-red seal mark in a line within a single-line rectangle and of the period, Imperial kilns, Jingdezhen, 1736-95

Stopper: coral, pagoda form

Height: 6.3 cm
Mouth: 0.7 cm
Neck: 1.3 cm

This bottle forms part of a well-documented group of similar Imperial bottles that bear either iron-red Qianlong or iron-red Jiaqing seal marks. The one feature on this group that differs between the Qianlong and Jiaqing examples is the base of the ogival gilt surround that frames the flower panels, which is truncated by an iron-red floral scroll, perhaps begonia, on many of the Qianlong marked bottles but never on the Jiaqing examples. In all the Jiaqing bottles the panels extend fully to the foot. This helps to build a chronology for the group. At some point late in the Qianlong reign, the truncated panel was dropped in favour of the full panel. The subject of these floral panels is discussed by Hui and Sin, *An Imperial Qing Tradition*, no. 2, where they illustrate a very similar Qianlong-marked bottle with truncated main panel and formalized iron-red floral scrolling on the narrow sides and suggest that the floral scenes represent the legendary 'nine flowers of autumn', which traditionally include marigold, chrysanthemum, yellow hibiscus, begonia, asters, cockscomb, Joseph's coat, rose mallow, and sweet olive. Whilst some of these flowers are present on our example, there also appear to be additional flowers though one cannot rely fully on the botanical accuracy of each artist. The motif is traditionally named *Jiu qiu tu* ('nine autumn painting') or *Jiu qiu tong qing* ('nine autumn festival').

Like nearly all the examples of this group the Qianlong marks are written satisfactorily though they are not particularly fine and there is no foot ring. The bottle is supported on the flat base and as a result the mark is often quite worn.

For a very similar bottle with an iron-red Qianlong four-character mark, see Moss, Graham, and Tsang, *A Treasury of Chinese Snuff Bottles: The Mary and George Bloch Collection*, Vol. 6, Part 2, Arts of the Fire, pp. 354-355, no. 1157 and from the Carl F. Barron collection, see Moss, *The Barron Collection: Illustrated Handlist*, ICSBS Convention, Boston, 2008, p. 44, no. 2713.

For a similar Jiaqing-marked bottle in the Imperial Collections, with the floral panel extending fully to the foot, see *Snuff Bottles in the National Palace Museum*, p. 125, no. 89.

For a more rare example with a figural scene on one side and for a wider discussion of the group as a whole see Hughes, *The Blair Bequest: Chinese Snuff Bottles from the Princeton University Art Museum*, p. 166, no. 204.

(CBL C 237)

224

Porcelain, relief moulded and painted in bright enamels on each main face with an identical scene depicting a single bat flying alongside a peach tree with five large fruit, rising from green and blue rockwork above breaking waves on which floats a single blossom, the narrow sides and the neck painted in iron-red and bright enamels with further scrolling foliage and flower heads, with everted waisted neck (restored) and gilt mouth, the slightly convex base is white glazed with an iron-red four-character seal mark

Qianlong four-character iron-red seal mark in a line within a single-line surround and probably late in the period or after his abdication, Imperial kilns, Jingdezhen, 1736-99

Height: 6.1 cm
Mouth: 0.7 cm
Neck: 1.7 cm

As with the previous example, this bottle forms part of a well-documented group of similar Imperial bottles molded with peaches and bats above waves and that bear either iron-red or underglaze blue Qianlong or Jiaqing seal marks. However, our bottle differs in one obvious respect, in that it depicts five peaches on each side rather than the usual nine peaches that appear on all the other published bottles. The reason for this difference is uncertain. It is not that five peaches are in any way inauspicious; there are numerous recorded vessels made during the Yongzheng and Qianlong reigns that depict groups of three, five, six, and eight peaches rather than the more common nine but it is unclear why the craftsmen would choose to stray from the norm. It could have been a special commission and might be a clue to chronology for the group. The artist also chose to use a far more naturalistic colour for the fruit rather than the more usual 'unnatural' pink enamel seen in the rest of the group. Pink was certainly available to the artist as evidenced in the blossom floating in the waves below the tree and on details of the floral scrolling used on the narrow sides and neck. Actually, the depiction of five peaches, though more rare, is probably more effective as it gave the artist the opportunity to flesh out, so to speak, the voluptuous peaches and presents a more balanced composition.

In this case the moulded panel to each side is identical suggesting that the same mould was used. In quite a few examples of this group the panels on each side are different (see No. 225, in this publication).

The depiction of bats, *fu*, and peaches, *shoutao*, forms the auspicious rebus 'May you possess blessings and longevity', *fushou shuangquan*, the bat being a pun for 'blessings', *fu*, and the peach being a symbol of longevity. According to Moss, Graham, and Tsang, *A Treasury of Chinese Snuff Bottles: The Mary and George Bloch Collection*, Vol. 6, Part 2, Arts of the Fire, pp. 363-365, no. 1161, where a 'nine-peach' bottle with underglaze blue Qianlong mark and underglaze blue floral scrolling on the narrow sides is illustrated, the design probably represents one of the three 'Isles of the Blessed' where minerals, springs, and plants promote longevity. Bartholomew, *Hidden Meanings in Chinese Art*, p. 221, no. 7.55.1, illustrates a Yongzheng *doucai* (contrasting colours) dish painted with bats, *fu*, hovering above waves or a sea, with a peach tree growing from a cliff which she notes forms the rebus 'May you be blessed by the mountain of longevity and sea of blessings', *shoushan fuhai*. The depiction of a floating flower in the waves below may be an allusion to marriage or springtime.

Our bottle cannot stand unaided suggesting that it may have originally formed part of a boxed set. See also the entry for the following bottle in this publication regarding the possible dating of bottles with reversed 'S' elements in the *Qian* character of the reign mark.

For an example of an iron-red Qianlong-marked bottle with the nine-peach design but identical stylized formal scrolling on the narrow sides, see Hughes, *The Blair Bequest: Chinese Snuff Bottles from the Princeton University Art Museum*, p. 188, no. 243.

(CBL C 241)

223 (mark)

224 (mark)

223

224

225

Porcelain, relief moulded and painted in bright enamels with a different scene on each main face, one side depicting a single bat, and a peach tree with nine fruit rising from rockwork above waves with three floating blossoms, the other side with a more unusual garden scene of narcissus, bamboo, orchids, *lingzhi*, peony, and blue rockwork, the narrow sides painted in iron-red and bright enamels with further scrolling foliage and flower heads, with everted waisted neck (repaired) and gilt mouth, the slightly convex base is white glazed with an iron-red six-character seal mark

Qianlong six-character iron-red seal mark in a line within a single-line surround and late in the period, Imperial kilns, Jingdezhen, 1736-95

Stopper: coral on gilt metal

Height: 6.4 cm
Mouth: 0.7 cm
Neck: 1.7 cm

Once again, this bottle forms part of the same relatively rare group of similar Imperial bottles moulded with peaches and bats above waves on one side and narcissus, *lingzhi*, bamboo, and rockwork on the other mentioned in the previous entry in this publication that bear either iron-red or underglaze blue Qianlong seal marks but do not appear to be recorded with Jiaqing marks. The moulding on this bottle might even be considered better than that on the previous bottle, with relatively close attention paid to how the enamel sits fairly precisely over the moulded design. Interestingly, the moulded panel on one main face is of the more ubiquitous 'nine-peach' design and unlike the 'five-peach' bottle has three flower heads rather than one floating in the waves below the tree. See the previous entry for a discussion of the scene's meaning. According to Bartholomew, *Hidden Meanings in Chinese Art*, pp. 158 and 189, nos. 6.34.13 and 7.25.4, the depiction of this group of plants and rocks has numerous possible meanings. The narcissus, *shuixianhua*, and the peony, *fuguihua*, form the rebus 'May the immortals bring you prosperity', or 'May you be blessed with longevity, wealth, and honour', *shenxian fugui*. The narcissus has the word 'immortal', *xian*, in its name. Also the collection of fungus (*lingzhi*), narcissus (*shuixian*), bamboo (*zhu*), and rock (*shoushi*) form the rebus 'May the fungus immortal congratulate you on your birthday', *zhixian zhushou*. The fungus and the second character of narcissus, *xian*, make up 'fungus immortal', the bamboo is a pun for 'congratulate', *zhu*, and the rock symbolizes longevity. The symbolism might suggest that these particular bottles were made to be given as birthday gifts by the emperor.

As with the previous bottle, this does not stand unaided suggesting that it may have originally formed part of a boxed set.

Similarly, the Qianlong mark is not well written but again the bottle probably dates to late in the Qianlong reign or, as suggested by Moss, Graham, and Tsang, *A Treasury of Chinese Snuff Bottles: The Mary and George Bloch Collection*, Vol. 6, Part 2, Arts of the Fire, pp. 366-367, no. 1162, dateable to between 1795 and 1799 on account of the reversal of the 'S' element in the lower-left quadrant of the *Qian* character of the reign mark, which may indicate a change in formalization of the seal script adopted by the Qianlong emperor after his abdication in 1795 but before his death in 1799.

For a near identical bottle from the Nancy B.W. and Y.T. Lee Collection see Hui, Kwong and Sin, eds., *A Congregation of Snuff Bottle Connoisseurs*, pp. 94-95, No. 107 and another is illustrated by Low, *More Treasures from the Sanctum of Enlightened Respect*, pp. 177-178, no. 163. For an example with the same garden scene on both sides of a bottle with an underglaze blue six-character Qianlong mark, see Hughes, *The Blair Bequest: Chinese Snuff Bottles from the Princeton University Art Museum*, p. 189, no. 244, and p. 188, no. 243, for an example of an iron-red Qianlong-marked bottle with the nine-peach design on both sides but identical stylized formal scrolling on the narrow sides.

(CBL C 242)

225 (mark)

225 (two views)

226

Porcelain, painted in bright enamels on one main face with a floral scene depicting blue rockwork with sprays of musk mallow, aster, or daisy, and amaranths within a simple moulded border with traces of gilding, the reverse side painted in black with a 28-character poetic inscription followed by two iron-red seal marks, the slightly rounded narrow flattened sides and neck painted in underglaze blue with stylized leafy floral scrolling, an everted waisted neck and pale-coffee glazed mouth with gilt, the glazed flat rectangular base with an underglaze blue four-character seal mark

Qianlong four-character underglaze blue seal mark in a line to the base and a two-character Qian and Long seal in iron-red to one main face and of the period, Imperial kilns, Jingdezhen, 1736-95

Stopper: amber

Height: 5.5 cm
Mouth: 0.7 cm
Neck: 1.8 cm

The 28-character poem is unusual in that after the title of four characters, the poem is split in to two five-character lines followed by two-seven character lines. It reads:

Yi chu yu xi
Chang bie shen pai hui
You yi chu jiang bin
Nai zhi ai yu lian xiang zhe
Bu shi dang nian xing Xiang ren

This translates as:
'The Songs of Concubine Yu'
A sad person separated walks aimlessly
Still remembering the bend of the Chu River
Who knows the person who loved you
Not the person called Xiang

This is followed by the two iron-red seal characters *Qian* and *Long*.

The poem is based on an episode in the story of Xiang Yu, overlord of the State of Chu and his concubine Yu Ji. Xiang's troops are hopelessly defeated in their penultimate battle with Liu Bang, the King of Han in a fight for supreme power over China. Xiang's encampment is surrounded by his enemies and Yu does her best to distract him from his troubles but in vain. That night she takes her life to relieve Xiang of all responsibility for her safety. In his sorrow, he slits his own throat before flinging himself into the raging torrents of the Chu River.

The Qianlong mark to the base of this bottle is partially defaced to the *Qian* and the *long* characters but happily both of these are clearly visible on the two iron-red square seals, which complete the inscription on one main face. As with all bottles from this group there is no foot ring; a glazed base serves as the support.

Two bottles in the Imperial collection today, which are presumably a precursor of our bottle, are painted with the identical 28-character poem in clerical script, *lishu*, on one side and a very similar floral scene with variations on the other, are illustrated in *Gugong Complete Snuff Bottles*, p. 198, no. 308, and p. 204, no. 314. Both the poem and the floral scene on both bottles is painted on a heart-shaped panel reserved on a turquoise ground with floral decoration. Both poems also have the addition of two iron-red seals that read *Qian* and *long*.

As a general rule, when there is a poem inscribed or written on one side of a snuff bottle, the scene that is depicted on the reverse side is invariably related in some way to the poem and this bottle is no exception. Mallow flowers are a symbol of loyalty. Like the sunflower, the mallow turns to follow the path of the sun, which represents the Emperor. It is most appropriate that a poem about an Emperor relinquishing his beloved concubine for the good

of his people should depict this flower. As a gift to a loyal official or minister, the sentiment would have been much appreciated. Alternatively, it is not difficult to believe that it might have been given to an official whose loyalty was in question, as a sort of 'warning shot across the bows'.

Interestingly, the flower, here described as mallow, on account of its correctly-drawn palmette long-pointed leaves with serrated edges and wide-open cup-shaped bloom with five broad flaring petals with wavy edges is almost indistinguishable from the corn or opium poppy, though that is usually depicted with its signature globular seed pod. According to Low, *Chinese Snuff Bottles from the Sanctum of Enlightened Respect III*, pp. 206-208, nos. 176-177, where he illustrates two bottles of quatrefoil shape, each painted with a 'Songs of Concubine Yu' poem on one side and flowers on the other, the mallow are described as corn poppy for two reasons.

One, they may well represent poppy, after all the mallow and poppy images can be indistuinguisable and two, the story goes that when concubine Yu, killed herself, she like Xiang, slit her throat, magnificent blooms sprang from the spot where her blood was shed and these became known as 'Yu Meiren' one of the Chinese names for corn poppy.

Clearly our bottle, whose flattened spade shape with large recessed panel and everted neck, echoes the two previous bottles, No. 224 and 225 in this publication (and originally based on Imperial jade bottle forms), and must be related to these courtly porcelain bottles which invariably have a floral scene on one side and a poem on the other, usually bear Qianlong marks and occasionally Jiaqing marks, and have stylized floral scrolling in enamels or underglaze blue on the narrow sides and neck. For further discussion see Hughes, *The Blair Bequest: Chinese Snuff Bottles from the Princeton University Art Museum*, pp. 164-165, no. 203.

(CBL C 230)

226 (mark)

一曲虞兮
徘徊猶
別神
憶楚江濱那知
愛玉嬌香者不
是當年姓項人

226 (two views)

Porcelain, the main octagonal faces moulded with circular convex panels and each painted in a similar manner in bright enamels, one main face with rock-work with peony, chrysanthemum or aster, amaranth, and sweet olive, a similar depiction and disposition of plants on the other side but with peony, magnolia, and rockwork, each circular panel outlined with a single underglaze blue circle enhanced with gilt and surrounded by eight equally-spaced underglaze blue dots ringed in gilt at the octagonal points at the bottle's perimeter, the flattened narrow sides and neck painted in underglaze blue with leafy floral scrolling enhanced with gilt and divided by iron-red and gilt flower heads, with everted waisted neck with gilt mouth, the flat rectangular glazed base with an underglaze blue four-character seal mark.

Qianlong four-character underglaze blue seal mark in a line within a single line surround to the end of the period, Imperial kilns, Jingdezhen, 1736-95

Stopper: coral glass and turquoise glass disc collar

Height: 5.55 cm
Mouth: 0.6 cm
Neck: 1.65 cm

In recent years, the theory that the unusual octagonal form was introduced to the Imperial Court in Beijing from the West in the form of pocket watches was generally accepted. Whilst this may in fact be the case, Moss, Graham, and Tsang, *A Treasury of Chinese Snuff Bottles: The Mary and George Bloch Collection*, Vol. 5, Part 2, Glass, pp. 296-297, no. 801, now suggest that it is equally as likely that such forms evolved independently as a result of experiments in faceting techniques and glass production.

What can be said is that the form was taken up by the Imperial glassworks probably in the early years of the eighteenth century, perhaps in the final years of the reign of the Kangxi emperor, but certainly we find this octagonal form reproduced as a glass snuff bottle as early as the reign of the Yongzheng emperor, see Hughes, *The Blair Bequest: Chinese Snuff Bottles from the Princeton University Art Museum*, p. 199, no. 136, for an enameled example and Moss et al, op cit, pp. 302-303, no. 804, for a transparent ruby-red bottle.

Apart from a small group of porcelain bottles made under the auspices of Tang Ying between 1728 (when he was appointed assistant supervisor at the Imperial kilns in Jingdezhen after five years as foreman of the artisans in the Beijing Palace workshops) and 1756 (after some 20 years as the director of the Imperial kilns), there are few existing porcelain bottles from Jingdezhen that we can confidently date prior to the last quarter of the Qianlong emperor's reign. (See Moss, *JICSBS*, Spring 2009, 'The Influence of Tang Ying on the Production of Imperial Porcelain Snuff Bottles'). Why more porcelain bottles were not produced earlier is addressed at length by Moss, Graham, and Tsang, *The Art of the Chinese Snuff Bottle: The J & J Collection*, Vol.1, pp. 360-361, no. 209, but the cause appears to be a combination of factors including a decline of quality in the enameling workshops at Court in the 1760s; that glass and enamel bottles made at Court were often indistinguishable from porcelain, negating the need for porcelain examples; and that the inherent qualities of porcelain—translucency and sonority—are hard to appreciate in such a small object.

The decoration on this bottle is quite magnificent and suggests the hand of an extremely competent and confident artist or draughtsman. The combination of bright enamels, underglaze blue, and delicate gilding is extremely well balanced as is the spacing of the floral scene. In other bottles of this group there is a tendency to fill in the entire paintable surface with decoration but here we have as much, if not more, space than we have painting that adds a delicacy to the entire bottle. Similarly the gilding on the underglaze blue floral areas at the neck and narrow sides is also of the highest quality. Even the underglaze blue Qianlong mark is quite well written for this group and not surprisingly, the 'S' element of the *Qian* character is written correctly (reading like the European 'S') suggesting a production date prior to its apparent reversal in 1796 (when it reads like a European 'Z').

The floral decoration on our bottle has several possible readings. According to Bartholomew, *Hidden Meanings in Chinese Art*, p. 74, 3.21, the osmanthus (*Osmanthus fragrans*) or sweet olive, an evergreen shrub or small tree native to southwestern China bears many tiny but fragrant yellow flowers used to

flavour tea and wine. It blooms in the autumn around the time of the Moon Festival and is associated with lunar legends. Its Chinese name is *guihua*, and the word *gui* is homophonous with the word for 'noble' or 'distinguished' *gui*. The peony, *mudan*, is amongst the most popular botanical motifs in Chinese art. Bartholomew notes, ibid, p. 155, no. 634, that the early history of the flower is closely associated with royalty. Sui and Tang dynasty emperors are recorded as growing them in their palaces. It is also known as, *fuguihua*, 'flower of wealth and honour'. The white magnolia (*magnolia denudata*) she notes, ibid, pp. 152-153, nos. 6.28 and 6.28.4, is called *yulan* in China and is an emblem of purity. In combination with the peony, *fuguihua*, it can form the rebus 'May your noble house be blessed with wealth and honour', *yutang fugui*, and she illustrates an eighteenth-century Imperial porcelain dish from Jingdezhen with a similar subject.

For other octagonal porcelain bottles that relate to ours, see Hughes, op cit, p. 163, no. 202; Kleiner, *Treasures from the Sanctum of Enlightened Respect: Chinese Snuff Bottles from the Denis Low Collection*, pp. 158-159, No. 136; Hui, Kwong and Sin, eds., *A Congregation of Snuff Bottle Connoisseurs*, pp. 90-91, No. 101, from the Lily B.Y. and Y.B. Fung Collection, which interestingly has the same poem and depiction of mallow as the previous bottle in this publication.

(CBL C 236)

227 (side view)

227 (mark)

227 (two views)

228

Porcelain, painted with garden settings in underglaze blue, enamels, and gilt with a scholar seated on rockwork awaiting his assistant carrying a wrapped *qin* below pine on one side and another scholar clutching a *lingzhi* fungus his assistant looking on and waving a fan, below a willow on the other, each with a simple gilt-line surround, both sides with extraordinary rock forms painted in underglaze blue and highlighted in gilt with concentric rings around a pierced center, the narrow sides with simple low-relief lion-mask and ring handles and underglaze blue, iron-red, and gilt floral decoration which continues on the waisted neck, an everted rim, the mouth with a pale-coffee glaze and gilt, the oval foot ring thinly glazed, the white-glazed concave base with an iron-red seal mark

Qianlong four-character iron-red square seal to the base and of the period, Imperial kilns, Jingdezhen, 1735-1796

Stopper: coral, turquoise collar

Height: 5.8 cm
Mouth: 0.7 cm
Neck: 1.7 cm

Whilst the subject of this bottle may be no more than a rural scene of a scholar gentleman and his assistant at various pursuits, as is usually the case, there are a number of other possible readings. The subject also appears to revolve around the subject of longevity as pine, rocks, *lingzhi*, and the elderly gentleman and boy can all be interpreted as related to that theme, whilst the addition of a willow, *liu*, on one side, can be read as a symbol of rebirth or springtime when it sprouts green shoots. The signs of growth also represent the coming of prosperity. According to Williams, *Outlines of Chinese Symbolism and Art Motives*, pp. 427-428, Buddhists view the willow as a symbol of meekness and it provided the poets of the Tang and the painters of the Song dynasties with a regular subject since it is also associated with beauty, suppleness, and frailty and therefore an emblem of the fairer sex. If only the title 'Master of the Rocks' had not already been assigned, there could be no more appropriate a title for this artist. The treatment of the *taihu* rocks is highly idiosyncratic and the curious forms are other-worldly.

The shape of this bottle can probably be best compared to an unmarked moulded bottle illustrated by Moss, Graham, and Tsang, *A Treasury of Chinese Snuff Bottles: The Mary and George Bloch Collection*, Vol. 6, Part 2, Arts of the Fire, pp. 368-369, no. 1163, which unlike our bottle has no lion-mask mock-ring handles or foot ring. The mark on our example with the 'S' element of the *Qian* character reversed so it reads like a European 'Z' suggests a production date between 1795 and 1799 (see entry No. 225 in this publication).

The handles on our example are uncommon on this particular form and presumably were a short-lived experiment. The combination of iron-red and underglaze blue for the decoration of the narrow sides was a feature that was certainly very popular at the end of the eighteenth and the beginning of the nineteenth centuries. The unusual use of a mixture of underglaze blue and enameling on both the pine and the willow and also on the *taihu* rocks seems to echo, to some degree, the techniques used in both the production of *doucai* enamels (joined colours) and *wucai* enamels (literally five colours but more correctly as 'full compliment colours'), see Cort and Stuart, *Joined Colours: Decoration and Meaning in Chinese Porcelain*, pp.15-16. In *doucai* production incomplete images are painted in underglaze cobalt first and then subsequently enameled with overglaze pigments to form a complete unit, and in *wucai*, five colours, but in fact often greater or fewer numbers are used, to form a full compliment of colours to create a lavish design. Generally the *wucai* palette is darker than that of *doucai* and therefore our bottle presents something of a hybrid.

(CBL C 251)

228 (mark)

229

Porcelain, each side with a moulded oval panel painted in bright enamels and iron-red with figural scenes, each depicting ladies in interior settings, holding scrolls or *ruyi* sceptres and at various tasks, the interiors with a variety of furniture, screens, doorways, and windows, all the panels set against a washed underglaze blue ground with gilt floral decoration and iron-red and gilt flower heads at the shoulder corners and gilt flower heads at the lower body, with everted waisted neck and gilt flat rim, the foot ring also gilt and the concave base white and with an iron-red four-character square seal mark

Jiaqing four-character iron-red square seal to the base and early in the period, Imperial kilns, Jingdezhen, 1796-1820

Height: 6.9 cm
Mouth: 0.8 cm
Neck: 1.7 cm

The subject of this bottle appears to be that of the female quarters at Court. Each of the four panels on our bottle depict two elegant ladies at various activities set within an interior space set with side tables, *tiaozhou*, large screens, *zuopingfeng*, possibly inset with *dali* marble panels, moon windows, and doorways revealing glimpses of further rooms. In one a bowl of fruit, perhaps peaches, sits on a tall stand, *xiangji*, and in another a spittoon, *zhadou*, sits on the floor. The paired ladies appear to be quite busy as they gesticulate and look around their surroundings, some holding scrolls, others clutching court sceptres. From the late Qianlong period onwards the depiction of courtly interiors was very popular particularly within this well-documented group of paneled vertical bottles with underglaze blue and gilt ground decoration. For other examples of this shape and method of decoration, see *Gugong Complete Snuff Bottles*, p. 193, no. 303; Hughes, *The Blair Bequest: Chinese Snuff Bottles from the Princeton University Art Museum*, p. 167, no. 206; Yee-wan Pang, ed., *Heavenly Creations*, p. 112, no. 173; and for subject matter see Yee-wan Pang, ed. Ibid, p. 107, no. 160 and Hughes, op cit, p. 176, no. 220.

It is informative here to quote the remarks by Moss, Graham, and Tsang, *A Treasury of Chinese Snuff Bottles: The Mary and George Bloch Collection*, Vol. 6, Part 2, Arts of the Fire, pp. 541-543, no. 1243, concerning ceramic snuff bottle output in the last decades of the Qianlong reign and the beginning of the Jiaqing reign, which in effect, can be looked upon as a single stylistic group.

From 1796 to the death of the retired Qianlong emperor in 1799, there was a rare overlap of a few years where both the abdicated and the sitting emperors inspired production with their creative input, and the reign marks of either one might be used on wares produced. Bottles such as this and the next [one an octagonal cylinder bottle, the other a square cylinder bottle – similar to ours], despite their Jiaqing marks are indistinguishable stylistically from their late-Qianlong counterparts and, as we have pointed out, it is even possible that such a bottle might actually predate one that was made and given a Qianlong mark in those first few years of the Jiaqing reign. Many of the bottles with painted designs from the period share the same enamels, decorative scheme with underglaze blue borders picked out with gold enamel, and, in many cases, range of shapes.

Our bottle, whilst bearing a Jiaqing mark. must surely have been produced at a very similar date to the recorded Qianlong marked examples of the same basic design. A date early in the Jiaqing reign, probably soon after 1796, would be plausible. However, unlike the known Qianlong marked examples of this type which are often unmoulded, the refined details of ours such as the concave foot treatment and truncated underglaze blue ground at the neck and foot suggests they were, with these extra refinements, made in response to the Qianlong examples and the later mark bears this out. The mark on this bottle is not particularly well written. This might be explained by the difficult and confined concave surface on which the calligrapher had to write.

(CBL C 254)

229 (mark)

228 (three views)

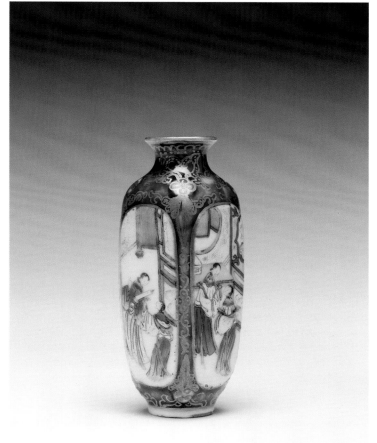

229 (two views)

230

Porcelain, painted in bright enamels within circular panels on each main face with female immortals including Magu in garden settings, one with two female immortals, one holding a giant magical peach, the other with a hoe over her shoulder supporting a basket of flowers on a garden terrace below pine, the other side with a single female immortal holding a *lingzhi* fungus in her raised left hand and a caparisoned deer to her side loaded down with flowers, fruit, and a ribboned gourd vessel in a similar setting, the narrow sides painted with a lime-green ground with colourful stylized scrolling lotus, the neck slightly everted, the rim gilt, the neck interior glazed, the foot edge painted in pink with a band of purple dots, the oval foot-ring unglazed but with traces of gilding, the glazed white base with an iron-red seal mark in a line

Jiaqing four-character iron-red seal in a line to the base and of the period, Imperial kilns, Jingdezhen, 1796-1820

Height: 6.1 cm
Mouth: 0.6 cm
Neck: 1.7 cm

A small group of very similar bottles of mostly quatrefoil shape with yellow or lime-green grounds painted with panels of paired female immortals is well recorded and whilst the shape of our bottle appears to be unique to the group, the remaining decoration, arrangement of figures, and background design are extremely comparable. In all cases the bottles bear well-written formal four-character Jiaqing seal marks in a line. One example can be found in the Imperial collections today, see *Gugong Complete Snuff Bottles*, p. 216, no. 327. Interestingly it appears to have its original porcelain stopper, which is imitating an imperial or official hat for formal dress. Others are illustrated by Kleiner, *Chinese Snuff Bottles: The White Wings Collection*, pp. 116-117, no. 78, formerly in the Bess J. Cohen Collection and sold at Sotheby's New York, 3 October 1980, lot 111; and subsequently illustrated by Souksi, *Merveilles de la Miniature Chinoise*, no. 70; and Moss, Graham, and Tsang, *A Treasury of Chinese Snuff Bottles: The Mary and George Bloch Collection*, Vol. 6, Part 2, Arts of the Fire, pp. 552-553, no. 1248.

Another example of small spade shape with scenes more comparable to ours, is illustrated by Low, *Chinese Snuff Bottles from the Sanctum of Enlightened Respect III*, p. 209, no. 178 and previously illustrated by Kleiner, *Chinese Snuff Bottles from the Collection of John Ault*, p. 70, no. 120. Another unique example depicting three figures on one side and two on the other is illustrated in *Heavenly Creations*, p. 107, no. 161, from the Anthony K.W. Cheung Collection.

In all the other bottles referenced each of the panels has two female immortals variously arranged in the garden setting, The Kleiner-Souksi and *Gugong* examples being identical depictions and perhaps from the same boxed set, whilst the Bloch example varies. Ours, and the Low bottle, are the only examples where a single female immortal is placed alone on one panel (alongside her deer). This panel appears to depict Magu, the goddess of longevity, the female equivalent of Shoulao, the god of longevity. According to Bartholomew, *Hidden Meanings in Chinese Art*, p. 191, no. 727, she is often depicted accompanied by a deer and could brew longevity wine from the fungus of immortality, *lingzhi*. In our portrayal she holds a large *lingzhi* spray in one hand and a gourd hanging on the deer's side further indicate her immortal status.

The other panel appears to, once again, depict Magu, this time holding a hoe over her shoulder from which is suspended a basket of peaches and flowers and a gourd tied at her waist standing with another female immortal or attendant who holds a large peach-coloured vessel which is tied at the neck with a cloth wrap and may well represent a jar of fungus wine. Interestingly the *Gugong* and Kleiner bottles both show a female holding a gold-decorated ewer and cover, which presumably represents the same motif. In point of fact, all four immortals in these two examples carry an attribute of the female immortal Magu, perhaps suggesting that each one is an attendant of the goddess. Possibly, each might be a separate manifestation of Magu, though it seems highly unlikely that they would depict the same goddess twice within one image.

According to Bartholomew, *Hidden Meanings in Chinese Art*, p. 191, no. 727, an image of Magu is hung in banquet halls for women's birthday parties. Perhaps this bottle was intended as a birthday gift to high-ranking women at Court.

In shape, as previously mentioned our bottle appears to be unique within the group of 'Magu' decorated bottles but is comparable to others in the same overall group of Imperial bottles. For two examples see *Gugong Complete Snuff Bottles*, p. 205, no. 315 which is much closer in colour scheme and format; it also has a pink border at the foot, circular panels (with a floral scene and a poem), and the same lime-green ground with stylized floral decoration below a gilt rim. It bears a Qianlong seal mark. Another, with a Jiaqing seal mark also an identical shape but differs in having a ruby-red ground. This seems to suggest that all were produced within a few years of each other and that the Jiaqing *Gugong* bottle, and indeed our example, probably date to between 1796 and the first few years of the nineteenth century.

(CBL C 250)

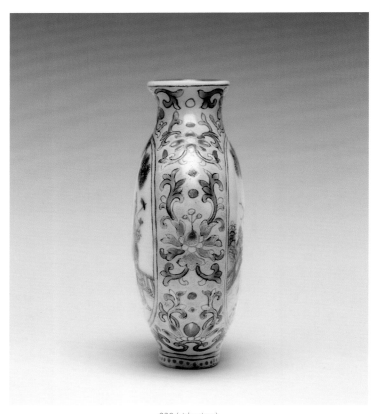

230 (side view)

230 (mark)

230 (two views)

231

Porcelain, very finely moulded in low relief and painted identically in bright enamels on each main face with a pair of quails below sprays of wild grain (millet, rice, or reeds) on a small rise with flowers and rocks, the narrow sides painted with a pink ground with colourful stylized lotus and other floral scrolling, with short cylindrical neck, the mouth rim gilt, the neck interior glazed, the foot edge painted in pale blue with a band of darker blue dots, the oval foot unglazed but with traces of gilding, the glazed white base with an iron-red seal mark

Jiaqing four-character iron-red seal in a line to the base and of the period, Imperial kilns, Jingdezhen, 1796-1820

Stopper: jadeite on gold collar (marked), silver spoon

Height: 5.7 cm
Mouth: 0.6 cm
Neck: 1.9 cm

Published: Chapman, 'The Chester Beatty Collection of Snuff Bottles', *Arts of Asia*, March-April, 1988, p. 61, fig 12.

This bottle is clearly related to the previous bottle in this publication and many of the comments made there apply here.

Though a magnificently moulded example and extremely well painted, the pink enamel appears to have been very slightly over-fired in the kiln causing the surface to bubble unattractively in some places. Identical examples of this bottle can be found in the Imperial Collections today. One is illustrated in *Gugong Complete Snuff Bottles*, p. 218, no. 329. Another seven examples (from an original boxed set of ten, though three are missing and have been replaced with alternates) are illustrated in *Snuff Bottles in the Collection of the National Palace Museum*, Taipei, p. 130, no. 94. The floral decoration on the narrow sides and neck is painted absolutely identically to these examples in respect of colour and every twist and turn of the scrolling design and the panels of quails might even be from the same mould.

According to Bartholomew, *Hidden Meanings in Chinese Art*, p. 245, no. 8.22.2, the subject of our bottle, quail, *anchun*, and ears of grain, *sui*, forms either the rebus 'May you have peace year after year', *suisui ping'an*, or 'May there be peace and good harvest', *shuang'an jiahe*. The first character of the word for quail, is homophonous with the second character of peace, *ping'an*. Similarly an ear of grain, *sui*, is a pun for 'year', *sui*. Multiple ears therefore standing for 'year after year'.

Bird paintings have been a popular subject in Chinese art since before the Song dynasty. The Song emperor, Huizong (reigned 1101-25; died 1135) was particularly fond of them and a number of his own extremely competent paintings are recorded, see Wu, *Tales from the Land of Dragons: 1000 Years of Chinese Painting*, pp. 54-55 and pp. 140-141, no. 13 (a parakeet); and Cahill, *Chinese Painting*, p. 73 (a pair of finches). He also painted sparrows, pheasants, cranes, and mandarin ducks amongst others. These paintings were invariably in hand scroll form. However a large number of bird paintings from this era come down to us in the form of circular fan paintings, and many of these would have been known at Court. It is tempting to suggest that such paintings might have been the stimulus behind snuff bottles like these where the snuff bottle shape provided a perfect canvas for these circular images. It is also well recorded that the Qianlong emperor loved these Song dynasty bird paintings. So much so that he even painted his own copies of them. For an example of this, 'Two chicks waiting to be fed', which copies the work of the Southern Song painter Li Di (active late twelfth to early thirteenth century), includes an inscription suggesting that the emperor attempted his copy not simply because he appreciated the skills of the Song master but because he saw a moral in the subject matter: his duty as Emperor was to see that his subjects do not go hungry, see Zhang Hongxing, *The Qianlong Emperor: Treasures From the Forbidden City*, pp. 132-133, no. 75.

The gold collar on the stopper is marked once with the characters *chi jiu* (red gold) and twice with the characters *cheng chang* (possible maker's or shop mark). However the stopper is not original to the bottle. Porcelain bottles of this type were usually made with porcelain stoppers.

(CBL C 246)

232

Porcelain, with an allover pink enamel ground painted with floral scrolling centered by a stylized lotus with other flower heads, probably stylized begonia, a waisted neck and everted rim, the mouth with traces of gilding, the neck interior glazed, the base is reduced by polishing, though the original glazed white base has a partially readable iron-red seal mark

Qianlong four-character iron-red square seal to the base and of the period, Imperial kilns, Jingdezhen, 1735-1796

Stopper: coral, turquoise collar

Height: 6.4 cm (reduced)
Mouth: 0.5 cm
Neck: 1.5-1.9 cm (lobed oval)

The overall decoration on this bottle appears to be a derivation from the backdrop decoration usually confined to the narrow sides and necks of a wide group of Imperial bottles produced in the Qianlong reign. For a number of examples of Imperial Qianlong-marked bottles from the Qing Court Collection, see *Gugong Complete Snuff Bottles*, p. 207, no. 317, which has near identical floral decoration on a pink ground to the narrow sides and neck and ibid, p. 195, no. 305 for a spherical bottle with an allover pink sgraffito ground with scrolling floral decoration. This bottle, like ours, also has a very clearly and neatly written four-character iron-red seal mark, though its is within a single line square. Other Qianlong examples with the narrow sides painted in a similar fashion from the Imperial collections are illustrated in *Snuff Bottles in the Collection of the National Palace Museum*, Taipei, pp. 114-118, nos. 74, 76, 81, and 82. See also the previous bottle, No. 231, in this publication for a Jiaqing example. The bottles themselves may well be modeled on a group of ceramic vessels made during the Qianlong reign at Jingdezhen which were commissioned for the Palace and which are usually quite simple vase forms with a single colour ground, often turquoise, pink, ruby-red, and yellow amongst the most popular, all with stylized floral scrolling with intersecting tendrils set out in a formalized symmetric pattern, see *Chinese Ceramics: Ching Dynasty*, pp. 240, 241, and 243 and *Qing Imperial Porcelain*, nos. 93, 95, and 96 for various examples of the group.

The lobed cross section of the bottle may well represent a begonia flower which would certainly make sense with the depiction of stylized begonia flower heads depicted above and below the larger central lotus on each main face and again on the narrow sides. The shape may also simply be a compressed lobed version of a more standard *meiping* form. A bottle of identical from is illustrated in *Zhongguo biyanhi zhenshang* ('Gems of Chinese Snuff Bottles'), p. 126, no. 133, it has a turquoise ground and similar floral scrolling around the body.

The decoration on our bottle can also be compared to that on another bottle illustrated by Moss, Graham, and Tsang, *A Treasury of Chinese Snuff Bottles: The Mary and George Bloch Collection*, Vol. 6, Part 2, Arts of the Fire, pp. 352-353, no. 1156, where the authors speculate on the influence of Tang Ying. Another example from the Ko Family Collection was sold at Christie's London, 14 June 1971, lot 80 was decorated on a turquoise ground.

The foot of our bottle must have been damaged at some time and then polished down.

(CBL C 272)

231 (mark)

232 (mark)

231 (two views)

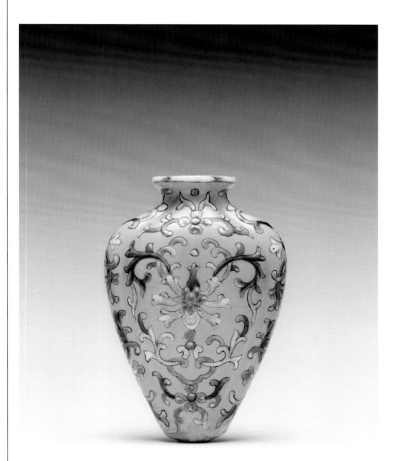

232 (two views)

233

Porcelain, painted in underglaze blue, some pale enamels, iron-red and gilt, in the *doucai* palette, in a continuous scene with eight foreigners dressed in European clothing and each bald at the top of the head and with curly locks to the sides, each holding a Daoist attribute including an umbrella, *ruyi* sceptre, coral branch, scroll, rhinoceros horn, and with various mythical animals in their midst including a white elephant, *qilin*, two Buddhist lions and a camel-like beast, all set in a rocky landscape below clouds at the rounded shoulder, the waisted neck with a band of five bats, the interior glazed, the glaze with an overall widely spaced crackle of two types, pale-brown and grey, the circular foot ring unglazed, the circular base white-glazed with an underglaze blue six-character mark within two circles

Yongzheng underglaze blue encircled six-character mark in regular script in two vertical lines to the base, Jingdezhen, 1820-1870

Height: 8.5 cm
Mouth: 0.9 cm
Neck: 1.7 cm

The scene depicted of 'eight barbarians bearing tribute', *Baman Jinbao*, was a popular one. For the neighbouring states of China to enjoy protection from the Qing Empire and remain at peace, tributes had to be given on regular occasions to the Emperor. The standard number of tribute bearers painted on snuff bottles was eight, which represents the number of tributary states on China's border. These tributary nations, far from appearing aggrieved at this subservient act, outdid each other in their desire to impress the Emperor with their own sophistication and their gifts often displayed their own nations' cosmopolitan, cultivated, and worldly view. The snuff bottles that commemorate such embassies do so in a spirit of memorializing the symbolic act of paying tribute rather than portraying an actual event. As a result the scene is often a curious mixture of a menagerie of real and mythical animals, Daoist emblems, and balding foreigners in Western dress.

This type of cylindrical-ovoid bottle, with this scene or a variant of it, more often than not painted solely in underglaze cobalt blue, appears to have made its appearance in snuff bottle production sometime in the first half of the nineteenth century. Examples are often unmarked and ours may be the only example with an apochrophal Yongzheng mark. The most common mark, it seems, to be found on this type of bottle is a perfectly acceptable Xianfeng mark (1851-1861). For an example, see Kleiner, *Chinese Snuff Bottles from the Collection of John Ault*, p. 102, no. 179, which appears to be painted less loosely than our example and with less verve. It is also painted with a more standardized formal neck decoration than ours (trefoils or *ruyi* lappets with dots), which might suggest that our bottle dates slightly earlier. An unmarked blue-and-white bottle whose depiction is actually much closer in sentiment to ours is illustrated by Moss, Graham, and Tsang, *A Treasury of Chinese Snuff Bottles: The Mary and George Bloch Collection*, Vol. 6, Part 3, Arts of the Fire, pp. 815-816, no. 1382, where the authors note that a similar example had already entered an English collection by 1896 thus giving us a positive Guangxu period terminus ad quem for this type of bottle. The authors date their bottle between 1840 and 1870.

Besides the plain blue-and-white bottles already mentioned, there appear to be two other variants. One with the inclusion of underglaze copper red, see Hui and Sin, *An Imperial Qing Tradition*, p. 36, no. 29, which is unmarked, and the second with the inclusion of pale enamels, *doucai*, as in our example.

In *doucai* ('joined colours') wares, incomplete images are painted in underglaze cobalt first and then subsequently enameled with overglaze pigments to form a complete unit. Here the additional enamels—pink, yellow, green, and iron-red—are used sparingly to give extra life to the scene.

(CBL C 255)

234

Porcelain, of peach-shaped cross section, moulded to form a wrapped and stitched traditional xylographic book, painted in bright enamels and iron-red with a scholar seated in a canopied boat playing a *qin* below overhanging trees and on the opposite bank a seated fisherman a pole by his side and a fish in his left hand, with bamboo to one side, this continuous scene divided on a flattened edge by the chapter and page numbers written in iron-red, the cylindrical neck is painted with an iron-red diamond-cell pattern band, the rim is gilt and brown glazed, the interior glazed, the peach-shaped foot ring unglazed, the base glazed white with an iron-red seal mark

Jiaqing iron-red square seal mark to the base and possibly late in the period, possibly Imperial, Jingdezhen, 1796-1820

Stopper: glass imitating emerald or jadeite

Height: 7.6 cm
Mouth: 0.8 cm
Neck: 1.4 cm

The implication of the book shape is that the scenes are pages from a polychromed wood-block print. The inscription includes the words *juan yi* (chapter one) written above and the pages numbers *yi* to *ba* (one to eight) below.

The scholar seated in his canopied boat is playing the classical and ancient musical instrument with seven strings, the lute or zither, generally referred to as the *qin*. The *qin* was considered one of the 'Four Scholarly Pursuits' that a scholar gentleman should master —the others being chess (*qi*), books (*shu*), and paintings (*hua*). Interestingly if we extrapolate from the actual design of the bottle itself, we can come up with a total of three pursuits, with only chess missing. Opposite him, seated on a riverbank, is a contented fisherman, who in this depiction probably represents one of the 'Four Noble Professions', the others being woodcutter, farmer, and scholar (here represented by the *qin* player). Close attention to detail has been paid by the artist in details like the 'spotted' bamboo frame that supports the canopy of his boat. This is not just regular bamboo, *zhu*, but the much rarer variety called, *Xiang fei zhu*, which comes from Hunan province that is instantly recognizable by this unusual spotted effect. The numbering of the pages and the title and the bottle shape itself are extremely well conceived, and the change in shape from a cylinder to a peach-shaped cross section is seamless. Quite why so few bottles of this attractive shape exist is a mystery but perhaps the whole group of oddly moulded bottles was the production of a certain kiln at Jingdezhen that made fewer batches than others or perhaps they were the product of an independent kiln that simply had less demand to fill.

The unusual design of our bottle is perhaps related to the enthusiasm for moulded porcelains during the second half of the Qing period. The glazed interior also enjoyed resurgence at this time, particularly from the Jiaqing period onwards. Whilst the Jiaqing mark on our bottle is poorly written and the firing of the porcelain has left the glaze a little grey, there seems no palpable reason not to believe that it dates to late in the period, though it conceivably might date to a few decades later. Certainly, the few others of this shape that are recorded are dated from 1840 onwards and all depict an aspect of ceramic production, which ours patently does not. One example is illustrated by Moss, Graham, and Tsang, *A Treasury of Chinese Snuff Bottles: The Mary and George Bloch Collection*, Vol. 6, Part 3, Arts of the Fire, pp. 868-869, no. 1411, painted in rather subdued colours of black and iron-red with a potter at his wheel; another of the same subject was illustrated in the *JICSBS*, Spring 1990, p. 27, figs. 3-4, and another is published by Kleiner, *Chinese Snuff Bottles from the Collection of John Ault*, pp. 88-89, painted in bright enamels and depicting the gathering of porcelain paste from the ground. The Ault bottle is dated to between 1840-1860 and the Bloch bottle to between 1850-1920.

Another example in blue and white from the Ko Family Collection is painted with a figure seated on an ox and a lengthy inscription regarding an exiled official, see Christie's London, 9 October 1974, lot 7.

Other less directly comparable bottles, which in concept at least are similar, are illustrated by Moss et al, ibid, Part 2, Arts of the Fire, pp. 527-528, no. 1236 and ibid, Part 3, pp. 862-863, no. 1408.

234 (mark)

(CBL C 248)

233 (two views)

234 (two views)

235

Porcelain, painted in bright enamels, iron-red and gilt, in a continuous scene with a story from *Dream of the Red Chamber* depicting various seated officials at a banquet in a roofed courtyard, with rockwork and bamboo to one side in a garden, a faint gilt inscription on an iron-red canopy to one side, below a rounded shoulder and small cylindrical neck with a blue enamel *ruyi* band, the interior glazed, a very pale overall crackle to the glaze, the circular foot ring unglazed, the circular base glazed white with a underglaze blue seal mark

Jiaqing underglaze blue four-character square seal mark to the base and possibly late in the period, Imperial kilns, Jingdezhen, 1796-1820

Height: 8.5 cm
Mouth: 0.6 cm
Neck: 1.2 cm

The gilt inscription on the iron-red canopy that hangs above main table in this banquet scene reads:

Rongxi tang zhu yu qing liang xiao

This translates as:
A fine night of celebrations in the Rongxi Hall

If it were not for the gilt inscription on this bottle, the scene might easily be mistaken for any random Chinese banquet taking place in a hall or courtyard. However the naming of the Rongxi Hall allows us to identify the scene as depicting part of a chapter from the well-known mid-eighteenth-century novel by Cao Xueqin, *Hong Lou Meng* ('Dream of the Red Chamber'). The story is massive in scope with hundreds of characters, many female, and is famed for its penetrating observation of aristocratic social mores under the Manchu rulers. It gives a glimpse in to real life and intrigue in China's last feudal dynasty. 'Red Chamber' is a reference to the sheltered quarters where the daughters of wealthy families lived. The Rongxi Hall refers to the mansion owned by one of the two branches of the Jia clan, the House of Rongguo and the House of Ningguo, illustrious families around whom part of the story is woven.

The scene on our bottle is most likely taken from Chapter 17 (or Chapter 14 in some editions), when a group of parents visit the Rongguo household to celebrate the 'Feast of the Lanterns'. In our depiction, the mothers are no doubt in the ladies' quarters and the fathers are seated around the hall at various tables enjoying food and wine below a line of lanterns.

The dating of this bottle should be straightforward enough as it carries a Jiaqing reign mark on its base. However the quality of the painting style and the range of enamel colours used could quite easily date this to the Daoguang period or even later. The shape is also one that was used more extensively in the mid- to late- nineteenth century, though it certainly exists earlier. Also to be taken in to account is the speed at which the novel would have disseminated through society to the point that an image like this would be instantly recognizable. I am reliably informed that the first recognized publication of the novel was in the 56th year of the Qianlong reign (1791) and that the book was illustrated. However it is uncertain whether the illustrations were drawn for the publication or were taken from prints already in existence. What we can say is that at least by 1791 woodblock prints of the story existed. Therefore a Jiaqing reign mark on a bottle painted with a scene from the novel is perfectly possibly rather than just conjecture. Another troubling question arises regarding the blue enamel of the trefoils or *ruyi* lappets with dots painted at the neck, which as discussed in the entry to No. 233 in this publication, is unreservedly dated to the Daoguang period at the earliest by Ault, and more likely the Xianfeng era or later. Arguing in favour of an earlier dating of the bottle, however, is that there seems no reason whatsoever to add an erroneous Jiaqing mark to a bottle possibly made in the Daoguang or Xianfeng era. A mark of the illustrious Qianlong emperor might be an option but a mark of the previous ruler seems inconceivable.

We are left with the possibility that it is a perfectly genuine Jiaqing bottle, presumably late in the reign but simply of poor quality, or that indeed it is of later manufacture and bears an apochryphal mark.

(CBL C 260)

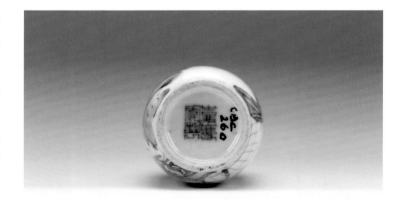

235 (mark)

235

235 (detail)

236

Porcelain, with moulded design of a central chrysanthemum flower head within an S-scroll surround bordered by vertical key-pattern bands to the narrow facetted sides, leaf lappets above the foot and small leaf-lappet bands divided by *ruyi* cloud lappets at the narrow edge and in a band on the stepped shoulder, the waisted neck plain, all under a quite thick turquoise glaze which extends over the oval foot flat

Jingdezhen, 1790-1840

Height: 6.0 cm
Mouth: 0.8 cm
Neck: 1.6 cm

The body of this bottle would have been high-fired initially and then the turquoise glaze would have been applied before a second lower temperature firing in the coolest part of the kiln, at the back beneath the chimney flue, see Kerr, *Chinese Ceramics: Porcelains of the Qing Dynasty, 1644-1911*, pp. 87-88. This glaze was first used at Jingdezhen in the fifteenth century but due to its relative instability was infrequently employed. Improvements in the glaze (a mixture of copper fluxed with potash) in the Qing dynasty reestablished its popularity.

This appears to be quite a rare design. There is one other identical bottle in the collection, which is white glazed, that utilizes the porcelain paste, *huashi*, slippery stone, formerly erroneously called 'soft paste' (CBL C 307). It is not illustrated in this publication. It is a very attractive shape and it seems odd that so few were made.

The chrysanthemum, *juhua*, is a symbol of autumn and has the resilience to grow in the face of harsh frosts and inclement weather. It thus became a symbol of longevity and many legends tell of its life-enhancing properties. It is also the flower of the ninth month. Here it is combined with the *ruyi* (at the shoulder) another long-life symbol to enhance the reference.

This obviously relates to the following two molded bottles and forms part of a much larger group of usually quite small molded monochrome and polychrome bottles that were produced at the end of the Qianlong reign and into the Jiaqing era but which are often unmarked.

Whilst clearly not equivalents to our bottle, it is still interesting to compare it with two other monochrome bottles from that larger group that may well have come from the same kiln and which use chrysanthemum heads as their main decoration, albeit both in a repeating pattern within hexagonal cells, see Kleiner, *Treasures from the Sanctum of Enlightened Respect*, p. 178, no. 154, and Moss, Graham, and Tsang, *A Treasury of Chinese Snuff Bottles: The Mary and George Bloch Collection*, Vol. 6, Part 2, Arts of the Fire, pp. 464-466, no. 1208, that has a Jiaqing mark and, whilst a much finer bottle, does show the range of output for the potters at Jingdezhen.

(CBL C 280)

237

Porcelain, moulded with a design with the *ba jixiang* (eight Buddhist emblems) in two horizontal rows with trailing ribbons but each treasure spaced diagonally from the one on the other row, a third row of conjoined lotus heads above the tapering foot with simple small raised dots, all in unusually high relief on a low-relief key-pattern ground set, with high rounded shoulders with *ruyi*-cloud lappets and a key-pattern band below the short everted rim with a band of small dots, all under a turquoise-green glaze, the mouth and the circular foot ring gilt, the slightly concave base turquoise-glazed and with a six-character manganese seal mark

Qianlong manganese six-character rectangular seal mark to the base, probably Imperial, Jingdezhen, probably 1796-1820

Stopper: turquoise and gilt porcelain stopper (possibly a replacement)

Height: 6.3 cm
Mouth: 0.6 cm
Neck: 1.9 cm

This bottle again forms part of the larger group of moulded bottles mentioned in the previous entry in this publication. They are wide and varied and include moulded decoration of the 'Eight Buddist Emblems' (*ba ji xiang*), dragons, eighteen *louhan*, and nine Buddhist lions, set against lower-relief grounds of waves, diaper cell, and clouds mostly reticulated. The neck and foot borders also vary but are typically a combination of key pattern, *ruyi* lappets, and bands of simple dots.

See Bartholomew, *Hidden Meanings in Chinese Art*, p. 185, no. 7.18 for a full description of the 'Eight Buddhist Emblems' or 'Eight Auspicious Symbols' which comprise the Wheel of Law, *lun*; Conch, *luo*; Canopy (or sometimes a flag, the Standard of Victory), *san*; Parasol (or umbrella), *gai*; Lotus, *hehua*; Vase, *guan*; Twin Fish, *yu*; and the Endless Knot, *panchang*. See also the entry for No. 240 in this publication.

Many bottles of this group bear erroneous Qianlong marks and ours is no exception. That being said, this bottle is actually an extremely well moulded example that might well have been produced at the very beginning years of the Jiaqing reign. The waisted baluster shape is rare and the extremely deep moulding is also unusual for an unreticulated bottle and further suggests, in combination with the other factors listed, that this bottle was a little more special than the standard production. The use of a manganese enamel to write the mark was an unusual one when gilt marks are the norm and our example with the 'S' element of the *Qian* character reversed so it reads like a European 'Z' might also suggest a production date between 1795 and 1799, see the entry for no. 225 in this publication for further discussion. For an iron-red decorated bottle from the Bragge collection with the same 'reversed S-element' Qianlong mark, possibly even using a manganese enamel, see a watercolour illustration from a rare leather bound hand-painted volume published in 1874 to accompany the catalogue, *Bibliotheca Nicotiana. A Catalogue of Books about Tobacco Together with a Catalogue of Objects Connected with the Use of Tobacco in All its Forms*, sold at Christie's, New York, The J & J Collection, Part IV, 22 March 2007, lot 20, p. 48, where other moulded bottles from the larger group are also illustrated.

For a turquoise-glazed bottle of similar design though less deeply moulded and of more rounded shape, see Kleiner, *Chinese Snuff Bottles from the Collection of John Ault*, no. 130.

(CBL C 281)

237 (mark)

236

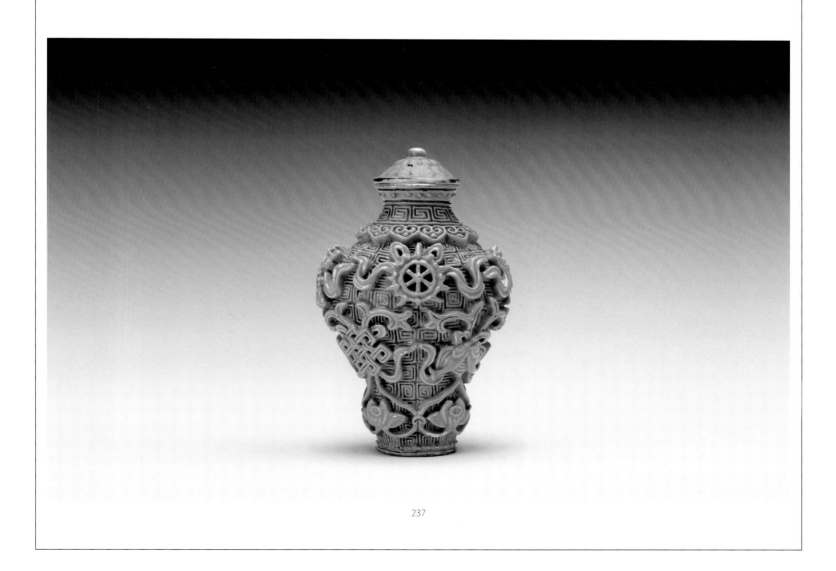

237

238

Porcelain, moulded in relief with the *ba jixiang* (eight Buddhist emblems) in vertical pairs divided by stylized lotus flower heads with trailing scrolls all in high relief on a key-pattern ground divided by *ruyi* lappets at the foot and shoulder and further key-pattern at the waisted neck below a band of small dots at the slightly everted rim, all under a coral glaze with gilding on the upper layer of relief, the mouth also gilt, the oval foot ring unglazed, the flat base coral-glazed and with a gilt four-character seal mark

Qianlong gilt four-character square seal mark to the base and probably late in the period, Imperial kilns, Jingdezhen, 1796-1820

Stopper: porcelain, metal collar

Height: 6.0 cm (without stopper)
Mouth: 0.6 cm
Neck: 1.9 cm

The differing layout of the 'eight Buddhist emblems' within the whole group of moulded bottles shows that the artist-craftsman was at liberty to arrange his 'emblems' in whatever order suited the shape of the bottle, in either paired vertical or alternate format. The choice of hibiscus or lotus to frame these were also optional, as was the choice of ground decoration, more usually key pattern but also clouds, cells in a diamond formation, and even waves. This bottle is one of the best examples of this moulded group. Unfortunately time has not been a good friend and the foot has many chips. If not for the 'reversed S-element' in the Qianlong mark in this bottle (see the entry for the previous bottle in this publication), it would be tempting to suggest that this was indeed a rare example of this group produced prior to 1796 when the Qianlong emperor was still on the throne, so fine is the modeling and enamelling.

This bottle, perhaps even more so than the previous bottle, also compares well to the Bragge bottle mentioned in the previous entry in this publication, though ours has a gilt mark rather than a probable manganese version. It is also identical though less rubbed than a bottle illustrated by Kleiner, *Chinese Snuff Bottles: The White Wings Collection*, pp. 129-130, no. 87. It may even be from the same mould, which the author mistakenly points out were wooden. Whilst we know that wooden moulds were used in the production of moulded gourd bottles, there was a very good reason for this; they were lightweight and had to be supported by the mother plant. In ceramic bottle production it seems far more likely that the moulds would have been made from the handiest material available, porcelain paste of some kind, which the craftsmen also knew how to manipulate to their needs. This would also follow the tried and tested formula used throughout porcelain production in Europe at the equivalent time. For instance in the production of scent bottles, plaster of Paris moulds were used extensively, though master models in lead and wax exist of Chelsea scent bottles, from which the mould maker would make the plaster moulds. In England, as opposed to the Continent, small hollow objects were usually made using the slip technique, in which liquid slip was poured into the moulds rendering the porcelain quite thin and was a major reason for the success of English manufacturers over their Continental competitors. We also know from surviving moulds at various early ceramic kiln sites, for instance the classic twelfth- and thirteenth-century 'Ding' white wares in Hebei province, that stoneware moulds made from a slightly greyish compact stoneware clay were considered the best moulds, see Medley, *The Chinese Potter*, pp.110-111, fig. 73.

According to Kerr, *Chinese Ceramics: Porcelain of the Qing Dynasty, 1644-1911*, pp. 91-94, iron-red or coral-red first made its appearance in Jindezhen in the fourteenth century. It is matte in tone and thinner than other overglaze enamels because rather than being fully dissolved in the glaze it is only suspended as a colourant. As a result, the surface of this enamel is often rubbed, as is clearly visible in our example. In its earlier manifestations, the iron-red was a dull tomato red colour but by the Qing period the high alkaline glaze had less lead added and a soft and luminous tone was achieved.

The use of a cell ground and higher relief decoration imposed over it suggests that the makers of our bottle modeled their techniques on cinnabar lacquer equivalents or other vessels and objects. Whilst no other lacquer bottle of this exact design appears to be recorded we can say with some certainty that some of the moulded bottle group appear to have been made in direct imitation of other media, like turquoise, lapis lazuli, and possibly even jade.

The stopper is a later addition.

(CBL C 293)

239

Porcelain, moulded in low relief on each main face with a circular panel, one depicting two Daoist immortals, Fuxing and Luxing, standing amidst clouds on a wave ground, one holding a *ruyi* sceptre, the other holding a scroll (repaired), the other panel with Shoulao holding a peach with a bat and a crane nearby amidst clouds on a wave ground, the narrow sides of the bottle moulded in extremely high and dense relief with the various Daoist attributes and numerous bats and clouds, all under a coral glaze, the mouth gilt, the oval foot ring unglazed, the concave oval base coral-glazed and with a partially gilt four-character seal mark

Jiaqing partially gilt four-character square seal mark to the base and of the period, Imperial kilns, Jingdezhen, 1796-1820

Height: 6.0 cm
Mouth: 0.6 cm
Neck: 1.9 cm

The subject of the 'Three Star Gods' was a popular one. The three represent the God of Good Fortune, Fuxing, holding a scroll; the God of Wealth, Luxing, holding a *ruyi* sceptre, symbolizing wish fulfillment; and the God of Longevity, Shou, more popularly called Shoulao, holding the peach of immortality and watching a flying bat and a crane, other long-life symbols, nearby. The high-relief Daoist emblems, *ba xian*, which surround the circular panels, further reinforce the longevity symbolism. The clouds on both sides of the bottle, *yun*, can also represent good fortune, *yun*. Therefore, in all likelihood, this bottle was presented as a birthday gift.

All of the eight Doaist immortal attributes including the gourd and iron crutch of Li Tieguai, the fish drum (bamboo tube and two metal beaters) of Zhang Guolao, the basket of flowers or peaches of Lan Caihe, the sword and fly whisk of Lu Dongbin, the lotus or bamboo sieve of He Xiangu, the fan of Han Zhongli, the flute of Han Xiangzi, and the pair of beaters for keeping time of Cao Guojiu, are present on the narrow sides and neck of this bottle and it is indeed an impressive example of high-relief moulding, with each detail finely picked out on a ground of clouds that resembles or mimics the reticulated bottles that were also popular at this time.

Of at least ten bottles published with the design of the 'Three Star Gods', the Chester Beatty example here illustrated, one published by Stevens, *The Collector's Book of Snuff Bottles*, p. 96, no. 284, from the Dane Collection, one illustrated by Moss, *The Barron Collection: Illustrated Handlist*, ICSBS Convention, Boston, 2008, p. 47, no. 4031 from the Carl F. Barron collection and another illustrated by Hui, Kwong and Sin, eds., *A Congregation of Snuff Bottle Connoisseurs*, pp. 102-103, No. 118 use a circular format for the central panels and for the shape of the bottle. All the others are slightly taller and of a more compressed ovoid shape with a stylized bat border surrounding the central scenes and a wide range of enamels ranging from beige, iron-red, turquoise, and at least three with iron-red borders and multiple enamel central scenes. All would appear to be made at around the same time period early in the Jiaqing reign. For examples of the compressed ovoid form, see Moss, Graham, and Tsang, *A Treasury of Chinese Snuff Bottles: The Mary and George Bloch Collection*, Vol. 6, Part 2, Arts of the Fire, pp. 483-485, no. 1215, where the seven other published examples are listed. Moss also mentions an unusual feature applicable to the Bloch bottle, that of a separately luted foot. He suggests that some moulds did not include the neck and foot treatments. Our foot, and indeed our neck, may also be separately made and then luted. Clearly from the illustration of the remnants of a gilt mark on this example, the mark would appear to have been first painted in a wax resist. The base was then glazed and fired. Once removed from the kiln, the gilt mark would be added over the silhouette left by the wax resist. It seems quite a laborious, time consuming method but perhaps it was felt that the gilding painted directly on to iron-red was more easily rubbed, though in our example they were clearly wrong.

(CBL C 303)

238 (mark)   239 (mark)

238

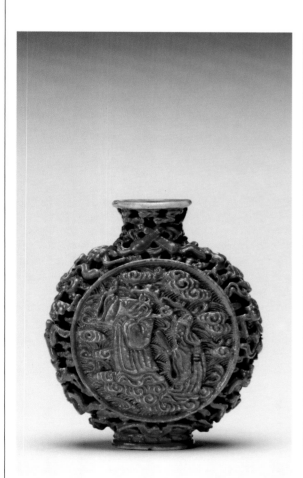

239 (three views)

240

Porcelain, of unusual fruit form, the exterior of the bottle moulded and fully reticulated with a dense abstract scrolling ground with the *ba jixiang* (eight Buddhist emblems), arranged equally-spaced around the body and pierced to reveal an unglazed interior body of the bottle beneath, the foot pierced in the form of a cash symbol, all under a thick white glaze with a faint blue tinge, the original stopper of twig form

Jingdezhen, 1790-1850

Stopper: porcelain, twig form

Height: 7.3 cm (with stopper); 6.2 cm (without stopper)
Mouth: 0.6 cm
Neck: no neck

Here we have an extremely unusual and rare bottle that clearly takes the moulded (and reticulated) group of bottles identified in the previous two entries as its starting point but adds another level of difficulty and ingenuity. Here the bottle is again clearly moulded as evidenced on the emblems themselves, where the glaze pools on the very low but overall even relief. Once the halves were joined together around a central interior bottle and when the paste was still in a semi-soft leathery state, the reticulation would have been cut. Here the degree of difficulty is patently obvious, as in some places the spacing is often wider than the scrolling tendrils that hold the entire bottle together. The shape too is a difficult one to manipulate and is probably part of the reason that quite a few cracks both at the foot and around the body are clearly visible. The shape appears to be fruit form, most likely an aubergine (or eggplant), although the carving of scrolling tendrils that cover the entire body suggest that the bottle is meant to represent a gourd, usually shown with scrolling vine tendrils. Both the aubergine and the gourd are auspicious and are recognized as fertility symbols because they both have numerous seeds and are fast growing.

For a full description of the subject of this bottle, the 'Eight Buddhist Emblems' or 'Eight Auspicious Symbols', see Bartholomew, *Hidden Meanings in Chinese Art*, p. 185, no. 7.18. They comprise the Wheel of Law, *lun*, symbolizing the turning wheel of Buddhist doctrine; the Conch, *luo*, symbolizing the far-reaching sound of the Buddha's teachings; the Canopy (or sometimes a flag, the Standard of Victory), *san*, symbolizing the victory of Buddha's teaching over all hindrances; the Parasol (or umbrella), *gai*, symbolizing protection and spiritual power; the Lotus, *hehua*, symbolizing purity; the Vase, *guan*, symbolizing the elixir of life; the Twin Fish, *yu*, symbolizing freedom from restraint; and the Endless Knot, *panchang*, symbolizing the infinite wisdom and compassion of Buddha. All these symbols are believed to bring peace and blessings. They entered the Chinese lexicon via Tibetan Buddhism probably in the thirteenth or fourteenth centuries. By the Qing dynasty they were so popular that they became integrated and interchangeable with the eight Daoist symbols (see the previous entry in this publication) sharing the same collective meaning of longevity. The scrolling tendrils that form the entire backdrop of the design and which are unending can also be seen as representing longevity and if the bottle represents a gourd rather than an eggplant, then the scrolling tendrils, *mandai*, are a pun for 'ten thousand generations', *wandai*. The cash or coin design cut to the foot of this bottle is a popular wealth-bringing motif.

The stopper must be original. Not only is this quite rare it also helps us to identify the model as that of a fruit, either an eggplant or a gourd. The fragile nature of the reticulation is clearly a reason for the damage to be seen at various places on this bottle, but still it is quite remarkable that it has survived even to this extent and is presumably also the reason that so few have survived.

For a reticulated white-glazed bottle moulded and carved with the same subject but of the more regular compressed shape applicable to the group, see Stevens, *The Collector's Book of Snuff Bottles*, p. 93, no. 264.

(CBL C 306)

241

Porcelain, each main side with a moulded and reticulated circular panel with a coiling dragon amidst clouds, the dragon rising on one side and descending on the other, both painted in iron red with a simple green enamel surround edged in black, all set on a sky-blue enamel ground painted with loose prunus flower heads with pink-spotted white petals and green centers all edged in black, the pierced work revealing the body of the bottle beneath, the panels divided at the shoulders at the narrow sides by small moulded lion-mask handles painted in iron-red with green ring handles edged in black, with cylindrical neck, glazed at the lip but unglazed to the interior, the oval foot ring unglazed and the base glazed

Jingdezhen, 1850-1900

Stopper: coral glass, bone finial, gilt metal collar

Height: 5.0 cm
Mouth: 0.6 cm
Neck: 1.2 cm

Again we have a most unusual shape. This does not appear to conform to any well documented group. There are, in fact, two in the Beatty Collection. They are both from different moulds however. The other example, which we are not publishing, whilst having almost identically reticulated oval dragon panels, is very slightly bigger than this example both in the height of the neck, (0.5 cm taller) and the width across the handles (0.2 cm wider). It is also very differently painted. Whilst the reticulated panel is iron-red enameled, the border is blue rather than green and the remainder of the bottle is clear glazed and undecorated with the exception of slightly larger mask handles painted in pale blue with darker blue spotting and with iron-red and gilt rings that are, like our bottle, unusually painted rather than moulded as one might expect. Even though the mallet is compressed slightly in both examples, unless the bottle was kept as a scholar's table bottle it would have been quite a difficult shape to carry around easily and may be one reason so few seem to have been made.

Overall, the quality is rather poor, both in paste and general enameling and finish. Surprisingly however, the dragon panels are startlingly well designed and finished. The use of a thick uneven sky-blue glaze and rather lumpy prunus flower heads combined with the unusual and slightly ungainly mallet form suggest a date of production probably between 1850 and 1900. Whilst Jingdezhen porcelain bottles, using a slightly darker blue glaze as the ground colour, are published bearing Daoguang reign marks, it seems highly unlikely, despite the very well modelled dragon panels, that our bottle could be this early. See Nicollier, *The Baur Collection: Chinese Snuff Bottles*, pp. 188-189, no. H73, for a Daoguang-marked bottle of compressed spherical shape with five-clawed dragon on a blue ground of rather uneven thickness; and Moss, Graham. and Tsang, *A Treasury of Chinese Snuff Bottles: The Mary and George Bloch Collection*, Vol. 6, Part 2, Arts of the Fire, pp. 683-684, no. 1315, for another Daoguang-marked bottle of compressed spherical shape with a circular panel on each side painted with a crane set against a blue ground which the authors call 'thick rather glutinous enamels' and painted with a cloud design, rather than the prunus flower heads of ours. A similar thick glaze was also employed at the Yixing kiln sites in Jiangsu province on the reddish-brown stoneware snuff bottles as well as a wide range of other vessels, most famously teapots. Interestingly, blossoming prunus branches occur frequently on enameled Yixing snuff bottles and perhaps there was some influence from Yixing on late production at Jingdezhen. For two examples see Moss et al, ibid, Part 3, pp. 963-964, no. 1459 and p. 954, no. 1454, for an example painted with a flowering prunus (plum) branch.

The black enamel, which is used to outline all the enamel colours on our bottle, may well serve as more than mere decoration. The outline itself, may actually act as a *cloison* does in cloisonné enamel manufacture, helping the unctuous glaze from running at these points of contact.

(CBL C 321)

240

241

Porcelain, moulded in a continuous scene with a scholar gentleman and an elegant lady standing in the doorway of a lakeside pavilion set on stilts, and surrounded by craggy rocks below clouds, surveying a scene of a gentleman and a lady in one boat and a single lady in another boat gathering freshly opened lotus dispersed around the lake on the reverse side, set between a band of moulded and iron-red painted *ruyi* lappets above the foot and a simple undecorated short everted rim, unglazed oval foot ring, white-glazed base with iron-red four-character seal mark

Jiaqing iron-red four-character square seal mark to the base and of the period, Imperial kilns, Jingdezhen, 1796-1820

Stopper: rose quartz

Height: 6.5 cm
Mouth: 0.7 cm
Neck: 1.7 cm

Lotus gathering had a long history and is described in many Chinese poems and paintings. Buds and blooms would be gathered in the cool calm dawn when the lotus was at its freshest and used for decoration in the house.

'Lotus-Gathering Boat' by the famous Tang dynasty female poet Xue Tao (and translated by Jeanne Larsen) is included in Mair, *The Shorter Columbia Anthology of Traditional Chinese Literature* (website), p. 106:

Lotus-laden
pushing through,
a single windblown leaf

tells the news: it's fall again,
time to fish
and sport

The moon-hare runs, the sun-crow flies,
Human chatter stills.

Pink tinted sleeves fill up the brook
And poling songs
Begin

Victor Mair in his footnotes to the poem beautifully describes how the scene that mingles the human world with the green realm of plants is evoked. The pink sleeves of the ladies' clothing also mirrors the rosy petals of the lotus and the 'single windblown leaf' describes the lotus gatherers' skiff. He also notes how the amatory nature of many poems associated with lotus invites us to read the verse with the old association of fishing and sexuality in mind. The reference to the mythic moon-hare and the sun-crow symbolise time's passing.

According to the website 'Other Women's Voices: Translations of women's writing before 1700' (http://home.infionline.net/~ddisse/):

> Xue Tao was the daughter of a minor government official in Xian, the capital of Tang dynasty China. In part because of her skill at poetry and calligraphy, she became the favorite concubine of Wei Gao, the military governor of the province. She befriended the major poets Bo Juyi and Yuan Zhen. Some 450 poems by Xue Tao were gathered in "The Brocade River Collection" that survived until the 1300s; today about 100 poems are extant.

It seems that our bottle captures perfectly the spirit of this poem and how tempting it is to believe that our scene may represent Xue Tao and Wei Gao standing on the terrace of a pavilion as she composes the poem.

This bottle belongs to a large group of moulded porcelain bottles that depict figural scenes, some historical, some mythical, that include the 'eight barbarians bearing tribute', *Baman Jinbao*, (see No. 233 in this publication); Su Dongpo's visit to the Red Cliffs; battle scenes from the epic *Romance of the Three Kingdoms*; and the *White Snake Story*. The group is usually quite finely

detailed and moulded, and shares the same general characteristics of compressed shape and bright colour. The majority bear Jiaqing marks, however a smaller group bear Qianlong marks and some no marks at all. This would suggest that the entire group was probably produced after Qianlong's abdication in 1795 but before his death in 1799.

On our bottle, as in the others, the patterning of the grounds is subtly achieved; a diamond-shaped key-pattern cell ground has been used for the floor surface within the pavilion, whilst a concentric semi-circular fan design has been used to denote water. Unusually the pictorial design does not stop at the shoulder where one might normally expect a band of stylized decoration to end but continues right up to the everted rim. Extremely finely detailed parts to the scene including the delicate use of iron-red spots on the lotus leaves to designate the leaf decay associated with lotus pads and the deftly depicted large tasseled cash symbol hanging on either side of the doorway are carefully delineated. Details like these are more often than not omitted from the scene, indicating that our bottle may be a cut above the norm.

Four very similar moulded bottles, differing slightly in enamel colours and some details are illustrated by Hughes, *The Blair Bequest: Chinese Snuff Bottles from the Princeton University Art Museum*, p.192, no. 249; Moss, *The Barron Collection: Illustrated Handlist*, ICSBS Convention, Boston, 2008, p. 49, no. 3077; Kleiner, *Chinese Snuff Bottles from the Collection of John Ault*, p. 76, no. 128; and Moss, *Chinese Snuff Bottles: 6. Chinese Snuff Bottles from the Collection of the Rt. Hon. The Marquess of Exeter, K.C.M.G.*, p. 47, no. c.60.

(CBL C 340)

242 (mark)

242 (two views)

243

Porcelain, moulded in a continuous scene with the scholar Mi Fu writing an inscription on a rock face whilst his young assistant patiently holds his ink stick, surrounded by rockwork, trees, and other vegetation, the reverse side appears to depicts Su Dongpo's famous visit to the Red Cliffs, three figures under the canopy of a boat enjoy conversation as their vessel passes high cliffs, a young maiden assists to the stern of the vessel and a boy appears to be nodding off whilst seated on a stool in the boat's prow, all is set between a simple turquoise band at the foot and rim, the mouth with a pale coffee glaze and traces of gilt, the interior unglazed as is the oval foot ring, a glazed-white base with iron-red four-character seal mark with traces of gilt

Jiaqing iron-red (with traces of gilt) four-character square seal mark to the base and of the period, Imperial kilns, Jingdezhen,1796-1820

Stopper: green glass with yellow glass disc collar

Height: 6.9 cm
Mouth: 0.8 cm
Neck: 1.7 cm

Like the previous bottle, also from the same generic group, the patterning of the differing grounds of water and land is achieved by the identical use of a moulded cell ground with the addition of foaming waves on our example to suggest a fast running river rather than a placid pond. Similarly the pictorial design does not stop at the shoulder but continues right to the base of the everted rim. Unlike the previous example there is no band of iron-red *ruyi* lappets to border the lower edge of the depiction. The shape of this bottle has been widened and lengthened purposefully to allow for a more complete canvas so to speak.

Like the previous bottle, the dating criteria remain the same, and a date between 1796 and 1820 seems most likely.

Our bottle appears to depict, on one side, the Song dynasty poet Su Dongpo (1036—1101) who was also known as Su Shi and who wrote his famous 'Prose Poem of the Red Cliffs', *Chibi Fu*, after two extensive trips with friends to the now famous cliffs in Hubei province in 1082. The other side of the bottle appears to depict the Northern Song dynasty poet Mi Fu (1050-1107) who was a famous calligrapher and painter noted for his love of strangely shaped stones and rock. He was born in Taiyuan in Shanxi province. The contemporaries Mi Fu and Su Dongpo were considered two of the four great 'Song Masters' and it seems appropriate that they should be depicted on the same bottle. However, Moss, Graham, and Tsang, *A Treasury of Chinese Snuff Bottles, The Mary and George Bloch Collection*, Vol. 6, Part 2, Arts of the Fire, pp. 474-476, no. 1212, suggest that it may be no more than an illustration of a standard literary pursuit (in a discussion of an identical bottle), in a country were scholars were prone to leaving graffiti on natural rock formations for posterity.

The figural scenes are each set against a simple open white-glazed moulded cell ground which cleverly silhouettes the figures and seems to throw them in to higher relief. The remainder of the decoration, particularly the surrounding rocks, is darkly enameled further focusing the eye on the two main scenes. Su Dongpo and his guests drink from wine cups as they dreamily drift along and the calmness of the scene is enhanced by the sleeping figure of a boy seated on a stool at the prow of their boat. The front edge of the canopy of their boat has an intriguing motif, which might be no more than an attempt to depict folds in the cloth but which is deceptively and tantalizingly similar to Chinese characters.

The other scene shows an elderly scholar in the act of inscribing a rock face with calligraphy whilst his boy assistant steadily holds his ink stone. The rock face however is very peculiar. It appears almost like a shaft of light from the heavens rather than as a natural formation and makes no real sense in the context of the otherwise moss covered rocks, unless it is meant to represent an area of rock that has been cleaned in preparation for calligraphy.

For other bottles depicting the same subject, see 'The Joseph Grimberg Collection of Snuff Bottles', *Arts of Asia*, November-December, 1993, p. 94, no. 35;

Moss, *Chinese Snuff Bottles: 6. Chinese Snuff Bottles from the Collection of the Rt. Hon. The Marquess of Exeter, K.C.M.G.*, p. 47, no. C. 60; Low, *Chinese Snuff Bottles from the Sanctum of Enlightened Respect III*, p. 241, no. 208 and a rare baluster shaped bottle of smaller size is illustrated by Hughes, *The Blair Bequest: Chinese Snuff Bottles from the Princeton University Art Museum*, p.193, no. 250.

(CBL C 341)

243 (mark)

243 (two views)

244

Porcelain, moulded in a continuous scene with *Baman Jinbao*, 'eight tribute bearers', three traveling by boat on one main face set against a white-glazed molded wave ground, a yellow banner flying from their mast is inscribed '*Jinbao*', the other side of the bottle depicts the remaining five, traveling by land, two walking and the others variously riding an elephant, a mule, and a Buddhist lion, some are holding tributes and others presumably have them stored away, set against moulded white-glazed cell grounds depicting land and water below colourful clouds, the foot edge and neck rim with a simple turquoise band edged in iron-red, the mouth with a pale coffee glaze and traces of gilt, the interior unglazed, restored turquoise-glazed oval foot ring, glazed-white base with iron-red four-character seal mark

Jiaqing iron-red four-character square seal mark (partially de-faced) to the base and of the period, Imperial kilns, Jingdezhen, 1796-1820

Height: 6.0 cm
Mouth: 0.6 cm
Neck: 1.7 cm

Like the previous two bottles in this publication, this example forms part of the same generic group.

The characters written on the banner flying from the boat's mast are most informative. It reads *Jinbao*, which can be read literally as 'bringing in treasure', and more specifically 'bearing tribute'. This useful inscription clearly establishes the exact depiction on the bottle as being the 'eight barbarians bearing tribute', *Baman Jinbao*. For the neighbouring states of China to enjoy protection from the Qing Empire and remain at peace, tributes had to be given on regular occasions to the Emperor. These tributary nations, far from appearing aggrieved at this subservient act, outdid each other in their desire to impress the Emperor with their own sophistication and their gifts often displayed their own nations' cosmopolitan, cultivated, and worldly views. The snuff bottles that commemorate such embassies do so in a spirit of memorializing the symbolic act of paying tribute rather than portraying an actual event. As a result the scene is often a curious mixture of a menagerie of real and mythical animals, Daoist emblems and balding foreigners in Western dress, see also the entry No. 233 in this publication for a *doucai* bottle painted with a different version of the same subject.

For other very similar examples differing only in enamel colours, see Christie's South Kensington, 4 October 1999, Chinese Snuff Bottles from the Gerry P. Mack Collection, lot 5; Moss, *Snuff Bottles of China*, pp. 126-127, no. 293; Hughes, *The Blair Bequest: Chinese Snuff Bottles from the Princeton University Art Museum*, p.194, no. 251 and Moss, *The Barron Collection: Illustrated Handlist*, ICSBS Convention, Boston, 2008, p. 47, no. 3328 from the Carl F. Barron collection. Another illustrating a different version of the same subject is published by Moss, Graham, and Tsang, *A Treasury of Chinese Snuff Bottles: The Mary and George Bloch Collection*, Vol. 6, Part 2, pp. 477-479, no. 1213, which oddly depicts only six of the eight tribute bearers.

(CBL C 344)

245

Porcelain, moulded in high relief in a continuous scene and painted in bright enamels with nine Buddhist lions playing with colourful ribboned balls, three painted in iron-red, two in blue, two in purple, one in pink and another in yellow glaze, some with the addition of green-glazed manes, each extremely well-detailed on a reticulated white-glazed cloud ground revealing the turquoise-glazed inner body beneath, all between a moulded coral-glazed band of *ruyi* at the foot and below a further band at the shoulder with key-pattern at the neck, the everted rim with moulded coral-glazed dots , the rounded mouth gilt, the interior unglazed, an oval glazed-white concave base forming the foot and painted with an iron-red seal mark

Jiaqing iron-red four-character square seal mark to the base and of the period, Imperial kilns, Jingdezhen, 1796-1820

Height: 6.7 cm
Mouth: 0.6 cm
Neck: 2.0 cm

This bottle also forms part of the well-documented larger group of moulded bottles mentioned in the previous entries in this publication (see Nos. 237-240 and 242-244). Whilst it follows in all respects the standard format of shape, background, and borders common to the group, it includes a few differences and one innovation. The method of glazing the entire surface of *ruyi*-lappets with thick iron-red enamel rather than simply highlighting the edges, both at the foot and neck, as well as in-filling the entire key-pattern band, is most unusual and helps to frame and silhouette the scene. Even more intriguing is the inner bottle, just visible through the reticulated clouds, which has been glazed in turquoise. Quite how this innovation was achieved is uncertain, though presumably as turquoise glaze is fired in a lower-temperature second firing, it could only have been added after the entire bottle was constructed and after the first high-temperature firing. Therefore it had to have been meticulously painted with a fine brush through the reticulation or a slip-glaze was somehow poured to the interior and tipped in the hand to cover the interior surface. Quite how this could be managed without spillage though is a mystery.

According to Bartholomew, *Hidden Meanings in Chinese Art*, p. 242, no. 8. 17.1, the subject of nine lions, *jiushi*, can form the rebus 'May all the members of the family live in harmony' or 'Nine generations under one roof', *jiushi tongtang*. The lion is also a military symbol and so nine lions together represent nine nobles with military power.

For a very similar bottle with the identical use of colours on each lion and ribbon and also the use of a solid iron-red to frame the scene and with only slight differences in the reticulation see Moss, Graham, and Tsang, *A Treasury of Chinese Snuff Bottles: The Mary and George Bloch Collection*, Vol. 6, Part 2, pp. 467-468, no. 1209, where the authors do not mention an interior bottle but say that the 'lowest plane' of the cloud design is painted green.

A vey similar bottle using the same type of mould in the Imperial Collections is illustrated in *Gugong Complete Snuff Bottles*, p. 218, no. 330, whilst the enamelling is worn, the mark is much neater and by a more confident hand than ours. Another from the Carl F. Barron collection is illustrated by Moss, *The Barron Collection: Illustrated Handlist*, ICSBS Convention, Boston, 2008, p. 47, no. 4043. For an example of the same design under a white glaze also with a Jiaqing mark, see Hughes, *The Blair Bequest: Chinese Snuff Bottles from the Princeton University Art Museum*, p. 204, no. 270.

Like the mark on the following bottle in this publication, the shape of the concave base gives the standard-sized mark here, a smaller appearance.

(CBL C 329)

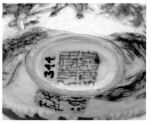

244 (mark)

245 (mark)

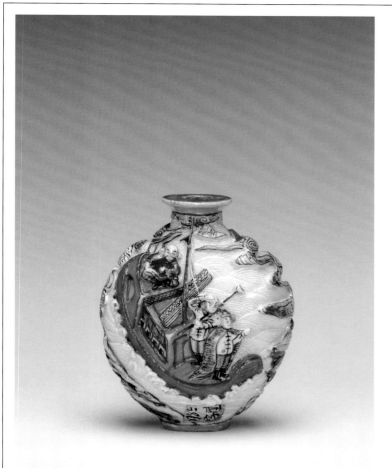
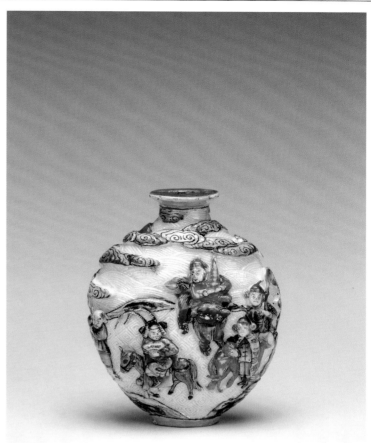

244 (two views)

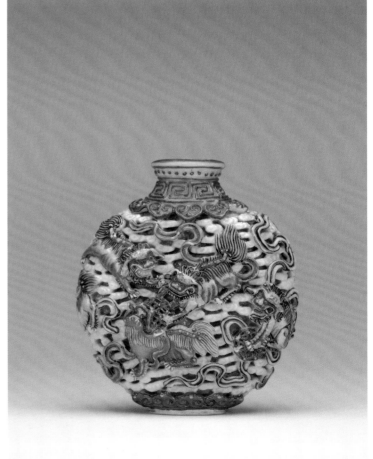

245 (two views)

246

Porcelain, moulded in a continuous design and painted in bright enamels with delicate use of iron-red with the *ba jixiang* (eight Buddhist emblems) evenly spaced around the body with flowing colourful ribbons, set against a reticulated white-glazed cloud ground revealing the inner body beneath, all between a molded coral-glazed band of *ruyi* and dots at the waisted foot and below a further band at the shoulder with key-pattern at the neck, the everted rim with moulded dots and a turquoise glaze, the mouth with traces of a coffee glaze and gilt, the interior unglazed, an oval glazed-white concave base forming the foot and painted with an iron-red seal mark

Jiaqing iron-red four-character square seal mark to the base and of the period, Imperial kilns, Jingdezhen, 1796-1820

Stopper: porcelain, hat form, possibly original

Height: 6.4 cm
Mouth: 0.6 cm
Neck: 1.9 cm

This bottle forms part of the well-documented larger group of moulded bottles mentioned in the previous entry in this publication (see Nos. 237-240 and 242-245).

For a full description of the The 'Eight Buddhist Emblems' or 'Eight Auspicious Symbols' which comprise the Wheel of Law, *lun*; Conch, *luo*; Canopy (or sometimes a flag, the Standard of Victory), *san*; Parasol (or umbrella), *gai*; Lotus, *hehua*; Vase, *guan*; Twin fish, *yu*; and the Endless knot, *panchang*, see Bartholomew, *Hidden Meanings in Chinese Art*, p. 185, no. 7.18. All these symbols are believed to bring peace and blessings. They entered the Chinese lexicon via Tibetan Buddhism probably in the thirteenth to fourteenth centuries. By the Qing dynasty they were so popular that they became integrated and interchangeable with the eight Daoist symbols sharing the same collective meaning of longevity. See also the entry for No. 240 in this publication for further discussion of the subject.

Our example is both finely moulded and deftly reticulated. It appears from the various published examples of this model, that the cloud ground has incised or moulded scrolling cloud edges under the white glaze and that these acted as guidelines for later reticulation. The patient handiwork of the reticulator, if you will, is evident in the fact that none of the published bottles appear to have identical reticulation. This makes each bottle within the group unique. The enamelling on our bottle is also of the finest of its type, with subtle gradation of tone both in the use of iron-red and the mixing of enamel colours. There is also an individual quality to the lightly painted iron-red *ruyi* lappets, which are handled differently at the foot and neck, and also to the key pattern.

See Moss, Graham, and Tsang, *A Treasury of Chinese Snuff Bottles: The Mary and George Bloch Collection*, Vol. 6, Part 2, pp. 436-437, no. 1194 for an identical creamy-white glazed example from a very similar mould. The entry includes a watercolour illustration of a similar enameled bottle from the famous Bragge Collection which was first published in 1874 in a rare leather bound hand-painted volume to accompany the catalogue, *Bibliotheca Nicotiana. A Catalogue of Books about Tobacco together with a Catalogue of Objects Connected with the use of Tobacco in All its Forms*. The volume was recently sold at Christie's, New York, The J & J Collection, Part IV, 22 March 2007, lot 20, p. 48, where other moulded bottles from the larger group are also illustrated. Another from the Emily Burne Curtis Collection is illustrated in the catalogue of the exhibition, *Chinese Snuff Bottles*, The Newark Museum, October 2-November 14, 1982, no. 19.

(CBL C 323)

246 (mark)

247

Porcelain, moulded in low relief in a continuous scene and painted in bright but worn enamels with a rare porcelain subject of the 'Cowherd and the Weaver Girl or Spinning Maid', depicting four ladies on one side near a rock table set with a wrapped *qin*, looking back to a boy, Niulang, the cowherd riding a buffalo descending steps from a frothy watery scene set amidst clouds, the other side continues with elegant ladies including Zhinu, the weaver girl, on a raised pavilion forecourt with her sister or attendant nearby in a river garden setting, the foot with a turquoise band and the neck with a similar band between a thin iron-red band and coffee-glazed rim, an unglazed oval foot ring and deep glazed base painted with an iron-red seal mark

Jiaqing iron-red four-character square seal mark to the base and of the period, Imperial kilns, Jingdezhen, 1796-1820

Stopper: coral with glass collar

Height: 6.4 cm
Mouth: 0.8 cm
Neck: 1.7 cm

This bottle is the last in this publication that forms part of the well-documented larger group of moulded bottles mentioned in the previous entry in this publication but which is much rarer than all the other examples despite sharing many of their traits (see Nos. 242-244).

The subject is a particularly uncommon one in the moulded porcelain snuff bottle oeuvre, despite being a very popular story that is celebrated each year on the *Qixi* festival of the seventh day of the seventh lunar month. The story goes that a humble young cowherd named Niulang happened upon seven celestial sisters bathing in a lake and, encouraged by his naughty ox, steals their clothing. Zhinu, the weaver girl, attempts to retrieve them but because she has been seen undressed by the cowherd, must agree to his marriage proposal. The marriage is a happy one on earth but not so in heaven, where the gods' fury at Zhinu for marrying a mortal is to recall her to the immortal world and with a stroke of a silver hairpin they draw a line across the heavens, forming a river that flows through the Milky Way separating the lovers. Zhinu is given the task of weaving colourful clouds in the sky and the unhappy Niulang spends the remainder of his mortal existence pining for his wife, with the exception of one occasion each year when the gods allow the couple to meet but on opposite banks of the heavenly river. In their anguish the magpies come to the rescue forming an avian bridge that spans the divide. At the end of the day when the time comes to separate, the lovers weep bitterly and the tears that fall are said to be the cause of the heavy rains that fall in this season.

Though our bottle does not show magpies, this is clearly the story depicted. In our scene, Zhinu is seated, with one of her sisters standing nearby holding a loom whilst in the distance Niulang enters the picture riding on the back of his ox. This may represent the annual visit of Niulang to the immortals' world—he is after all shown exiting the frothy swirling waves of a river on the back of his ox surrounded by colourful clouds—or it might depict the lovers' first meeting.

For another very rare example of an identical bottle to ours also with a Jiaqing mark from the Carl F. Barron collection, see Moss, *The Barron Collection: Illustrated Handlist*, ICSBS Convention, Boston, 2008, p. 47, no. 2788. For another which depicts the same scene but with the identical figure groupings in slightly different positions on a bottle of broader and more compressed form, see Hall, *Chinese Snuff Bottles III*, pp. 112-113, no. 66.

(CBL C 346)

247 (mark)

246 (two views)

247 (two views)

248

Porcelain, of naturalistic curled begonia leaves, formed with a large stalk running up from the base to the mouth and dividing and extending around the bottle and forming further lightly coloured variegated leaves, flower heads and buds, the body of the bottle enameled in a pea-green with black-enameled veins whilst some leaves are enamelled in a paler lime green with some pink shading and with veins either white glazed or touched in iron-red or pink, even insect holes are cleverly incorporated in the leaves, a large katydid, *guoguo*, in the lower portion of the bottle is picked out in iron-red as are the buds and flower heads, the mouth edge and interior unglazed, the stalk terminal forming the foot

Jingdezhen, 1790-1860

Stopper: coral with gilt metal collar

Height: 7.6 cm
Mouth: 0.6 cm
Neck: 1.0 cm (1.2 cm at edge with moulded stalk)

A number of naturalistic curled-leaf moulded porcelain bottles are recorded; most represent lotus. This may be the only one recorded that represents curled begonia leaves. As it is from a mould, one can only assume others must have also been made. Quite why such a successful model should not be more prevalent is a mystery.

According to Bartholomew, *Hidden Meanings in Chinese Art*, p. 232, no. 8.3, the begonia, *qiuhaitang*, has been a popular subject for Chinese artisans since the Song dynasty because of its characteristic oval flower formed by its four petals which has lent itself perfectly for shaped dishes. She illustrates a jade vessel of oval shape with canted corners that imitates the shape of the flower and which is further decorated in high relief to the centre with begonia branches, leaves, and flowers. She recounts that legend has it that a woman's tears created the begonia after she was deserted by her beloved and wept uncontrollably in her garden, nurturing the ground around her, which in return sent forth a begonia to comfort her. Because the plant blooms in autumn and the pink blossoms bear a slight resemblance to those of the spring-blooming crab apple, *haitang*, it is called 'autumn crab apple', *qiuhiatang*. She also illustrates an enameled bowl of the late Qing dynasty, which is painted with the same subject as our bottle, a katydid among begonia blossoms. The katydid is an auspicious insect because its name, *guoguo* (or *guoer* in some dialects) is close in pronunciation to the word for 'official', *guan'er*. According to Moss, Graham, and Tsang, *A Treasury of Chinese Snuff Bottles: The Mary and George Bloch Collection*, Vol. 5, Part 2, Glass, p. 367, no. 840, who illustrate a glass bottle with begonias to the sides, the sound *tang* in the name of the begonia, *qiuhaitang*, was probably intended to evoke the idiomatic expression *yutang fugui*, '[May your] magnificent hall [be filled with] riches'.

Begonia is a genus in the flowering plant family Begoniaceae of which there are more than 1500 species that are terrestrial herbs or undershrubs that occur in subtropical and tropical moist climates. Begonia is the common name as well as the generic name for all members of the genus. The leaves are varied but many, like those in our bottle, are variegated in shades of green, red, and pink and have serrated edges.

For other curled leaf bottles see Moss, Graham, and Tsang, *A Treasury of Chinese Snuff Bottles: The Mary and George Bloch Collection*, Vol. 6, Part 2, Arts of the Fire, pp. 518-522, nos. 1232 and 1233. The first depicts curled lotus leaves with a beetle, *jiachong* (which might also be a katydid), which the authors suggest hints at multiple offspring because of its ability to proliferate. They also note that its generic term calls to mind the term, *kejra* (civil-service examinations). By a play on words therefore, the beetle and the wrapping leaf it crawls on, also imply a wish for success in the examinations and a promising official career.

A crack running the entire vertical length of the bottle follows exactly the original line of the two-piece mould.

A paper oval label stuck to the bottle reads NP1091 above three Japanese *kana* (characters).

(CBL C 362)

249

Porcelain, of twin-fish shape, unusually moulded to appear as two leaping carp rising from frothy waves when viewed from each main side of the bottle but visible as a single fish when viewed from the narrow edge, the eyes of each fish are cleverly rendered by the exigent use of a simple black enamel dot placed on a circular disc of biscuit porcelain whilst the remainder of the bottle is under a fine white glaze, the scales and fins of the fish are moulded in low relief whilst the frothy waves that separate them are clearly in higher relief, the dorsal fins appear to have been incised after moulding, the fish heads cleverly mould together at the shoulder to form a single un-interrupted everted neck, the mouth white-glazed, the interior unglazed and the deeply concave base white-glazed and forming a narrow foot edge

Jingdezhen, 1780-1850

Stopper: jadeite with gilt metal collar
Height: 7.5 cm
Mouth: 0.6 cm
Neck: 1.4 cm

Published: Chapman, 'The Chester Beatty Collection of Snuff Bottles', *Arts of Asia*, March-April, 1988, p. 61, fig 13.

For an almost identical model of this bottle in ivory, see Kleiner, *Chinese Snuff Bottles in the Collection of Mary and George Bloch*, pp. 482-483, no. 317. At the time of publication, however, the bottle, which bears a Qianlong reign mark, was still believed to be of Chinese Imperial origin. The dating of the entire group of 'so-called' eighteenth-century Imperial ivory bottles, usually of compressed spade or spherical shapes, and thought to have influenced the ceramic bottle producers of Jingdezhen, has been turned on its head by a recent lecture and subsequent article by Moss, 'The Imperial Master', in *JICSBS*, Spring 2007 (see the entry to Nos. 174-176 in this publication). Moss reassigns the entire ivory group to a post-1854 production date in Japan. He even illustrates the Bloch ivory double-fish bottle (fig. 1) Therefore, a bottle, perhaps even from the same mould as ours, was the inspiration behind the Bloch ivory bottle. The addition of a Qianlong mark to the ivory example may therefore be quite important. Many of the ivory copies are made with poorly written marks that mirror the sometimes poorly written iron-red marks on the Chinese porcelain bottles. Our double-fish bottle is unmarked but it is conceivable that the porcelain example that the Japanese were copying from may have been marked. Certainly the quality of the moulding and the whole concept of the bottle allows for a late Qianlong or early Jiaqing dating for our bottle, even though it is also possible that ours dates to as a late as the Daoguang era.

The moulding is extremely sensitive with exquisite fine details in every aspect of the decoration from the delicately frothing waves to the irregular scales and the clever use of the biscuit itself and small dots of black enamel for the eyes. Even the dorsal fins appear to have been finished off after the moulding by the judicious use of a blade to incise the markings along their length. Sadly this fish has a small chip on its shoulder and a large crack that follows the original join of the two-piece mould down one vertical edge and across the concave foot.

The fish is an extremely popular subject in Chinese art. This example almost certainly depicts two carp (*liyu*). The Chinese characters for 'carp' (*liyu*) and 'profit' share the same sound, as do the characters for fish (*yu*) and 'affluence' or 'abundance', and given as a gift, this hidden meaning would most certainly be understood. The carp is also the fish associated with motifs for passing the civil service examinations. The story goes, according to tradition, that a carp swimming upstream in the Yellow River, fighting against the opposing current must leap the rapids of Dragon's Gate; the first to succeed transforms itself into a dragon. This story is a metaphor for a poor scholar who, by passing the civil service exams, raises himself to the status of high official. The addition of waves to the model here and the fish in a leaping pose is probably a direct evocation of this story. The combination of two fish together also suggests marital bliss and would have made a most suitable wedding gift.

For another twin-fish bottle in porcelain that lacks the high relief moulding of our example but is otherwise quite similar see Moss, *Chinese Snuff Bottles*: 5, p. 59, fig. 44. It is green glazed.

(CBL C 374)

248

249

250

Porcelain, modeled as a standing caparisoned elephant with an archaic vessel on its back, the head turned to its left, a blanket with colourful tassels and painted in blue and grisaille edged in iron-red and gilt with a scene of waves breaking on rocks below clouds, supporting an iron-red and gilt *gu*-shaped archaic vessel with a turquoise-glazed funneled interior that forms the mouth of the bottle, the body of the elephant finely painted with hair and wrinkles in shades of pale brown with the straps of the blanket carefully tied under the elephants head and tail, the edges of the feet picked out with simple toes, the underside of each foot unglazed

Jingdezhen, 1780-1830

Height: 4.0 cm
Mouth: 0.3 cm
Neck: 1.0 cm

There are a number of known models of elephant bottles. Most are kneeling or recumbent (see the following entry. No. 251, in this publication). Our example, which is standing, is amongst the more rare of the elephant models. At least three others are recorded. One is in the Seattle Art Museum and illustrated by Fuller, *Chinese Snuff Bottles in the Seattle Art Museum*, pl. 37, which has an integral faux wood base with a gilt six-character Qianlong seal mark (it also illustrated by Moss, *Chinese Snuff Bottles*, No. 5, p. 57, fig. 35); a second is illustrated by Hall, *Chinese Snuff Bottles X: The Button Collection*, no. 104; and another is illustrated in a mainland auction catalogue, China Guardian, Beijing, 24 October 1996, lot 3.

The elephant, *xiang*, has a long history in China. It once roamed plentifully in Bronze-Age China before becoming almost extinct and being driven to the country's fringe. During the Qing dynasty, real elephants carrying vases on their backs appeared in processions celebrating the emperor's birthday see Bartholomew, *Hidden Meanings in Chinese Art*, p. 237, no. 8.12. The word for elephant was also a pun for the word for 'sign', *xiang*, both pronounced and written in the same way. When an elephant is shown carrying a vase, *ping*, on its back it represents 'peaceful times', *taiping youxiang*. *Ping* being a pun for the word peace, *taiping*. Because of their auspicious symbolism elephants were a popular subject at Court. Large marble elephant sculptures line the famous Sacred Way that leads to the Ming tombs north of Beijing and various palaces and terraces within the Forbidden City are dotted with cloisonné enamel or bronze elephant vases, or incense burners either of elephant shape or with legs in the form of elephants, see *The Imperial Palace: Chinese Landscape Storehouse* (unnumbered pages and photographs) for interior views of the Taihedian (Hall of Supreme Harmony), popularly known as the Jinluantang, where Court examinations took place, which features cloisonné enamel elephant inspired incense burners and the Baohedian (Hall of Preserving Harmony), also called the Jinshentang and the site of many large banquets held by the various Qing emperors to entertain nobility, high officials, and generals, with further elephant cloisonné vessels.

Another view of the interior of the Taihedian with two massive metal models of caparisoned elephants supporting vases on their back flanking a gilt-wood throne is illustrated in *The Forbidden City*, fig 23.

See also No. 125 in this publication for a crystal bottle with a depiction of an elephant along with a European figure.

(CBL C 367)

251

Porcelain, modeled as a recumbent caparisoned elephant with a *zun*-shaped vessel on its back, the head turned to its left side, a blanket painted in bright enamels and edged in iron-red and gilt with a scene of a sun above waves on each side, the tassels extending under the body, the saddle supporting an iron-red and gilt truncated archaic vessel with a coffee-glazed rim with traces of gilt that forms the mouth of the bottle, the body of the elephant painted in a pale sepia with iron-red skin wrinkles with the straps of the blanket carefully tied under the elephant's head and tail, the underside of the body glazed and with traces of four spur marks on the elephants tucked legs for support during firing

Jingdezhen, 1780-1830

Height: 3.6 cm
Mouth: 0.6 cm
Neck: 1.9 cm

See the previous entry for discussion of elephant symbolism and its popularity at Court.

Unlike the previous example, this elephant is shown recumbent rather than standing and is the more common of the two models. This is quite curious really because amongst other media like cloisonné for instance, where elephants are depicted, they occur far more frequently standing rather than reclining. Nevertheless, we can see from the relatively large number of published recumbent elephant bottles, that this form would appear to have been more popular. It is certainly conceivable that the standing bottles may have been based on the larger standing models dotted around the Palace grounds whilst the recumbent ones might be based on the smaller cabinet fondling jades or bronzes, the likes of which could be seen in various curio cabinets around the palace or used as paperweights on scholars' desks. For a recumbent elephant jade carving of similar size and form, that a bottle like ours may have been based upon, see Watt, *Chinese Jades from Han to Ch'ing*, p. 75, no. 56.

There are several ostensibly similar moulds of the recumbent elephant published, though with minor moulding differences in the arrangements of caparisons, the sizes of the vases supported on the backs, and the degree of turn in the heads and with variations in the enamelling of the beast and also the detailing of the saddle clothes. The closest comparable example appears in a watercolour illustration from the famous Bragge Collection, which was first published in 1874 in a rare leather bound hand-painted volume to accompany the catalogue, *Bibliotheca Nicotiana. A Catalogue of Books about Tobacco together with a Catalogue of Objects Connected with the use of Tobacco in All its Forms*. A copy of which was recently sold at Christie's, New York, The J & J Collection, Part IV, 22 March 2007, lot 20, p. 51, where another of this type is illustrated with identical treatment of the elephants wrinkly skin and the details on the saddle cloth.

Others are illustrated in *Chinese Snuff Bottles from the Fernhill Park Collection*, pp. 6-7, nos. 1 & 3; Moss, *Chinese Snuff Bottles*, No. 5, p. 56, fi. 34 from the Givaudan Collection; Stevens, *The Collector's Book of Snuff Bottles*, pp. 98-99, no. 308; and Holden, *Rivers and Mountains Far from the World*, pp. 142-143, no. 58.

Four small spur marks on the underside of the tucked legs of the elephant show that this bottle was fired while supported on tiny ceramic pins that allowed the underside to be fully glazed. These small spurs, when snapped off after firing, seldom left more than tiny pinprick-sized imperfections to the glaze. The previous elephant bottle was also fired standing up but the underside of each foot was left unglazed so that it could stand freely in the sagger without the use of spurs. Another solution is to fire the bottles upside down, with rods inserted in their mouths.

(CBL C 369)

250

251

252

Porcelain, modeled as a reclining lady, her black hair tied in a simple ingot-shaped bun with colourful hairpins, nesting her right hand on her right cheek with her right leg bent over her out-stretched left leg, wearing a lime green jacket painted in grisaille with stylized flower heads and scrolling, each side split to reveal a yellow undergarment with a tassel hanging to one side down the left leg, holding a yellow cloth painted with grisaille clouds, her iron-red pants painted with gilt clouds, the bound foot of the left leg forming the stopper, the irregular opening with traces of a pale coffee glaze over a white glaze

Jingdezhen, 1790-1830

Stopper: porcelain (bound foot)

Height: 10.0 cm (with stopper); 9.1 cm (without stopper)
Mouth: 0.7-0.8 cm irregular
Neck: 1.3-1.5 cm irregular

The majority of published examples of this type of reclining female bottle have the left leg extended, forming the neck of the receptacle and the right leg tucked over it. Quite why this preposterous position was chosen for the bottles when two legs alongside one another would not only be easier to mould and easier to carry but could also have afforded an additional mouth, is not immediately clear. Possibly the bottle was meant to be placed down (as it is usually photographed) with the raised right arm and the knee of the bent right leg forming the support. It could also be argued that there was no necessity for the right arm to be raised as it is and yet, in such models they all do. This seems to validate the theory that both postures are somehow beneficial or necessary to one another. Whilst the bending of the leg to highlight the bound foot was certainly a subtle erotic gesture, one other possible explanation, and perhaps the most likely, though purposefully only vaguely hinted at, is that it in fact shows a lady reclining in bliss between bouts of opium smoking. Photographs of opium dens and opium smokers frequently show figures in this identical awkward position with one leg tucked over the other. The photographic images also show the head turned at a slightly akward angle, usually supported on a brick, box or pillow, see Martin, *The Art of Opium Antiques*, pp. 12-28, fig. 1, 3-4, 8-9. Fig. 8 is also noteworthy as it shows two women in the languid, unhurried aspect of smoking opium. According to the author, while smoking opium was traditionally a man's pastime, anecdotal (and photographic) evidence asserts that women smokers were not uncommon.

At the beginning of the nineteenth century, opium smoking was on the rise in China and despite its prohibition, the trade, encouraged by the British, grew quickly. Two opium wars in 1839 and 1858 ensued. The smoking of opium does not involve direct flames on the opium itself but rather an indirect heat, which vaporizes the active alkaloids. A small pea-sized 'pill' of opium was placed in a special pipe-bowl and held over an opium lamp, which directed heat to a specific point. The most comfortable and effective manner to do this was for the smoker to lie on his (or her in our case) side and 'guide' the pipe-bowl and 'pill' over the stream of heat and to inhale the vapour as needed. Though less effective, it was also sometimes mixed with tobacco and smoked.

However, the subject of opium would not have been condoned at Court. If indeed these reclining ladies were ordered by or sent to Beijing then presumably the fact that there were two possible readings of the subject, the obvious one erotic and the concealed one illegal, would have just been enough of a cover to sanction their distribution. It would also neatly answer why the figure is not moulded with an opium pipe.

It is quite interesting to compare the lime-green jacket of our lady with an informal lady's robe made from silk embroidered gauze from The Denver Art Museum illustrated by Reynolds, 'Chinese Costume at the End of the Qing Dynasty: American Collectors and the China Silk Trade', *Orientations*, Selected articles 1983-1997, p. 127-129, fig. 7, which is of the same ground colour and with similar decoration and which the author dates to the early nineteenth century on account of the simple trim around the collar, sleeves, and side edges.

The closest comparable example to ours appears to be one from the Lily B.Y. and Y.B. Fung Collection illustrated by Hui, Kwong and Sin, eds., *A Congregation of Snuff Bottle Connoisseurs*, pp. 98-99, No. 112, where she wears a very similarly coloured outfit.

(CBL C 376)

253

Porcelain, modeled as a reclining lady, her black hair tied in a simple ingot-shaped bun with colourful hairpins, nesting her right hand on her right cheek with her right leg bent over her out-stretched left leg, wearing a black-ground jacket painted with groups of green clouds, each side split to reveal an iron-red undergarment with a tassel hanging to one side down the left leg, holding a green-edged yellow cloth painted with pink clouds, her iron-red pants painted with gilt clouds, the bound foot of the left leg forming the stopper, the irregular opening with a white-glaze

Jingdezhen, 1790-1830

Stopper: porcelain (bound foot)

Height: 10.3 cm (with stopper); 9.7 cm. (without stopper)
Mouth: 0.5-0.7 cm (irregular)
Neck: 1.0-1.2 cm (irregular)

It seems that the raised right arm of the lady may well have been modeled separately from the two-piece figure mould and added after the porcelain was removed from the press mould and cleverly joined with the rest of the figure whilst still in a soft leathery state. It would then have been glazed and fired. Certainly the slightly lumpy character to parts of these arms; the fact that some touch the face with fingertips only and others with the palm resting against the cheek; and yet others raised but not touching the face at all, coupled with the differing angles of what often appear to be identically moulded heads suggest that their was some post moulding manipulation.

The mould lines on this bottle (and the previous one in this publication) are faintly visible under the glaze running down the entire length of the body from head to toe following the natural line of the shoulders, waist, hips, and legs. The eyes and possibly other facial details were probably worked with a blade after moulding. The enamel details on this and the previous bottle are quite magnificent from the delicately painted tassel, which hangs from the waist at one side, to the handkerchief held in the left hand and the scrolling tendril design on the jacket.

Though this ostensibly appears to be from the same mould as the previous bottle in this collection, there are in fact subtle differences in the size of the models and also in the depth of some of the moulding, particularly to the face where the features in this example are much softer.

The differing models of basically the same reclining lady subject include an example where the lady is folding her upper left leg at its knee and holding the foot with her left hand whilst resting her head on her right hand with her right elbow supporting the weight, which is illustrated by Stevens, *The Collector's Book of Snuff Bottles*, p. 100, no. 319, from the Metropolitan Museum of Art Collection, New York. Another slightly differing model in which the figure simply folds her left upper leg over the right, whilst resting her weight on her right arm and elbow on the ground is illustrated by Moss, *Chinese Snuff Bottles: 5*, p. 63, fig. 56 and formally in the Caretti Collection, Turin.

For models closer in modeling to both this and the previous bottle, see Hui, Kwong and Sin, eds., *A Congregation of Snuff Bottle Connoisseurs*, pp. 98-99, nos. 112 and 113, the first being closer in enamel colouring to the previous bottle in this publication, No. 252; Christie's, New York, 25 March 1998, lot 250; Hughes, *The Blair Bequest: Chinese Snuff Bottles from the Princeton University Art Museum*, pp. 218-219, nos. 297-299; Moss, Graham, and Tsang, *A Treasury of Chinese Snuff Bottles: The Mary and George Bloch Collection*, Vol. 6, Part 2, Arts of the Fire, pp. 504-506, no. 1224, Christie's, London, 19 February 1986, lot 395; and Bushell, *Oriental Ceramic Art*, p. 139, fig. 179.

A watercolour illustration of a bottle from the Famous Bragge Collection publication of 1874, *Bibliotheca Nicotiana*, which is identical in shape to both our bottles, through closer in colour to the previous bottle is illustrated in Christie's, New York, 22 March 2007, lot 20, p. 50.

(CBL C 378)

252

253

254

Porcelain, modeled as the Daoist figure Liu Hai, standing with his robes open exposing his chest and belly, the robes painted in a pale lime green with pale blue flower-head sprays all over, wearing a purple and grisaille tiger-skin wrap thrown around his shoulders, and iron-red pants with gilt floral decoration, a string of coins tied at his back hangs down his front where his mythical three-legged toad is grasping for the coins, the areas of exposed skin and the face have a pale sepia wash, with iron-red highlights, the hair is painted in a pale blue, the top of the head has a simple hole for the stopper, the underside of the shoes are glazed white with a pale coffee or sepia wash on the remainder

Jingdezhen, 1790-1820

Height: 8.0 cm
Mouth: 0.7 cm
Neck: none

The subject of the Daoist god Liu Hai was an exceedingly popular one. He was revered as the epitome of wealth and business success. He started life, according to Bartholomew, *Hidden Meanings in Chinese Art*, p. 150, no. 6.24 and Williams, *Outlines of Chinese Symbolism and Art Motives*, p. 403, as an historical figure named Liu Yuanying, also known as Haichanzi, who was a prime minister in the Han dynasty government and a proficient student of Daoist magic and medicine. It was rumoured that he possessed a specimen of the legendary three–legged toad of Chinese mythology that resided on the moon. (In legend, circa 2,500 BCE, the wife of a chieftain had stolen the elixir of immortality from her husband and fled to the moon. There, Xiwangmu, the Queen Mother of the West, transformed her in to the toad.) It was said that Liu Yuanying with the help of his toad could travel unimpeded anywhere he choose. Occasionally the creature would escape down the nearest well but Liu Hai could always tempt him back by dangling his string of coins like a fishing line and retrieve him. The toad, like Liu Hai, also became a symbol of wealth. In another version of the story, the toad lived in a deep pool exuding poisonous vapour and Liu Hai once again enticed him out with his string of coins before destroying it. The obvious metaphor being that greed can lead to ruin.

The various models of this figure generally show Liu Hai as a boy in a standing position, wearing similar clothing, with his string of cash looped around his neck and dangling at his waist and with the curious three-legged toad clambering at his front to grab the coins. It was obviously a standard depiction as it seldom deviates from this basic model. The only significant difference on some models is either the toad is placed under one foot and the coins are draped across the shoulder or the shawl of leaves or tiger skin on the shoulders is replaced with *ruyi*-like collars and the shawl is instead tied at waist level on his back. What does differ considerably however is the enamelling. Some are left plain, like the Bloch bottle mentioned above whilst others, like ours, are painted in a wide variety of enamels. Our bottle may well have been carved after moulding, particularly the facial details, which are very crisp. For two bottles of slightly differing dimensions that would otherwise be said to be from the same mould, see Moss, Graham, and Tsang, *A Treasury of Chinese Snuff Bottles: The Mary and George Bloch Collection*, Vol. 6, Part 2, Arts of the Fire, pp. 438-439, no. 1195 and Hui, Polak, and Sin, *Hidden Treasures of the Dragon*, pp. 98-99, no. 195. Neither is enamelled, but for a touch of pigment on the eyes and lips, and both are of a cream colour under a clear crackled glaze.

Interestingly, the modeling of the faces and the range of enamels used on our bottles can be favorably compared to much larger figures produced at Jingdezhen which are generally accepted to dating to either the late Qianlong or early Jiaqing periods. For various examples see Howard and Ayers, *China for the West*, vol. 2, pp. 613-617, nos. 642-647.

(CBL C 380)

255

Porcelain, modeled as two boys embracing a massive vase, one in an iron-red jacket with a gilt floral design over turquoise pants and black shoes, the other with a pale-blue jacket with a darker blue floral design over green pants and iron-red shoes, both with their hair shorn and with a small bun to each side, the vase between them is glazed in a vibrant lime-green and lightly incised with floral scrolling, sgraffito, and gilt at the rounded rim, the circular foot rim of the vase and the undersides of the boys' feet are unglazed and each supports the bottle, the deep base is glazed white

Jingdezhen, 1790-1840

Height: 5.7 cm
Mouth: 0.6 cm
Neck: 1.2 cm

This model is extremely rare in the snuff bottle oeuvre. Whilst bottles depicting a boy, or boys, clutching a double gourd are quite well recorded, models of two standing boys clutching a large vase are rarely seen. Only two other examples appear to be recorded. One from the Gerry P. Mack Collection is illustrated in a sale catalogue, see Sotheby's, New York, 25 October 1997, lot 264, where the boys are identically enameled and grouped as our example, though their heads are tilted in slightly different attitudes and where the vase, also enameled in green and incised with floral scrolling, is of baluster shape. The other from the Denis S.K. Low Collection is illustrated by Kleiner, *Treasures from the Sanctum of Enlightened Respect*, pp. 182, no. 158, and has a white vase with blue floral decoration held by two similarly dressed boys.

According to Bartholomew, *Hidden Meanings in Chinese Art*, pp. 63-64, nos. 3.4-3.4.4, in a society in which the absence of boys, *zi*, is a catastrophe it is important to have images of healthy boys at play, *yingxi tu*, or vessels and utensils decorated with them in the household to ensure the arrival of a son. However, a son is not enough, he must also succeed at the civil service examinations and become a distinguished official. Boys are often depicted holding a vase of flowers, usually lotus, implying a wish for harmony among sons and grandsons, *zisun hehe*. The act of carrying a vase, *ping*, alone is a pun for peace, *ping'an*. To present a vase means to wish the recipient peace. The incised floral scrolling on our bottle is generic but may well add another layer of meaning in being a pun on string-like vine, *mandai*, which stands for ten thousand generations, *wandai*.

There are well-known eighteenth-century vases of larger size that similarly depict two or more figures holding or supporting them. The earlier ones, it seems, were made for Imperial use in which the boys are Chinese and can number two, three, or more and which are marked with gilt Qianlong seal marks, see Ye, *Kangxi. Yongzheng. Qianlong. Qing Porcelain from the Palace Museum Collection*, p. 368, no. 49; Doyles, 18 March 2008, lot 2100, deaccessioned from the Depuy Collection located at the Carnegie Museum of Art Pittsburgh in 1958; Sotheby's, New York, 18 March 2008, Lot 117, a gilt-decorated brown-ground vase with three boys; and another with a green-ground vase supported on the backs of three boys was offered at Christie's, New York, 23 March 1995, lot 398. The slightly later ones, which are unmarked, were made, it seems, for export and depict adult Westerners rather than Chinese boys holding the vase form, see du Boulay, *Christie's Pictorial History of Chinese Ceramics*, p. 292, no. 5.

For examples of the more standard bottles depicting boys clutching gourds, see Stevens, *The Collector's Book of Snuff Bottles*, pp. 104-105, no. 353; Hughes, *The Blair Bequest: Chinese Snuff Bottles from the Princeton University Art Museum*, p. 220, no. 301; and Moss, Graham, and Tsang, *A Treasury of Chinese Snuff Bottles: The Mary and George Bloch Collection*, Vol. 6, Part 2, Arts of the Fire, pp. 440-442, no. 1196.

Whilst our bottle may well date to the closing years of the Qianlong era it just as easily could date, like so many of the moulded porcelain bottles of the group, to the heyday of production in the Jiaqing period.

(CBL C 382)

254

255

Porcelain, modeled as male and female figures, possibly court figures, the male standing and holding what appears to be a snuff bottle in his out-stretched right hand, his right thumb nail may have a pinch of red snuff placed on it for inhalation or it might depict a coral stopper, he is wearing unofficial dress comprising a black-trimmed yellow jacket painted with coral-red floral roundels, possibly orchids, over a deep sky-blue robe painted with black enamel floral scrolling, at his belt on his left side is what appears to be a belt hook and possibly a snuff bottle pouch partially obscured by his hanging left hand, a green cloth is tied further along the belt, the base of the figure formed by the shoes and underside of his robe, the white-glazed face with traces of sepia to the cheeks and with finely detailed hair around the top of the queue (pigtail) which hangs down his back, the other is a Han Chinese lady standing and holding a flower spray, probably orchid, against her chest in her right hand and a folded concentric fan in her left hand (partially missing), wearing unofficial dress comprising a dark-blue waistcoat, *xia pei*, with gilt borders tied with a pink sash at chest level that is tied at one side and hangs down almost to hem level, and a turquoise-glazed knee-length jacket painted with gilt *cymbidium* (orchid) flower sprays, and a white skirt, *mang chu*, with floral scrolling in blue and gilt, two tassels to her right side with very fine molding of details where the cloth folds and opens, her bound feet just visible beneath her skirt, the hair pulled at the sides and held in place by pink flower-head hairpins, the face finely detailed with pursed lips, gentle expression, and simple gold earrings, one bound foot chipped to the toe, her left hand damaged

Jingdezhen, 1790-1830

MALE
Stopper: red-stained bone/ivory

Height: 6.4 cm (without later stopper)
Mouth: 0.4 cm
Neck: no neck

FEMALE
Stopper: later addition

Height: 6.5 cm (without later stopper)
Mouth: 0.4 cm
Neck: no neck

Published: Chapman, 'The Chester Beatty Collection of Snuff Bottles' *Arts of Asia*, March-April, 1988, p. 60, fig 15.

These two bottles represent the zenith of achievement in the moulded figural bottle category. Of this group sadly only seven individual bottles are recorded. Originally it would appear that they were made in sets of three as we only know of three models of this particular type; the male figure with yellow jacket (probably a mandarin or official – see below), the Han lady with bound feet who may represent a concubine or third wife (these two represented here) and another figure of a Manchu lady possibly the second wife or another concubine. Of course other models may originally have existed making sets of a larger size but in their absence it is presumably safe to assume they were made in sets of three. There are three published figures of the Chinese lady with bound feet, three published figures of the male figure (mandarin) in yellow jacket, and only one additional figure of a Manchu lady holding a rigid oval fan. The whereabouts of all but one of these is known. The Bloch Collection has one of each, see Moss, Graham, and Tsang, *A Treasury of Chinese Snuff Bottles: The Mary and George Bloch Collection*, Vol. 6, Part 2, Arts of the Fire, pp. 509-511, no. 1226-1228; the Chester Beatty Collection has two, the official (mandarin) in the yellow jacket and the Chinese lady with bound feet, illustrated alongside; Princeton University Art Museum has one example of the Chinese lady with bound feet, see Hughes, *The Blair Bequest: Chinese Snuff Bottles from the Princeton University Art Museum*, p. 217, no. 296; and one other official (mandarin) in yellow jacket formerly in a private European Collection was sold by Sotheby's, Hong Kong, 5 November 1997, lot 2153 to an anonymous Japanese buyer.

The official or mandarin (indicated by the seventh rank mandarin's hat that the two other examples of this model exhibit—and without which the subject could not be identified as such) may be ethnically Manchu or Han Chinese as both were allowed to sit the lengthy qualifying examinations based on the Chinese classics leading to the rank of a mandarin at Court. According to Garrett, *Chinese Dress from the Qing Dynasty to the Present,* pp. 64-65, there were two orders of mandarin. The first, and more highly respected, were the civil mandarins—scholar officials who administered the government of China—and probably represented by our figure, whilst the second were military officials responsible for internal stability and external defence. These two orders were each formed of nine ranks each subdivided into principal and secondary classes. Our official wears unofficial dress with a long-sleeved waistcoat worn over a long black-edged blue robe. Garrett, ibid, p. 68, also notes that Manchu customs and the Manchu language were generally not adopted by the Chinese, however the regulations concerning dress did take root as a means of unifying the country and making Han Chinese officials indistinguishable from their Manchu counterparts. Unfortunately, the original stopper that would have formed the hat of the official is a replacement. However the two other known models of the official have identical hats that are believed to be the original stoppers, so we can say with some certainty that ours would have had the same wide black brim that it presently has but with the addition of a porcelain stopper that has a simple iron-red painted shallow cone surmounted by gilt spherical knob, see Moss et al, op cit, p. 509, no. 1226.

Garrett, op cit, p. 73, fig 124, illustrates a plain gilt hat knob, which she describes as denoting the seventh rank. She also notes (p.70) that in 1727 the Yongzheng Emperor had introduced hat spheres for less formal occasions to avoid confusion between ranks when insignia were not worn. The buttons or finials were made of either semiprecious stones or glass in descending order of rank: first rank, ruby, then coral, sapphire, lapis lazuli, crystal, opaque glass, and finally the seventh rank, gold or brass.

Attempting to describe the details of the right hand of the official is actually quite difficult. Prior to the publication by Moss, Graham, and Tsang, *A Treasury of Chinese Snuff Bottles: The Mary and George Bloch Collection*, Vol. 6, Part 2, Arts of the Fire, pp. 509-511, nos. 1226-1228, the hand was simply described as 'wearing an archer's ring' with no mention of a snuff bottle. Moss et al, ibid, however list the bottle as 'an official holding a snuff bottle in his outstretched right hand, which sports a jadeite thumb ring'. Later in the footnote it describes the 'amusing little touch of having the man offer us a snuff bottle. It appears to be a flattened white flask with a coral stopper, though not identifiable as depicting a vessel of any particular material, it is unquestionably intended as a snuff bottle.' Whilst this may well be the case, other readings of the curious depiction are possible.

The detailed illustration of the hand shows that whatever the craftsmen was trying to convey involved a touch of turquoise enamel, a touch of iron-red enamel, and thin black enamel lines that run over the iron-red enamel, around the turquoise enamel and over the wrist. Because of the low-relief moulding of the hand it is quite hard to judge which digit is the thumb (it could either be lying over the forefinger or tucked under it). If, indeed, the official is wearing an archer's thumb ring, then it is difficult to see what represents the snuff bottle, though the upper curved surface which has the iron-red patch painted to it might represent the 'flattened white flask' mentioned by Moss (though it might just represent the forefinger of the hand). The turquoise enamel which may well represent a thumb ring might also represent the lower part of the bottle clutched in the palm of the hand, perhaps a jade bottle and perhaps the iron-red enamel rather than representing a coral stopper actually represents snuff powder resting on the thumb and thumb nail itself prior to being snorted. The inclusion of the black enamel outlines is puzzling.

Our figure also appears to have a belt hook at his waist and also a pouch, possibly for his snuff bottle, and a handkerchief, though these are all slightly obscured by the edge of his jacket and his left hand. Because robes did not have pockets, small items were either tucked inside sleeves or suspended from a sash or a girdle tied at the waist in a variety of shaped purses. Garrett, op cit, p. 91, notes that snuff bottles were easy to carry, either tucked in the

256
(four views)

sleeves of robes or suspended in a purse and she illustrates a stiffened card snuff bottle holder with an embroidered red silk cover, fig. 175.

The other figure represents a Han Chinese lady, identified as such by her bound feet, and may be the third wife or concubine of the official. Manchu ladies did not bind their feet. She is wearing unofficial dress, which often had wide bands of decoration around the edges and could be accompanied by a sleeveless jacket. The colours of pale blue and green were favoured in the spring and summer. The flowers on both the male and female figures appear to be forms of cymbidium or orchid, which might be another clue to identifying these two figures. Whilst wives took the same rank as that of their husband and would wear complimentary insignia at semi-informal gatherings, the fact that she is probably holding an orchid as well as having them as robe decoration seems to suggest the significance of this particular flower, making it unlikely that it is merely a decorative element in the design.

Interestingly, the theme of cymbidium was among the wood carving commissioned in 1818 by the Jiaqing Emperor for his summer palace, the Yuanmingyuan, see Bartholomew, *Hidden Meanings in Chinese Art*, p. 67, no. 3.8.1. Whilst there may be no link between this fact and the appearance of them on the robe, what we can say is that cymbidiums were definitely a popular subject in the Jiaqing reign, which falls inside the date range suggested for this bottle.

According to Garrett, op cit, pp. 98-113, under Manchu rule Han Chinese women were not required to wear official attire and most were in fact keen to retain their pure Chinese identity and took care not to wear Manchu-style clothing. The wives of Chinese noblemen or high-ranking officials were expected to wear quasi-official formal dress on ceremonial occasions when their husbands wore the court robe. An official's principal wife wore red, the dynastic colour of the Ming, while the second wife wore blue and the third wife green. Our lady may well be a third wife or a concubine. According to John Vollmer (personal communication) while a Manchu man might have taken a Han woman as a consort or concubine it was rare for Han women to be the principal wives of Manchu men.

She also appears to be wearing either a skirt, *gun*, or a *mang chu*, which comprises a pair of pleated or gored aprons with panels back and front which are worn beneath a knee-length jacket and tied at the waist. The embroidered decoration stops at the point where the skirt meets the jacket and because of the pleating that widened towards the hem and swung gracefully as the wearer walked, it allowed for ease of movement. The skirt was tied at the waist by means of a tie just as the dark blue sleeveless jacket or stole, *xia pei*, was held together by a tie to one side, also. Both of these ties are clearly visible on the right side of our figure, one painted in pink enamel, the other in iron red.

Hair styling was one of the more time-consuming personal activities. Scrupulous attention was paid to this enterprise. Unfortunately our lady (and indeed the Princeton-Blair bottle) are missing their original stoppers so we cannot see the full splendour of the ingot-shaped topknot or bun that is still present in the Bloch example, however the ornamentation on the side of the head consisting of artificial (or real) flowers or hairpins with gilt trimmings is still very much in evidence. Another indication that our lady may be the third wife rather than the concubine of the official is the high hairline. According to Garrett, ibid, p.103, prior to marriage, a woman had the hairs on her forehead removed in a process called *kai mian*, literally 'opening the face' (a practise that dates back to the Shang dynasty, c.1600-1100 BCE). The hair was then put in a bun. Han Chinese women also pierced their ears and our lady is wearing simple gold earrings. The Han Chinese tradition of foot binding probably began in the Tang Dynasty and was initially confined to the elite classes and was perhaps an indication of the wealth of the household, with well-born girls free from manual labour. At some point erotic overtones slipped in to the picture but by the nineteenth century the practise was widespread across the classes. Manchu women were forbidden to bind their feet by royal decree.

(CBL C 375 & 379)

256 (three views)

257

Porcelain, painted with two gourd tendrils which begin at the shoulder of the smaller upper gourd and twist around the bottle form before splitting into other more numerous tendrils and variously sprouting leaves in two shades of green, flower heads in white with green centres and gourds in shades of yellow and white and green and white, all outlined in black enamel and set against a pale lemon-yellow ground cold painted with brown dapples to represent natural discoloration, the rim and mouth of the bottle glazed white, the neck interior glazed, the interior unglazed, the rounded base painted with an iron-red seal mark

Qianlong iron-red four-character seal mark in a line on an unenamelled glazed white rectangle, Imperial kilns, Jingdezhen, 1735-1796

Stopper: jadeite on gilt metal collar

Height: 6.4 cm
Mouth: 0.6 cm
Neck: 1.9 cm

The gourd as a form was a very popular one, particularly at the Imperial Court where a variety of vessels of this shape are well recorded. As a snuff bottle shape it was certainly used in the early Yongzheng enamels made at the Imperial workshops as attested to by an example from the Palace Collection illustrated in *Gugong Complete Snuff Bottles*, p. 85, no. 133. Like our bottle, though smaller, it is a of compressed double gourd shape and has a yellow ground enamel colour painted with vine tendrils and gourds. The only real difference in the design is the addition of bats. It has a four-character Yongzheng reign mark in regular script. Our bottle is definitely a natural progression from this enamel type. Illustrated in the same publication, p. 201, no. 311 and also part of the Palace Collection, is a porcelain double gourd bottle, of which quite a few are published, including one illustrated by Low, *More Treasures from the Sanctum of Enlightened Respect*, p. 174, no. 160, which has an orange-beige ground with a gilt design of tight scrolls, painted with fruiting, leafy, gourd-vine very similar to ours, but with the addition of moulded gourds near the waisted centre. It bears a black enamel four-character square seal mark of the Emperor Qianlong. According to Moss, Graham, and Tsang, *A Treasury of Chinese Snuff Bottles: The Mary and George Bloch Collection*, Vol. 6, Part 1, Arts of the Fire, pp. 341-342, no. 1115, who illustrate an identical bottle, it may date to as early as the 1740s, sharing as it does with the newly-attributed Tang Ying porcelain bottles from Jingdezhen, the thinness and delicacy of the porcelain, similar seal marks, minute scroll ground, and general overall exquisite quality. Whilst are bottle does not quite share the same sonority or delicacy as the Bloch bottle, nor the moulded gourds, internal glazing and slightly smaller size; the style and quality of the painted vine tendrils, leaves, and gourds are definitely comparable as is the single coloured ground. In fact the naturalistic addition of passages of pale brown dapples over the surface of the entire gourd powerfully evokes the natural discoloration of the gourd as it matures. The authors also suggest that it might be fruitful (pun probably intended) to link the series of bottles of which the Bloch bottle belongs to, with an order from the Qianlong Emperor in 1758 for 'nine gourd-shaped snuff bottles' to be made at Jingdezhen. Our bottle, which has a less Imperial mark in iron-red and lacks the necessary features to link it with the Tang Ying group, was probably produced in the last quarter of the eighteenth century. Our bottle can also be linked with a group of early glass bottles of double-gourd shape, some with yellow grounds which also bear Qianlong reign marks, see *Masterpieces of Snuff Bottles in the Palace Museum*, pp. 118-119, nos. 107-108. Interestingly the nearest equivalent use of brown dappling on a glass bottle, is a moulded bamboo-form example with a Yongzheng mark also in the Palace Collection, where the dapples are meant to imitate the spots on the famous *Xiang fei zhu* variety of bamboo, see *Snuff Bottles in the Collection of the National Palace Museum*, p. 93, no. 28.

See Bartholomew, *Hidden Meaning in Chinese Art*, p. 61, no. 3.3 for an explanation of the gourd as an important auspicious symbol. It is a natural symbol of fertility because of its numerous seeds. The plant can produce large gourds,

gua, and small gourds, *die*, and when depicted as such as in our example can form the rebus '*guadie mianmian*', meaning 'ceaseless generations of descendants'. The string-like vines and tendrils, *mandai*, can be read as a pun on *wandai*, 'ten thousand generations' further emphasizing the rebus.

The bottle is made from a two-piece mould, though the vertical join lines are not visible on the exterior of the bottle. Unfortunately, the bottle does not stand unaided, suggesting that it may have been part of a boxed set originally. As a result of its inability to stand, the vagaries of time have been unkind to the widest points on the compressed main faces of the bottle, where the enamel has worn thin. The yellow ground enamel of the bottle stops neatly at the base forming a glazed white rectangle on which the iron-red mark is written. Slight over-firing to base of lower gourd has caused a slight grey bubbling to the surface of the yellow enamel.

(CBL C 461)

257 (mark)

257 (two views)

258

Porcelain flask, painted on one side with an open hand-scroll depicting a hut on a promontory in a mountainous wooded landscape in shades of black and grey, and similarly on the other side with an ogival panel with a cluster of low buildings in a similar mountain setting, all set against a pale blue enamel ground with scrolling peony tendrils in white and shades of green, with peony heads in pink and white enamel, the slender cylindrical neck with a castellated border in blue on yellow above a turquoise band, a rounded rim, the neck interior partially glazed, one side with four spur marks from original firing

Jingdezhen, 1730-1830

Height: 9.3 cm
Mouth: 0.9 cm
Neck: 1.45 cm

A very similar flask is illustrated by Bushell, *Oriental Ceramic Art*, p. 139, fig. 179, with slight variance in the landscape depiction but following the identical format of grisaille-decorated leaf-shaped panels on a floral ground. Large flask forms are unusual. The nearest comparable to ours is listed above. Three other flasks are published which are all of leaf shape and are enameled in the darker famille verte palette and usually dated to the Yongzheng reign on account of the similarity of design with a well-recorded group of Yongzheng-marked dishes, see Christie's Hong Kong, 29-30 October 1995, lot 716; Hughes, *The Blair Bequest: Chinese Snuff Bottles from the Princeton University Art Museum*, p. 162, no. 201; and White, *Snuff Bottles from China: The Victoria and Albert Museum Collection*, p. 116, no. 4. This would place all three at the earliest known production date for snuff bottles and certainly for porcelain examples.

The use of pink-and-white enamel for the peony flower heads on our flask, colours that were not introduced to the Jingdezhen kilns until about 1720, clearly indicates that our bottle date from no earlier than that year. In the West, the use of a predominant pink in the colour palette (derived from gold), led to these wares being called famille rose whilst the Chinese appellation is more vague with four interchangeable terms: *fan cai*, 'powdered colours'; *ruan cai*, 'soft colours'; *yang cai*, 'foreign colours'; and *falan cai*, 'enamel colours'. See Kerr, *Chinese Ceramics: Porcelain of the Qing Dynasty, 1644-1911*, p. 106. Chinese ceramics painted with pink enamels are recorded in Western inventories as early as the 1730s. 'Augustus the Strong,' the Elector Frederick Augustus I of Saxony, had assembled a magnificent porcelain collection at Dresden, which included famille rose wares, before his death in 1733. During the Yongzheng period (1723-35) and in to the Qianlong era, the subject of fan, scroll painting, and fruit-shaped cartouches set against a monochrome ground with flower heads dispersed over the surface was a popular one, see Kerr, ibid, p. 110, no. 92, for a vase in the Victoria and Albert Museum dated to between 1730-1750 with such a design. Our flask takes its inspiration from such designs though it was probably made later in the Qianling period.

Certain features on our flask, like the restrained use of relatively thick pink enamel on the peony and a measured, even modest, use of the lemon-yellow glaze is reminiscent of Yongzheng production, whilst the white-enamelled scrolling tendrils on a pale blue ground are more suggestive of Qianlong production. Once again, as we must rule out any connection with this flask and the magnificent ceramics produced by Tang Ying, and as we know of no other private kilns that might have produced a flask such as this, then the most likely date of production must fall in the fourth quarter of the eighteenth century. The unglazed interior of the flask suggests that it may well date to late in the reign also.

The painting on the hand-scroll and the leaf-shaped panel is reminiscent of the orthodox school painting in the earlier manner of Ni Zan, one of the four Yuan masters, or perhaps one of the four Wang masters. All such generic scenes were published in 'Mustard Seed Garden Manual of Painting' in 1679 and became the template for many artists in the eighteenth century.

There seems to be little question that this type of flask was made with the storage of snuff powder in mind. The neck is extremely small in relation to the size of the flask, being just 1.1 cm. from shoulder to rim, less than a ninth of the actual flask size. The small opening would have been perfect for the fitting of a regular stopper to ensure that moisture was kept out of the bottle. Flasks of this kind were presumably far too cumbersome for everyday conveyance and were probably kept on the scholar's table and used as a receptacle to store snuff. It does not stand unaided. In order to fire a flask of this size which has no foot ring or unglazed exterior surface and to allow for free flow of heat in the sagger, it either had to be supported by a rod through the mouth, which was probably impractical on a flask this size, or it had to be supported by small spurs. The minute remnants of these four spur marks are just visible on the enamel that surrounds the scroll painting on one side.

(CBL C 462)

258 (two views)

METAL & ENAMEL

259

Metal, of tapering cylindrical shape with high rounded shoulder below two stepped collars and a tall cylindrical neck, very finely engraved and inlaid in gilt around the body with numerous individual scenes comprising: fisherman in boats, small buildings on islands, fisherman on a bank, lotus sprays, a gathering of *weiqi* players, birds on a peach branch, pavilion and pagodas on fantastic rockwork, willow, birds amidst prunus, paired birds, monkeys poking sticks at a wasp's nest, pine trees and deer on grassy knolls, this is gilt, the body of the bottle is heavy and black whilst the base, shoulder collar, and neck appear to be of more coppery type and are separately made and conjoined with the body, the neck has an interesting marbled effect to the exterior, the body is made from a single sheet of metal folded around its vertical axis, the surface is the base is slightly concave and appears to have a rivet at its centre

1720-1880

Stopper: gilt-metal (not original)
Height: 8.1 cm
Mouth: 1.1 cm
Neck: 1.4 cm

This most unusual and rare bottle almost defies classification. The appearance of the neck with a wide collar between the shoulder rim and the cylinder of the neck itself suggests that it might originally have been made to be fitted with a cover rather than a stopper, and that it may not have started life as a snuff bottle at all but as a container of another kind. It has since gained a stopper, which appears to be made from a Chinese jacket button. On the other hand the mixed-alloy wood-grain decoration on the neck's exterior is a difficult one to attain. It entails the twisting, turning, and hammering of mixed sheets of metal (akin to the making of marble cake). The method was particularly popular in Japan where it was called *mokume* and required great skills to bring the underlying colours to the surface in a manner suggestive of figured wood with wavy lines and knot-like markings. To hide such craftsmanship with a cover seems counter-productive.

The basic concept of gilt decoration set against a darker ground was particularly favoured during the Song and Ming dynasties, in a wide ranging group of bronze archaizing vessels with gilt highlights culminating in the famous works of Hu Wenming and the inlaid work of Shisou, see *Arts from the Scholar's Studio*, pp.178-179, no. 157, for a water vessel by Shisou dated 1541 or 1604 and pp. 134-135, no. 103, for an incense burner by Hu Wenming dated to 1613. Whilst we know that metal as a ground material was used in early enamel snuff bottle production both in painted Beijing enamels and in cloisonné, the previously lauded Shunzhi dated (1640s) metal bottles thought to have been the earliest snuff bottles made, have now been assigned a late production date. So few comparable metal bottles are published, with two exceptions, that it is quite difficult to confidently assign a production date.

An almost identical bottle is illustrated in an exhibition catalogue by Randall, *From the China Trade to the Imperial Court*, no. 24, which is dated to between 1700 and 1800. It bears a two-character mark (not illustrated), which is translated as 'imitating the Ming' and where he notes that this type of bottle is so far unrecorded.

A second, with a different neck from the Humphrey K.F. Hui Collection is illustrated by Hui, Kwong and Sin, eds., *A Congregation of Snuff Bottle Connoisseurs*, pp. 186-187, no. 228, where it is compared to another from the Emily Burne Curtis Collection which is illustrated on the front cover of the *Journal*, ICSBS, Summer 1991, and which like the Randall bottle compares very closely with ours. A third bottle, perhaps better described as a jar, may give us a clue to the origins of this type. It formed part of the Ko Family Collection and was purchased in China between 1920 and 1943. It is illustrated in the sale catalogue, Christie's London, 14 June 1971, lot 167. Admittedly of much smaller and squatter form than the Beatty bottle, it does however share common stepped-shoulder treatment and gilt inlay of figures in a landscape. From the rather poor black and white illustration it might also share the unusual marbled neck.

The other nearest equivalent bottle appears to be a bronze bottle inlaid in gold, that comes very close in sentiment, illustrating as it does a landscape scene with figures set amongst trees and rockwork on one side (and a poem on the other) but which is of an entirely different oval shape, see Nicollier, *The Baur Collection: Chinese Snuff Bottles*, pp. 360-361, no. H169. Our bottle is of course incised and then gilded but the end product appears quite similar with gilt decoration set against a dark ground. Nicollier dates the bottle between 1800-1880, as did Kleiner, in personal communication with her. Interestingly, the Baur bottle can also be favorably compared to a cyclically dated Yixing bottle illustrated by Moss, Graham, and Tsang, *A Treasury of Chinese Snuff Bottles: The Mary and George Bloch Collection*, Vol. 6, Part 3, Arts of the Fire, pp. 938-940, no. 1447, which the authors date to 1763 (making it the earliest known Yixing bottle). The two bottles, whilst differing in materials, certainly appear to share some characteristics; similar form, a gilt poem, and a gilt landscape on main face, and comparable ground colour that perhaps suggests a link between them. The Baur bronze bottle (and indeed ours) may well be inspired by this type of Yixing stoneware bottle.

However, based on the shape and decoration a plausible, if wide, dating can be proposed. The shape is certainly one seen in seventeenth-century Jingdezhen ceramic wares but which persisted well in to the nineteenth century. The decoration of gilding and gilt inlay has a long Chinese history as previously mentioned, it also was a favoured media of the Japanese, particularly in relation to the metal workshops producing swords and sword fittings. The Japanese popularized a method of 'pickling' alloys to produce different surface colours. Perhaps the most famous, which bears a strong resemblance to the surface of our bottle, was called *shakudo* which was an alloy made up of approximately 95% copper and 5% gold, which after immersion in a 'pickling' substance said to be a form of cupric sulphate, turned the surface of the copper to a lustrous 'raven' black. The Japanese made various metalwork vessels of this kind for the Dutch market in the seventeenth and eighteenth centuries. Our bottle definitely appears to have a black patination to the suface and may well be produced by the same methods used in Japan. The scenes engraved and then gilded on our bottle, however, are unquestionably Chinese and therefore we appear to have an object that was strongly influenced by Japanese metalwork methods. Yet another group of wares similar to the Japanese ones comes under the genric term Tonkin ware which again use a dark metal ground with gilt decoration and inlay and which have been attributed to the Tonkin Bay area in the South China Sea. Its proximity to Gaungzhou however may well be a clue to the possible source of our bottle.

The myriad scenes are wonderfully rendered and though all are worldly subjects, the juxtaposition of seemingly random vignettes gives the appearance of a world caught between reality and dream. The wide ranging subjects do have a common naturalistic bucolic thread running through them but individually the scenes can be read as wishes for longevity, a happy marriage, harmony, promotion to high rank, and may even refer to the realm of the immortals, one of the four noble professions (fisherman), and one of the four scholarly pursuits, *weiqi* (chess). There are almost certainly other Daoist references mingled within the scenes.

The construction method of our bottle is clear from the 'fold' line that runs vertically down the bottle and which is cleverly disguised in the decoration running down the centre of a pine tree, the centre of the pagoda, and further rockwork and trees visible on one side. The bottle started life as a simple copper sheet that was then folded, perhaps around a wood mould, and hammered and shaped to the required form. The gilding was added to the bottle after the 'pickling' of the surface and after the chasing had taken place, as evidenced by a number of places where the gold is missing and the underlying copper surface is revealed in empty channels and punched dots. The underside of the base was made separately and is concave and is finished at the centre with what appears to be the hammered head of a rivet. The neck and collar were also made separately.

(CBL C 490)

259

259 (detail)

260

Metal, silver inlay decoration, each main face applied with a heart-shaped panel and inlaid with a fourteen-character inscription, the rounded narrow sides inlaid with leafy floral scrolling and possibly stylized bats centred by applied relief lion-mask handles, the cylindrical neck inlaid with a band of key-pattern, the flat oval base inlaid with a stylized *shou* character within a lotus petal surround

1830-1910

Stopper: Silver inlaid with malachite and coral

Height: 5.5 cm
Mouth: 0.7 cm
Neck: 1.5 cm

Provenance: Possibly Y. Okita, Nara, February 1915.

The inscriptions on each side can be read as two seven-character lines that read:
Ye fu lu jin bu ping chu
Mo shun xiang wan gu dao
De jian za ru tian jian pu
Wan shu jiu shi yi liang peng

This translates as:
The gentleman on the road sees the uneven places (and rude people)
Grinding and breaking in his chest ten thousand ancient blades, (anger)
The obtaining of swords has suddenness like increasing one's sturdy retainers (makes one powerful and strong)
The loss of books drums out the memories of fine utensils (and friends)

The rather odd juxtaposition of images evoked by the poem probably suggests the contrast between the speed of the sword and the slow pace of learning. The same contrast can be found between civil (*wan*) and military (*wu*) virtues.

Our bottle does not exude the same grace nor attention to detail as the gold-inlaid bronze bottle illustrated by Nicollier, *The Baur Collection: Chinese Snuff Bottles*, pp. 360-361, no. H169 cited in the previous entry, No. 259. The bottle actually displays quite poor workmanship in its finish, particularly in regard to the soldering of the various constituent parts that make up the whole. The neck, the heart-shaped panels, the repoussé handles and the foot are all separately attached and the body is made from one sheet, or possibly two, that is folded along the vertical axis. However, solder is clearly visible along various join lines. The mouth is also very slightly off centre and the stopper is not original.

Despite the fact that this bottle is decorated with a silver inlay, it in many ways is as much, if not more, comparable with the Yixing bottle also cited in the previous entry (Moss, Graham, and Tsang, *A Treasury of Chinese Snuff Bottles: The Mary and George Bloch Collection*, Vol. 6, Part 3, Arts of the Fire, pp. 938-940, no. 1447), because of its similarity in shape, the poetic inscription on a shaped panel and the mask handles on the narrow sides.

(CBL C 491)

261

Cloisonné, the body with five registers of simple wire and enamel decoration on a tarnished copper ground, the upper gourd with two registers of green enamel dots and C-scrolls, the waisted centre with a register of white enamel dots, the larger lower gourd with a similar register in green enamel above a band of chrysanthemum petals in white enamel at the foot and forming a concave base, the mouth plain copper with a screw thread interior for the stopper, the interior appears unenamelled

1840-1910

Stopper: copper of stalk form, screw thread (possibly added)

Height: 6.2 cm (without stopper)
Mouth: 0.4 cm
Neck: 0.7 cm

See the entry for the following bottle for the significance of the gourd shape.

The method of enamelling, whilst resembling champlevé, is in fact a cloisonné that has been left partially unfinished. The simple difference between the two methods is that champlevé requires the scooping out of the ground surface to form the cells that will hold the enamel whilst cloisonné requires the soldering of metal wires to form the cells. This is the case here. The bottle was almost certainly intended to be fully enameled, as there would be no good reason to waste quite so much effort trailing wire around the body to form cells that would not be used. It might also be that after the first firing of the green and white enamels the end product was simply considered complete.

Moss, Graham, and Tsang, *A Treasury of Chinese Snuff Bottles: The Mary and George Bloch Collection*, Vol. 6, Part 1, Arts of the Fire, pp. 252-253, no. 1115, illustrate a cloisonné bottle that is partially enameled and note that it seems this type was almost exclusively confined to snuff bottles produced at court in the mid- to late Qianlong period. Our bottle is certainly later and almost certainly not an Imperial production. However the basic idea of producing such a design may well have its origins in bottles such as those.

The stopper may be the original one as suggested by the well fitting screw thread to both the stopper and the neck interior although one might expect to find an enameled stopper. The silk thread attachment that ties the stopper to the bottle is certainly old though it might have been a later addition in either China or Japan.

(CBL C 489)

260

261

262

Cloisonné, decorated with numerous trailing gourd tendrils, leaves and fruit in different shades of blue which cover the entire white ground surface and trail under the slightly concave base which is also fully enameled and forms the foot, the neck rim and mouth copper, the interior unenamelled

1780-1850

Stopper: cloisonné

Height: 7.2 cm (without stopper)
Mouth: 0.6 cm
Neck: 1.4 cm

Turquoise was certainly the most popular ground colour in general cloisonné production in the eighteenth century. It is also the case in cloisonné snuff bottle output. This bottle is therefore quite unusual in its use of a white ground and decoration in two shades of blue. The use of this colour combination, whilst rare in eighteenth-century production is certainly recorded. For two examples of Qianlong Imperial wall vases with floral decoration in blue on a white ground see *Enamel Ware in the Ming and Ch'ing Dynasties*, National Palace Museum, Taipei, pp. 124 and 126, nos. 46 and 48. The gourd form was also popular in eighteenth-century cloisonné vessel production that included snuff bottles. For an example of a large Qianlong-marked double-gourd vase similarly decorated with trailing gourd vine and smaller gourds, see Brinker and Lutz, *Chinese Cloisonné: The Pierre Uldry Collection*, no. 294, and a snuff bottle of twin double-gourd shape, no. 254.

For a near identical cloisonné enamel bottle of the same colour from the A.W. Bahr Collection, 1916, see Glickman, *Chinese Snuff Bottle Mania*, p. 94, fig 2.56, which may be the only other example published.

Interestingly some worthwhile comparisons can be made between our bottle and an unusual blue-and-white double-gourd porcelain bottle illustrated by Moss, Graham, and Tsang, *A Treasury of Chinese Snuff Bottles: The Mary and George Bloch Collection*, Vol. 6, Part 2, Arts of the Fire, pp. 413-414, no. 1184. It is dated to the latter part of the Qianlong reign or the early part of the Jiaqing reign and besides a slimmer upper gourd is quite similar. It is interesting to note that the authors make a clear reference to the 'distinctly linear style' of the cobalt blue painting. They continue, 'the entire subject is defined by line, to which washes are then added to lend body. If one removed all the washes and left only the lines and dots, the design would still be complete'. How tempting it is to suggest that artisan producing the Bloch bottle was in fact basing his work on the linear lines of a cloisonné bottle. The solid blue outlines on the decoration on the porcelain bottle clearly echo those found on the strong outlines formed by the *cloisons*, which hold the enamels in place on our bottle. The strong likelihood is that our bottle may well be of a similar date to that proposed for the Bloch bottle making this link all the more pertinent.

The next closest comparison with a cloisonné bottle appears to be another illustrated by Moss et al, ibid, Vol. 6, Part 1, pp. 263-265, no. 1119, which is dated to the Qianlong period. It is of compressed spherical shape with blue flower heads and turquoise leaves on a white ground. The stopper on our bottle is decorated with five flower heads that do not relate to the gourd decoration on the body of the bottle and would in fact be better suited to the Bloch bottle; the enamel is more 'glassy' and darker than that on the rest of our bottle indicating that it is a later addition, albeit a clever one.

See Bartholomew, *Hidden Meaning in Chinese Art*, p. 61, no. 3.3 for an explanation of the gourd as an important auspicious symbol. It is a natural symbol of fertility because of its numerous seeds. The plant can produce large gourds, *gua*, and small gourds, *die*, and when depicted as such as in our example can form the rebus *guadie mianmian*, meaning 'ceaseless generations of descendants'. The string-like vines and tendrils, *mandai*, can be read as a pun on *wandai*, 'ten thousand generations' further emphasizing the rebus.

(CBL C 488)

263

Cloisonné, decorated on both sides with stylized descending archaistic key-pattern *chilong* possibly forming stylized *long* characters below green *ruyi* lappets at the everted rim and with red dots spaced unevenly running down the narrow sides, the neck rim, mouth copper, the interior unenamelled, the deep oval foot also copper

1720-1820

Stopper: cloisonné of mandarin hat form (original)

Height: 6.7 cm (without stopper); 8.0 cm (with stopper)
Mouth: 0.6 cm
Neck: 0.7 cm

Whilst this bottle can be assigned an eighteenth-century date with some confidence, the decoration itself actually owes more to seventeenth-century cloisonné production. It would be very bold to suggest that this bottle might date to the Kangxi reign, but of the few contenders for that crown, this just might be one of them. Moss, Graham, and Tsang, *A Treasury of Chinese Snuff Bottles, The Mary and George Bloch Collection*, Vol. 6, Part 1, Arts of the Fire, p. 36, mentions two other possible contenders, one formerly in the Ault Collection and now the Marakovic Collection (*JICSBS*, Spring 1987, front cover, top left) and one from the J & J Collection (Moss, Graham, Tsang, *The Art of the Chinese Snuff Bottle, The J & J Collection*, Vol. 2, p. 443, no. 265). Whilst there are no known Kangxi-marked cloisonné bottles published, there are certainly features on this bottle that are consistent with well-recorded seventeenth-century cloisonné production. For a number of examples of seventeenth-century cloisonné vessels that have very similar colour combinations with stylized *chilong* key-pattern designs, see Brinker and Lutz, *Chinese Cloisonné: The Pierre Uldry Collection*, no. 212, for a *fangzun* vessel with very similar decoration above the foot and around the body; and *Enamel Ware in the Ming and Ch'ing Dynasties*, National Palace Museum, Taipei, p. 81, no. 13, for a *gu*-shaped vessel dated the first half of the seventeenth century with similar *chilong* on the central lobe; and also p. 96, no. 25, for a rare Kangxi-marked box with lotus spray decoration, that uses a similar limited palette of turquoise, blue, and red (with an additional white replacing the green of our example). However, it should also be mentioned that in the eighteenth century, the use of seventeenth-century decorative motifs did not cease, as evidenced by a seventeenth-century style *gu*-shaped beaker bearing a Qianlong mark and a large unmarked flask dated to the Qianlong period, both of which have stylized *chilong* key-pattern designs similar to our bottle, see ibid, p. 127, no. 49, and pp. 150-151, no. 65 respectively.

Moss et al, op cit, Vol. 6 Part 1, p.20, note that whilst there is some confusion as to the exact date of the establishment of the earliest enamelling facility at the Court, it likely dates to some point in the 1690s. Certainly the existence of a small group of Kangxi Imperially marked painted enamel bottles would suggest that it could not have been later than the early 1700s. Of course it is also quite possible that this bottle was not even a product of the Court workshop, after all it does not bear any reign mark, but was in fact an order from the private cloisonné workshops which had been producing vessels for the Court for hundreds of years. Canton, Yangzhou, Hangzhou, and Beijing, appear to have had significant private workshops, which satisfied Imperial demand, see *Enamel Ware in the Ming and Ch'ing Dynasties*, National Palace Museum, Taipei, pp. 46-52.

The subject of dragons, which are Imperial by implication, may also be a clue to the intended destination of this bottle. The stopper is definitely the original and is of mandarin court hat form. It is adorned with four motifs that are most likely no more than decoration but which might be read as stylized *shan* (mountain) characters, though why this would be alternately written, first correctly and then up-side, is unknown. The areas of white visible in the illustration appear to be chalk deposits from the infilling of small areas of missing enamel.

(CBL C 485)

262

263 (two views)

264

Enamel on copper, painted in a continuous scene with two four-clawed dragons, *mang*, one ascending, the other descending, each successfully clutching a flaming pearl in clenched claws, one dragon painted primarily in orange and pink, the other in green, pink, and brown, amidst pale blue and white enameled clouds on a black enamel ground between two lines at the foot and floral scrolling on a pink band at the neck, the circular neck rim copper, the interior unenamelled and the oval foot ring also in copper and the slightly concave base enameled white and bearing an aubergine four-character regular mark

Yongzheng aubergine four-character mark in regular script to base, Guangzhou, 1723-35

Height: 7.2 cm
Mouth: 0.9 cm
Neck: 1.2 cm

The somewhat provincial quality of the enamel (not the painting technique, which is exquisite) is here self-evident and well represents the output of the Gaungzhou workshops at this time early in the eighteenth century. As is often the case with these early enamel products, the surface exhibits 'stretch marks' clearly visible around the head of the green dragon and flaking, particularly noticeable to the lower edge extremities and the neck, which are a common kiln fault, indicating uneven shrinkage between the enamels and the ground material during the cooling process. The method of painting, primarily using a wash effect is standard for this southern centre and quite unlike the meticulous stippling techniques of Beijing production. The profile of this bottle, a compressed elongated oval shape, is also wholly consistent with a well-recorded group of Yongzheng-marked enamel bottles though the shape continued to be made in the Qianlong era. For another Yongzheng-marked example of identical shape though painted with deer in a landscape not dragons, see Kleiner, *Chinese Snuff Bottles in the Collection of Mary and George Bloch*, pp. 38-39, no. 20.

Unmarked examples of identical shape with attributions to 1720-1760 are legion, see Hughes, *The Blair Bequest: Chinese Snuff Bottles from the Princeton University Art Museum*, p. 254, no. 353; Low, *Chinese Snuff Bottles from the Sanctum of Enlightened Respect III*, pp. 24-25, nos. 9-10; and Moss, Graham, and Tsang, *The Art of the Chinese Snuff Bottle: The J & J Collection*, Vol. 1, pp. 300-301, no. 181.

For two examples of Yongzheng-marked bottles painted with two dragons amongst clouds but with yellow grounds, see Tsang and Moss, *Snuff Bottles of the Ch'ing Dynasty*, p. 49, no. 7; from the Fuller Collection at the Seattle Art Museum; and Low, op cit, p. 21, no. 6.

According to Xia, *Masterpieces of Snuff Bottles in the Palace Museum, Gugong biyanhu xuancui*, p. 19-21, the main centres where enamelware was produced during the Qing dynasty included the enamel workshops in the Qing court (under the Qing Imperial Internal Affairs *Zaobanchu* – Manufacture Department), elsewhere in Beijing and also Gaungzhou and Yangzhou. Regarding snuff bottle production he notes that apart from the enamel workshop under *Zaobanchu* of the Qing court, Guangzhou was the key producer. At Court he notes that the majority of enamellers came from Guangzhou while the minority were from Jiangxi (presumably Jingdezhen). He goes on to record that Yinzhen (the Yongzheng emperor) 'advocated black colour' and ordered bottles with designs on a black ground to be made. Whilst these seem to refer to bottles ordered from the Court workshops, they no doubt also included orders from Guangzhou.

Other black-ground bottles with Yongzheng marks are illustrated by Xia, ibid, p. 43, no. 4; Moss, Graham, and Tsang, *A Treasury of Chinese Snuff Bottles: The Mary and George Bloch Collection*, Vol. 6, Part 1, Arts of the Fire, p. 292-294, no. 1131; and Kleiner, *Treasures from the Sanctum of Enlightened Respect*, pp. 8-9, no. 6, though all three are of a different shape and decoration than ours.

The depiction of a dragon set amongst clouds chasing a flaming pearl can be traced back in Chinese painting to at least the ninth century, see the entry for No. 211 in this publication. The earliest was a three-clawed creature, preceded in the thirteenth century by five-clawed (eventually reserved for Imperial use) and four-clawed varieties (reserved for the lower ranks). Occasionally this system was overruled but only when granted by the ruling Emperor of the day. On an Imperially-marked bottle like ours, one would expect to see five-clawed dragons, *long*, reserved for Imperial use but instead we have the four-clawed dragon, *mang*, which were the dragons reserved for officials of lower than Imperial rank. This bottle therefore was probably a special order to be given away by the Emperor to more lowly courtiers. It might even be the case that the Emperor did not waste the finer quality Beijing workshop enamels by giving those as gifts but ordered from Gaungzhou instead.

According to Williams, *Outlines of Chinese Symbolism and Art Motives*, p. 318, the flaming or wish-granting pearls, *baozhu*, which are clutched in the claws of both dragons on our bottle, appears in a variety of subjects in Buddhist legends, but most usually in association with the dragon. It is found amongst the Hundred Treasures of Buddhism, *baibao*, and is a symbol of wealth.

Chips to lower edge extremities reveal a copper-red ground with a chalky layer covered in the base enamel.

(CBL C 469)

264 (mark)

264 (two views)

Enamel on copper, painted on each main face on a black ground with baskets of colourful flowers and other objects, one side with a decorative square woven basket with waisted neck and pierced body revealing a variety of flowers within and further flowers bursting from the rim including peony, plum, and chrysanthemum, the upright square handle tied with a red cloth or sash and alongside the basket is a *ruyi*-scepter tied with a blue cloth or sash, the other side with a rounded woven basket with similarly pierced body revealing a plethora of flowers within and with peony and magnolia bursting from the rim, the upright square handle tied with either a necklace of beads or a twisted thread for a hanging basket and alongside is a blue dish on a red stand filled with peaches, both scenes divided by a single copper ridge that runs down the vertical axis on the narrow sides, a simple white band centred by a blue line forms the simple register below the copper rim and above the oval copper foot ring, both with traces of gilt, the interior enamelled white, the slightly concave base enameled white and bearing a partially visible manganese four-character regular mark

Partially visible Yongzheng manganese four-character mark in regular script to the base, Guangzhou, 1723-35

Stopper: amethyst or tourmaline, gilt metal collar (not original)

Height: 4.8 cm
Mouth: 1.00 cm
Neck: 1.2 cm

Aa mentioned in the previous entry in this publication, according to Xia, *Masterpieces of Snuff Bottles in the Palace Museum, Gugong biyanhu xuancui*, p. 19-21, the two main centres for producing enamelware during the Qing dynasty were Beijing and Gaungzhou. Unfortuantely no dates are given for the start of production at either site, though mention of the arrival in Beijing of Chinese and European enamellers from Guangzhou in the Kangxi reign (1662-1722) are noted. They include Pan Chun, Huang Ruixing, Ruan Jiayou, and Yang Shizhang. Mention is also made of foreign enamellers including the Frenchman Gravereau in 1717 and another French missionary, Chen Zhongxin (his given Chinese name), in 1719 . From this one might assume that the Guangzhou workshops were more advanced than those in Beijing but we cannot be sure. However, according to Moss, Graham, and Tsang, *A Treasury of Chinese Snuff Bottles: The Mary and George Bloch Collection*, Vol. 6, Part 1, Arts of the Fire, p. 276-279, no. 1124, production in Guangzhou must predate 1712, on account of a Guangzhou enamel panel painted with a Western woman in a landscape (illustrated by Gillingham, *Chinese Painted Enamels*, no. 13) with a partially readable cyclical date almost certainly corresponding to 1712. Moss et al, op cit, p. 288-289, no. 1129, also observe that whilst there is ample evidence of courtly production at Guangzhou during the Yongzheng reign, the same cannot be said of Beijing palace production. This is certainly borne out by the paucity of palace examples. The authors suggest that the Yongzheng emperor seems to have concentrated his attention at Court on enamelling on porcelain leaving the Guangzhou workers to produce a fair proportion of what was required. Interestingly Xia, op cit, p. 20, notes that the Yongzheng Emperor set up an additional enamel workshop in the Yuanmingyuan complex north of Beijing to increase output and for convenience when he was living there. He continues that the production of enamel-painted vessels (though not specifically bottles) was in its prime during the Yongzheng emperor's reign. Regarding painted enamel bottles, he later notes that Emperor was 'very enthusiastic' and every year sent decrees to the enamel workshops for bottles of 'every description' sometimes only ordering one at a time and on other occasions several dozens. Sketches or wooden models would be made at the workshops and presented to the Emperor for approval. The repertoire of shapes and decoration on bottles increased in his reign. As mentioned in the previous entry, the emperor was very fond of black grounds and in this bottle we have another quite rare example. The combination of black and a flamboyant extensive use of the 'newly introduced' pink enamel are wholly consistent with a Yongzheng date.

Another early feature of our bottle is the copper ridge that runs the entire vertical length of the narrow sides. This is a feature found on a group of early bottles that was probably phased out by the end of the Yongzheng period. It is rather unsightly but was the probably simplest and most practical way to join two halves

of a bottle in the early phase of enamel bottle production. For other examples of early enamel bottles with a similar ridge on the narrow sides see, Moss et al, op cit, pp. 276-285, nos. 1124 and 1127, where the authors note that another feature suggesting an early experimental phase of enamelling is the unenamelled interior, which is not the case with the interior of this bottle which has a white enamel coating. The same authors illustrate two other bottles worthy of comparison, pp. 290-294, nos. 1130 and 1131. The first is identical in shape and very similar in its dimensions. It bears a very neat brownish-black enamel Yongzheng mark written in a single line in regular script and like our bottle is painted with a purely Chinese subject of lotus, *shou* characters, bats, and foliage on a yellow ground and is similarly bordered at the neck by blue and white bands. They mention the inner metal neck (though do not illustrate it) which is sometimes found on these bottles, and a concentric line that runs around the mouth of our bottle as well but partially hidden by gilt seems to mirror this technique. The second bottle is of double-gourd shape and painted with flowers and a 'tied-sash' in a predominately pink palette on a black ground and has a similar partially defaced four-character Yongzheng mark. The painting style of the floral decoration on this Bloch bottle is so similar to ours it is tempting to suggest that they are from the same hand. Moss et al heap praise on the masterly hand that painted their bottle claiming, quite rightly, that the painting matched anything produced at the Palace workshops. Note is also made of the fact that the black ground was not an overall ground on which the design was then painted but a final phase of enamelling as indicated by the minute gaps between the floral decoration and the black enamel which most likely was the last colour added.

The baskets of flowers on our bottle are associated with the Daoist immortal Lan Caihe and are a symbol of longevity. Individually and conjoined the various flowers are representative of multiple readings. Peony, *fuguihua*, alone are a symbol of wealth and rank whilst in combination with white magnolia, *yulan*, they evoke the idiomatic expression 'May your noble house be blessed with wealth and honour', *yutang fugui*, see Bartholomew, *Hidden Meanings in Chinese Art*, p. 137, no. 6.6.2.

Peaches denote longevity, whilst the square basket or vase, *fanghu*, can be read as a pun on one of the isles of the immortals, *fanghu*, Bartholomew, *ibid*, p. 227, no. 7.62.1. Plum blossom, *meihua*, are emblematic of perseverance and purity. Chrysanthemum, *juhua*, is another symbol of longevity and when combined with peony, *mudan* (or *fuguihua*), forms the rebus 'May you enjoy long life, wealth, and honour', *changshou fugui*. The ribboned or cloth-tied *ruyi*-sceptre (or wish-granting wand) is one of the eight Daoist treasures, *babao*. When combined with a vase, *ping*, filled with flowers it forms the rebus 'May you have peace and fulfillment of all wishes', *ping'an yuyi*. When combined with the flowers of the four seasons, *sijihua* (we appear to have the peony for spring, the chrysanthemum for autumn, the plum for winter and possibly the rose for summer is tucked in the basket somewhere) it forms the rebus 'May everything be as you wish during the four seasons', *siji ruyi*, Bartholomew, ibid, p.265, no. 9.12.5. The coloured sashes, *shoudai*, tied to one basket handle and enveloping the *ruyi*-sceptre represent longevity, *shou*, but if read as wrapping, *fu*, it can also mean good fortune, *fu*.

(CBL C 467)

265 (mark)

265 (two views)

265 (detail)

Enamel on copper, painted in a continuous scene in bright enamels on a vibrant lustrous sea-blue ground with various groups of paired birds in a lake setting, one main face painted with two phoenix standing in mirror image on pierced rockwork holding *lingzhi* in their beaks and looking lovingly over their backs towards each other, two cranes on further rocky ground nearby surrounded by blooming peony, whilst a plump yellow bird sits in the branches of a *wutong* (parasol tree) above whilst its pair plunges in a death-defying dive nearby, only the wing tip visible from this viewpoint , the scene continues on the reverse with a pair of mandarin ducks quacking together on the rippling waters of the lake surrounded by further blossoming peony, whilst two pairs of dark-feathered birds fly or walk on a rocky area in the background, one narrow side of the bottle is divided by the very straight trunk of the *wutong* tree, a white band at the neck with a single pink line below the copper neck rim and mouth, the interior with an unevenly coated enamel, a thin simple white band above the oval copper foot ring, the slightly concave white enameled base painted with a black enamel six-character mark in regular script

Qianlong black enamel six-character mark in regular script in a horizontal double line to base, Guangzhou, 1735-96

Stopper: enamel official's hat form with copper collar and gilt copper spoon (original)

Height: 8.4 cm (with stopper); 7.8 cm (without stopper)
Mouth: 0.8 cm
Neck: 1.1 cm

The form of this bottle, a compressed elongated oval, is actually very similar with a well-recorded group of Yongzheng-marked Gaungzhou-made enamel bottles but as it was a popular shape its use continued in the Qianlong era. For another Yongzheng-marked example of identical shape though painted with deer in a landscape not dragons, see Kleiner, *Chinese Snuff Bottles in the Collection of Mary and George Bloch*, pp. 38-39, no. 20.

For a similar unmarked bottle depicting different paired birds and painted on a white ground, see Moss, Graham, and Tsang, *The Art of the Chinese Snuff Bottle: The J & J Collection*, Vol. 1, p. 303, no. 182, which is dated to 1736-1760. It also appears to have an identical original matching stopper based on the design of an official's hat with integral metal finial. Ours is unquestionably the original stopper with a simple design of a vibrant plum blossom on the identical blue ground to the body. See the entry for No. 256 in this publication for a discussion of the finials of officials' hats and the descending order of rank based on them. Five other examples of enamel bottles made for the inner court as tributes from Guangdong officials are illustrated in *Tributes from Guangdong to the Qing Court*, p. 88 and pp. 132-133, nos. 51-55. All have Qianlong marks of four or two characters in black enamel and all have official hat type stoppers attached to gilt copper spoons just as ours does. The stoppers however are slightly higher domed than ours and with more floral decoration than our single plum (*prunus*) flowerhead. One of the bottles illustrated has a cartouche of a pair of mandarin ducks.

Just like No. 264 in this publication, this bottle well represents the fairly early output of the Gaungzhou workshops in the first half of the eighteenth century. As is often the case with these early enamel products, the surface exhibits 'stretch marks' clearly visible around the entire bottle, almost appearing like the fine *craquelure* found on old master canvases. It is a common kiln fault, indicating uneven shrinkage between the enamels and the ground material during the cooling process. Whilst the style of the painting borrows something from Beijing output, the method of painting, primarily using a wash effect is standard for this southern centre and quite unlike the meticulous stippling techniques of Beijing production.

The subject of a phoenix, *feng*, singing under a Chinese parasol tree, *wutong* (see below), with a rising sun, visible as a very small red sphere on the narrow side of our bottle, represents 'red phoenix paying homage to the sun' *danfeng zhaoyang*, see Bartholomew, *Hidden Meanings in Chinese Art*, pp. 160-161, nos. 6.37.2-6.37.4. The sun symbolizes the *yang* or male principle of

brightness and warmth as well as righteousness and promotion and can be read as a wish for 'all the good things in life' for the recipient of this bottle. According to Krahl, 'Plant Motifs of Chinese Porcelain', *Selected Articles from Orientations*, 1982-1998, p.160, *paulownia* and *wutong* are virtually indistinguishable from each other (both are from the same *tong* family). Whilst their blossoms differ these are seldom depicted. According to legend, the *wutong* is the only tree on which the phoenix perches, a fact that can help to identify it. The presence of a pair of phoenix on our bottle seems to confirm this identification. The phoenix, *feng*, and the peony, *fuguihua* forms the rebus 'May there be wealth, rank, and good fortune', *fugui jixiang*. When the 'king of birds' is paired with the 'king of flowers', they augur great blessings and prosperity. The male phoenix, *feng*, and female *huang*, surrounded by numerous birds is an extremely popular subject and can be interpreted in several ways; either as 'hundred birds courting the phoenix', *bainiao chaohuang* or *bainiao chaofeng* which can represent the relationship between a ruler and his officials, or more simply, the subject of paired birds symbolizes both conjugal bliss and a wish for progeny. More specifically, according to Bartholomew, op cit, p. 161, no. 6.37.4, the phoenix, *feng*; immortal crane, *xianhe*; mandarin ducks, *yuanyang*; wagtails, *jiling*; and orioles, *huangying* (these last two might easily be the birds depicted in the upper portion of this bottle), together form the rebus 'Picture of the Five Relationships', *lunxutu* or *wuluntu*. These five relationships according to the *Book of Changes* (*Yijing*), and the *Book of Odes* (*Shijing*), are the relationship between father and son, *fuzi zhidao*, represented by the cranes (when the father crane calls, his son harmonizes); husband and wife, *fufu zhidao*, represented by the mandarin ducks (who mate for life); the relationship between brothers, *xiongdi zhidao*, represented by wagtails; the relationship between friends, *pengyou zhidao*, represented by the orioles (when an oriole sings it seeks the voices of friends). Bartholomew illustrates a Ming dynasty painting of the same subject.

Based on the similarity with known Yongzheng enamel bottles, it is safe to assume that our bottle is probably an early product of the Qianlong era probably within the first two decades of the reign.

(CBL C 473)

266 (stopper)   266 (mark)

266 (two views)

267

Enamel on copper, painted in a continuous scene in bright enamels on a vibrant purple-cherry-red ground with an identical scene to the previous bottle, the only difference being a band of blue scrolls on a white ground at the neck and a not so well executed nor as harmonious a colour balance of the entire decoration, a simple oval copper foot ring and the very slightly concave white enamelled base painted with an arrangement of six blue dots reminiscent of a flower head

Qianlong, Guangzhou, 1735-96

Stopper: jadeite

Height: 7.8 cm (without stopper)
Mouth: 0.8 cm
Neck: 1.0 cm

See the full entry for the previous bottle No. 266, which differs only in ground colour, stopper, mark and minor areas of decoration.

The choice of background colour for this bottle and the previous example in this publication appears to be an arbitrary one. It is possible that the two bottles represent a night and day scene of the same subject. However, as one bottle bears an Imperial mark and the other does not, we can safely assume they were not made as a pair, despite the identical subject. The sphere in the sky of this bottle, is blue (rather than the red colour of the previous bottle) and might easily represent the moon, however the necessary appearance of a sun in one of the rebuses noted in the previous entry might negate this reading.

This bottle is obviously missing its original enamel stopper.

This bottle has a large area of missing enamel just below one shoulder. This has either been rather crudely restored or it may in fact be the original under drawing on the chalky beige ground, which would be a fascinating insight in to the basic techniques involved in producing such enamels (see side view). Like the previous bottle 'stretch-marks' have been over-painted throughout the surface to hide them. However, the choice of ground colour here does not contrast quite so well as the blue ground does, and the painting itself is not quite so well executed. It has also not weathered the years as well either. Because of a jammed stopper it was impossible to ascertain if the interior of the bottle was enamelled or not.

Even though this bottle is unmarked it is safe to date this bottle to a similar one attributed to the previous bottle probably within the first two decades of the Qianlong reign.

For another very similar enamel bottle painted with five paired birds on a yellow ground and with a brown enamel Yongzheng four-character mark to the base from the Emily Burne Curtis Collection, see the catalogue of the exhibition, *Chinese Snuff Bottles*, The Newark Museum, October 2-November 14, 1982, no. 34.

(CBL C 476)

267 (foot)   267 (side view)

267 (two views)

268

Enamel on copper, painted with five pink bats, *wufu*, flying amidst gourds, leafy tendrils, and five-petalled flower heads, all descending from the stalks on the neck of the smaller upper gourd below a thick blue line and two thin pink lines on a white band at the neck and a copper rim and mouth, the neck interior enamelled but the interior unenamelled, the exterior decoration continuing to the underside of the round-bottomed base

Qianlong, Guangzhou, 1735-96

Height: 5.0 cm
Mouth: 0.7 cm
Neck: 1.0 cm

The gourd as a form was a very popular one, particularly at the Imperial Court where a variety of vessels of this shape are well recorded. As a snuff bottle shape it was certainly used in the early Yongzheng enamels made at the Imperial workshops as attested to by an example from the Palace Collection illustrated in *Gugong Complete Snuff Bottles*, p. 85, no. 133, which has its original stopper, which is of official hat form with a simple loop finial. Like our bottle, though smaller, it is a of compressed double-gourd shape and has a yellow ground enamel colour painted with vine tendrils, gourds, flowers, and bats. It has a four-character Yongzheng reign mark in regular script. Another slightly taller bottle of more elongated gourd shape but also painted on a yellow ground with bats, vine and gourds is illustrated by Hall, *Chinese Snuff Bottles: Masterpieces from the Reitberg Museum, Zurich*, pp. 16-17, no. 2.

Our bottle follows a natural progression from these types and can also be linked with a group of early Qianlong-marked glass bottles of double-gourd shape, see *Masterpieces of Snuff Bottles in the Palace Museum*, pp. 118-119, nos. 107-108, the first has very similar decoration of vine tendrils, gourds, flowers, and bats and the second has roses painted on a yellow enamel ground. The most likely date of production for our unmarked bottle is probably within the first three decades of the Qianlong reign. The use of bands of decoration at the neck combined with the loose painterly quality of the decoration seems to confirm this attribution.

See Bartholomew, *Hidden Meaning in Chinese Art*, p. 61, no. 3.3, and p. 134, no. 6.1.1 for an explanation of the gourd as an important auspicious symbol. It is a natural symbol of fertility because of its numerous seeds. The plant can produce large gourds, *gua*, and small gourds, *die*, and when depicted as such as in our example can form the rebus *guadie mianmian*, meaning 'ceaseless generations of descendants'. The string-like vines and tendrils, *mandai*, can be read as a pun on *wandai*, 'ten thousand generations' further emphasizing the rebus. Bottle gourds, *hulu*, and bats, *fu*, together form the rebus 'May you have both blessings and wealth', *fulu shuangquan*, the word for bottle gourd, *hulu*, is close in pronunciation to the combined words for blessings, *fu*, and emolument, *lu*. The bat, *fu*, is also a homophone of blessings, *fu*.

The bottle does not stand without support due to the roundness of the base. It may have been part of a boxed set. The curious orange colour on the lower section of the gourd is the result of discoloration to an area of restoration.

(CBL C 480)

269

Enamel on copper, two conjoined bottles, each of the conjoined main sides painted rather cursorily with five bats, two in pink, two in blue, and the fifth in turquoise on one side; and two in pink, one in blue, one in turquoise and the fifth in white on the other side, all set amidst similarly coloured clouds on a red-dotted yellow ground, the neck rim and mouth of both openings in copper, the interior is white enameled, two simple circular copper foot rings with white enamel bases

Qianlong, Guangzhou, 1735-96

Stopper: coral glass, green glass collars

Height: 5.1 cm
Mouth: 0.8 cm and 0.9 cm
Neck: 1.2 cm and 1.15 cm

The unusual stippled background may have been an attempt at duplicating the stippled effect found on Beijing enamels or it may have been imitating another material, perhaps a textured gourd or bamboo, perhaps even a gold ground; from a short distance the stippling is invisible and the bottle appears as though the bats and clouds are on a gold ground. It can also be found on other Guangzhou enamel vessels and objects as a ground colour, see *Quanji 6* (Boda, *Zhongguo jinyin boli falang qi quanji*, [Complete compendium of Chinese artworks in metal, glass and enamel], Vol. 6, *Falangqi* [Enamels]), p. 122, no. 183, for a small 'mid-Qing' plaque with an almost identical decoration of bats and clouds on a red-stippled yellow ground; and p. 132, no. 199, for spittoon and cover with an identical ground.

It is quite unusual to find a twin bottle in enamelware and it may well be a copy of a porcelain bottle. The decoration is actually quite cursory and little bit slapdash. The bats have an almost comical 'cartoonish' look to them. There are ten in total which is an unusual number, five or nine being the norm, but probably attributable to the fact that we have two conjoined bottles and thus two sets of five bats rather than a full compliment of ten. The word for bat, *fu*, has the same sound as the word for blessing, *fu* and riches, *fu* and has thus become synonymous with this meaning. Bats, *fu*, and clouds, *yun*, form the rebus 'May you have good fortune or luck', *fuyun*. The word for clouds is homophonous with the word for fortune, *yun*. If one reads the pink bats as red bats, *hongfu*, flying in the sky, *tian*, the rebus formed is 'May your blessings be as vast as the sky or heavens'. Red, *hong*, and vast, *hong*, are similarly pronounced, see Bartholomew, *Hidden Meanings in Chinese Art*, p. 23, no. 1.1.5. Five bats, *wufu*, forms the rebus, 'May you have the Five Blessings', *wufu*, (old age, wealth, health, love of virtue, and a peaceful death). 'The Five Blessings' were first mentioned in the ancient Warring States text *Shangshu*, in the chapter entitled 'The Great Plan', *Hongfan*, compiled before the second century BCE. If the stippled ground, is indeed meant to imitate a gourd skin, *hulu*, then we have yet another reference to good fortune and fertility.

Oddly the mouths of the bottles are of slightly different sizes. The bottle with the wider diameter neck actually has a slightly smaller mouth. The stoppers are later additions.

For a very similar bottle from the C.F. Yau Collection, 1926 (Ton-Ying Company, New York), see Glickman, *Chinese Snuff Bottle Mania*, p. 46, fig 2.7.

(CBL C 481)

268 (two views)

269

270

Enamel on copper, painted in bright enamels on each main face with two ascending and confronted fish-tailed winged dragons resembling sea-horses spewing *lingzhi* or possibly spray from their mouths either side of a single blue enameled *shou* (longevity) character within an oval cartouche, all on a pale aubergine or lilac ground, the decoration continuous around the body and stops at the shoulder below simple dark blue enamel lappets on a pale blue ground which decorates the neck, an almost-square thick copper-rimmed mouth, the interior white enameled, the decoration continuing over the rounded base with no foot for support

Yongzheng / Qianlong, Guangzhou, 1720-50

Height: 5.1 cm
Mouth: 1.1 cm x 1.0 cm (rectangular)
Neck: 0.8 cm x 0.7 cm (rectangular)

Since robes lacked pockets, an essential part of courtly dress was the pouch or purse suspended from a girdle tied at the waist. Generally, the purses were embroidered by the ladies of the household who devoted much time to this task. There were also specialized shops providing this service. According to Garrett, *Chinese Dress from the Qing Dynasty to the Present*, p. 88, it was the custom of the emperor to reward his courtiers and officials, especially at the Lunar New Year, with purses containing jeweled charms. As a result of the purses' popularity and necessity it also became a standard form for enameled copper snuff bottles made in Guangzhou in the early days of production in the late Kangxi and Yongzheng periods and even in to the Qianlong reign. Interestingly many of the designs on the enamel bottles seem to take their inspiration from textile designs. One such example, of horizontal purse format, from the Imperial palace collections is illustrated in *Quanji 6* (Boda, *Zhongguo jinyin boli falang qi quanji*, [Complete compendium of Chinese artworks in metal, glass and enamel], Vol. 6, *Falangqi* [Enamels]), p. 122, no. 184. It also has its original ties with beads attached to loop handles presumably to allow for attachment to the waist girdle. The neck decoration of blue leaf lappets is similar to ours but slightly more sophisticated suggesting slightly later manufacture perhaps. It can be dated to the Qianlong period. Another bottle worthy of comparison, also of horizontal purse format rather than the vertical shape of ours is illustrated by Moss, Graham, and Tsang, *A Treasury of Chinese Snuff Bottles: The Mary and George Bloch Collection*, Vol. 6, Part 1, Arts of the Fire, p. 286-287, no. 1128. Like our bottle it appears to have a near identical pale aubergine or lilac ground; has rather baroque mythical phoenixes confronted around a *shou* character, where ours have mythical fish dragons confronted around a *shou* character; and is also unusual in having a rare rectangular-shaped mouth, technically quite difficult when it rises from a rounded shoulder. The authors date the bottle to between 1720-1750. Two further bottles, both from the Denis Low Collection, are important in establishing a likely Yongzheng or early Qianlong date for our bottle, one is illustrated by Low, *More Treasures from The Sanctum of Enlightened Respect*, p. 7, no. 4; the other by Kleiner, *Treasures from The Sanctum of Enlightened Respect*, p. 12, no. 8. The first bears a Yongzheng four-character regular mark and though called gourd shape, is more likely to be pouch-shaped. It is painted with a large pink bat supporting a blue *shou*-character medallion amidst floral scrolling on a yellow ground. The similarities speak for themselves. The second bottle has no mark but has a black ground indicative of early production (see No. 265 in this publication). More importantly, it is painted with two similar winged mythical creatures, which have have florid bodies and tails resembling fish, again surrounding a *shou* character and with blue lappets at the neck. Kleiner attributes the bottle to a 1720 to 1740 production date in Guangzhou.

The symbolism expressed by the combination of a *shou* character and *lingzhi* is one of longevity. The depiction of fish-like dragons may be a reference to the legend of the carp swimming upstream in the Yellow River, fighting against the opposing current and leaping the rapids of Dragon's Gate (Longmen) falls; the first fish to succeed transforms itself into a dragon. The story is a metaphor for a poor scholar who, by passing the civil services exams, raises himself to the status of high official (see also No. 24 in this publication). Depicting a pair of dragons, it might also be a metaphor for marital bliss.

The bottle does not stand unaided.

(CBL C 475)

271

Enamel on copper, painted in bright enamels on each main face with a descending bat in shades of pink above a large peony flower head with trailing leafy tendrils and divided by two magnificent descending phoenix whose twisting bodies continue on the narrow sides, each bird with a *lingzhi* held in its mouth, all set on a bright yellow ground between a single blue line on a white enamel band at the oval copper-rimmed foot and circular neck, the interior partially enameled, the shallow concave white base painted with a blue chrysanthemum flower head consisting of rings of concentric dots and simple strokes

Yongzheng/Qianlong, Guangzhou, 1723-50

Stopper: amethyst, quartz or pink glass, silver collar

Height: 5.0 cm
Mouth: 0.8 cm
Neck: 1.1 cm

The nearest equivalent bottle to ours appears to be one illustrated by Moss, Graham, and Tsang, *A Treasury of Chinese Snuff Bottles: The Mary and George Bloch Collection*, Vol. 6, Part 1, Arts of the Fire, pp. 290-291, no. 1130 which bears a Yongzheng four-character mark in regular script. Though neither quite as spherical in profile nor as compressed as our bottle, there are many features that do compare favourably. The overall colour scheme is certainly very close, with a lemon-yellow ground bordered by a blue and white band at the neck, and another band above the foot; a large single flower head, albeit lotus rather than peony, surrounded by variegated scrolling foliage; and a bat descending from the shoulder of the bottle. The only principal difference is the addition of a *shou* character at the centre of the Bloch bottle (which relates to the previous bottle in this publication), whilst ours has the addition of phoenix. However both are manifestly of the highest aesthetic order. There is nothing tentative in the execution of any part of the design and the curious almost human-faced bat has a singular appearance. The phoenixes seem to be a naturalistic borrowing from a mixture of fauna with crane heads, rooster beaks, swan necks, eagle wings and peacock tails and the balance of floral scrolling is superb. Though there are some minor technical issues in the firing of the enamel such as the usual 'stretch marks', the enamelling is extremely refined.

Moss et al, ibid, pp. 290-291, note that expert enamellers from Europe were, because of protocol, regularly forced to mark time in Guangzhou and prove their worth in this southern port before being invited to Beijing. The effect this had on the supposed 'provincial' centre was to lift the workmanship to a level of perfection during the Yongzheng reign. Our bottle can also be compared, or cross-referenced if you will, with another bottle in the Bloch collection, ibid, pp. 286-287, no. 1128, mentioned in the previous entry, that is of pouch or purse shape, and which like the Yongzheng-marked Bloch bottle referenced has a *shou*-character medallion at its centre but, more importantly in relation to our bottle, has the addition of two confronted phoenix on a floral ground. Another yellow ground enamel bottle of compressed ovoid shape painted with a large peony head and with similar scrolling foliage all set between blue and white bands at the foot and neck is illustrated by Moss, Graham, and Tsang, *The Art of the Chinese Snuff Bottle: The J & J Collection*, Vol. 1, pp. 300-302, no. 181. Interestingly it has a near identical blue enamel flower head on the base.

See also a bowl, cover, and stand with a Qianlong four-character mark from the Imperial Palace Collections illustrated in *Quanji 6* (Boda, *Zhongguo jinyin boli falang qi quanji*, [Complete compendium of Chinese artworks in metal, glass and enamel], Vol. 6, *Falangqi* [Enamels]), p. 90, no. 133, which has the same yellow ground painted with numerous similar multi-coloured flying phoenix amidst peony sprays but excluding bats. It was most certainly a type made for the Imperial Court, as indeed our bottle may be, despite being unmarked.

The subject of our bottle can be interpreted a number of ways. The phoenix, *feng*, dallying with the peony, *fuguihua*, is an auspicious design, *fengxi mudan* or *fengchuan mudan*, and according to Bartholomew, *Hidden Meanings in Chinese Art*, p. 160, no. 6.37.1, the phoenix, *feng*, and peony, *fuguihua*, form the rebus 'May there be wealth, rank, and good fortune', *fugui jixiang*. When the king of birds is paired with the king of flowers, they augur great blessings and prosperity. The phoenix is said to only appear at times of peace and prosperity. The author also notes, ibid, p. 54, no. 2.20, that the tail of five colours is symbolic of the five cardinal virtues of benevolence, *ren*; righteousness, *yi*; propriety, *li*; knowledge, *zhi*; and sincerity, *xin*. A bat, *fu*, descending, *jiang*, from the sky, *tian*, forms the rebus 'blessings descending from heaven', *fucong tianjiang*.

(CBL C 478)

270

271

Enamel on copper, painted in bright enamels on each main face with a European lady in an oval panel, on one side the lady is wearing a low-necked lace-trimmed pink dress and a wide-brimmed hat whilst a plump bird balances on her raised left hand in a landscape setting with bushes, trees, and a simple building, the other side with a lady in a lace-trimmed yellow dress with a pink shawl and a posy of flowers in her hair suckling a child at her breast, in a hilly landscape with bushes and a European-style castle or chateau, each oval panel set on dense floral scrolling with a dark black-dotted purple ground, below lotus lappets above the shoulder and between similar coral floral scrolling on yellow bands at the copper-rimmed oval foot and slightly waisted cylindrical neck, the interior white enameled, the shallow concave white base painted with a black enamel seal mark

Qianlong black enamel six-character seal mark to the base, Guangzhou, 1736-95

Height: 5.5 cm
Mouth: 0.9 cm
Neck: 1.2 cm

Published: Chapman, 'The Chester Beatty Collection of Snuff Bottles', *Arts of Asia*, March-April, 1988, p. 61, fig 19.
The Chester Beatty Library, Handbook, no. 100, p. 84.

It is widely acknowledged that the European-subject depictions on enamel and glass bottles borrowed their themes most likely from European prints or European enamels. However, so little work has been done on the use of decorative prints as a source material, it is hard to be sure which prints were copied, and when copied how much the enameller deviated from the source. It is certainly true that there was a lively trade in decorative prints via the East India Company in the eighteenth century. The major production centre for stipple engravings (the most common print type) was London and print makers from around Europe came to the United Kingdom to practice their craft. These engravings were then disseminated around the globe either through the officers of the various trading companies or indeed by private persons. Books with engravings were essential travel companions for the long and arduous journeys abroad. There is also no doubt that the missionaries would also have carried books and engravings, though more likely of a religious or scientific nature.

An artist that stylistically comes to mind when looking at the two ladies on our bottle is Francis Hayman (1708-1776). He was one of the most versatile of the English eighteenth-century artists and worked in the paint and print milieu. He was also a prolific book illustrator. He painted and produced prints primarily depicting themes of theatrical, literary, and historical subjects as well as portraits of luminaries of his day. He was a founding member of the Royal Academy in 1768. He even collaborated with his contemporary the Frenchman Hubert Francois Bourguignon (1699-1773), better known as Gravelot, who had revitalized illustrative engraving in England and to whom many English artists were indebted. Hayman's images were widely distributed through stipple engravings. Whilst his work may not be the exact source of our depiction, it was most certainly an artist working in a similar fashion and at a similar time who influenced the scene on our bottle. A wonderful oil painting of circa 1741-42 in the Victoria and Albert Museum, London (accession no. P.12-1947) by Hayman entitled the 'The Milkmaid's Garland' or 'Humours of May Day' depicts as the central focus of the painting two dancing ladies that could almost be the sisters of the two ladies on our bottle. Both wear floppy bonnets similar to the one worn by the lady holding the bird on one side of our bottle, and both dance in elegant silk or brocade gowns with laced stays that support and raise the breasts, narrow to a sharp point at the front, as well as define a slim outline. The lace sleeves and neckline of the undergarments in the painting are clearly comparable to those on our bottle. The rather unsightly smudging on the faces of both ladies on our bottle must surely be a rather crude attempt at imitating the stippled effect used on the original engraving. This must leave us in no doubt that a print source was the inspiration for this depiction.

The subject that the original print depicted is hard to ascertain without knowing the exact engraving. Our figures may have been single ones in the original or part of a much larger group. The fact that so many depictions of single Euro-

pean ladies exist on a wide variety of enamel and glass bottles (with or without children depicted) and often with the lady holding a posy of flowers or more rarely with a bird, as with this example, does however suggest that the original print probably had a similar simple image. The image of a lady suckling a child is most likely based on a depiction of the popular Christian subject of Charity, one of the three great virtues. On the other hand, the image may have been misinterpreted from the original engraving and what appears now like a child suckling at the breast may simply have been a misreading of an image of the Virgin Mary and the Christ child or a lady in a décolleté dress holding a child. The image on the other side of the bottle of a woman supporting a bird on her outstretched fingers can also be read in several possible ways. From a Western perspective it can be read as a simple pastoral scene, which is actually most likely the case here, but it might also derive from an image of Lesbia and her sparrow, a subject found in eighteenth- (Francis Wheatley, 1747-1801) and nineteenth-century (Sir Edward John Poynter, 1836-1919) paintings and based on the popular Latin poem of the same name by Gaius Valerius Catullus who lived in Verona at the time of Cicero in the first century BCE. However, the fact that on similar images of this subject a young boy is often inserted in to the scene seems to suggest that the former reading is correct, see an example of a Guangzhou enamel bottle with a Qianlong two-character black enamel mark depicting a scene of a European lady with a bird perched on her hand and a boy alongside her, illustrated in *Tributes from Guangdong to the Qing Court*, p. 88, no. 53.

From a Chinese perspective the subject would probably have read as a simple image of a lady with a pet bird as the keeping of caged birds for singing was extremely popular. If the bird is a quail, *anchun*, it certainly has the appearance of one, though they are rarely shown with human figures, it might be read as a pun for 'peace', *ping'an*. The Chinese artisans may also have seen a print image of this subject and misinterpreted it as relating to rank. Civil and military officials were officially distinguished by the insignia of different birds or animals that they wore, which on official occasions their wives also did.

The subject of ladies and children playing with birds is also known on Beijing enamels made for the court, sometimes though more rarely depicting Chinese ladies, see *Gugong Complete Snuff Bottles*, p. 110, no. 162, for a European subject example and pp. 104-106, nos. 156 and 158, for two Chinese-subject examples.

All bear Qianlong four-character marks in blue enamel, which seems to have been the regular (though not exclusive) method for marking bottles in the Beijing workshops. In Guangzhou it seems that other colours like the black of this example were just as acceptable. Another Beijing enamel bottle also with the same blue enamel mark is illustrated in *Masterpieces of Snuff Bottles in the Palace Museum*, p. 54, no. 19 and depicts the same subject of a lady in a décolleté dress with a child on one side, possibly suckling, and a lady holding a bird but with the addition of a child.

The ground decoration of our bottle is much more in keeping with Guangzhou production being less formalized and more loosely painted than their Beijing counterparts, which tended to employ a more spectacular use of contrasts, very often with dark grounds and masculine baroque interlocking scrolls, see Hughes, *The Blair Bequest: Chinese Snuff Bottles from the Princeton University Art Museum*, pp. 257-263, nos. 356-362 for various examples.

The pear shape of the bottle is most unusual in enamel snuff bottle production, the compressed spherical or oblate shape being the norm.

(CBL C 482)

272 (mark)   272 (detail)

272 (two views)

273

Enamel on gold, each main face decorated with unintentional cash-like symbols formed from four-petal gold flower heads on white-enameled diamond-shaped panels with curved sides set within deep blue-enamel circles, all below arch-like decoration at the shoulder formed by the curved octagonal band of gold dots on white enamel and gold leaves on dark blue enamel which encircles the neck, the neck with two bands of decoration, one is a serious of vertical and horizontal strokes on a pale blue enamel ground below a band of gold running vine on a deep blue ground, the mouth slightly concave and decorated with a swirling leaf design in gold on deep blue within a simple 25-point star polygon band in pale blue and white enamel, the narrow sides with vertical side panels of half-pearls, which again have the unintentional appearance of *ruyi* scepters, the lower third of the bottle applied with a thick band of upright leaf lappets each centred by half pearls, the oval gold base flat

1810-1830, Switzerland

Stopper: Enamel, gold, and half-pearls with domed crystal or glass hinged cover with pearl-set bezel, encasing a European watch face with Roman chapters, outer minute divisions, hinged to the casing the gold lid has the stamped number 4574, opening to reveal gilt brass full plate engraved with 'A' and 'R', with cylindrical pillars, verge escapement, brass balance, continental cock or bridge, an integral gold and enamel spoon

Height: 5.6 cm (with stopper); 4.5 cm (without stopper)
Mouth: 0.9 cm
Neck: 1.2 cm

PUBLISHED:
Chapman, 'The Chester Beatty Collection of Snuff Bottles', *Arts of Asia*, March-April, 1988, p. 57, fig 1.

The engraved letters 'A' and 'R' denote 'Avant' and 'Retard' for the purpose of altering the movement of the mechanism.

Snuff bottles of this type apparently made for the Chinese market are extremely rare. Including our two bottles, Nos. 273 and 274, in this publication, there appear to be six published examples. A pair of enamel bottles each of identical pattern is illustrated in *Snuff Bottles in the Collection of the National Palace Museum*, p. 88, nos. 23 and 24, and are painted with ogival fruit panels on a deep blue ground with floral decoration; another with a green enamel ground with oval panels from the Sandberg Watch Collection was sold at Antiquorum, Geneva, 31 March 2001, lot 50; and another with a red enamel ground and shaped floral panels was offered at Christie's, Hong Kong, 27 November 2007, lot 1671.

The unique pair of bottles from the Imperial collection mentioned above were, according to the text of *Snuff Bottles in the Collection of the National Palace Museum*, p. 39, apparently given as gifts from Europe. They state that they are champlevé enamel and that the cap of the stopper is a small clock which can be wound by a key (illustrated) and that a snuff spoon hangs down from it. The decoration on the sides of our bottle is a common-enough European decorative element that by rather fortuitous happen-stance resembles the Chinese cash symbol. Similarly and presumably unplanned, the pearl-encrusted side panels that run vertically on the narrow sides of our bottle resemble the official symbol of the court, the *ruyi* sceptre. If indeed this bottle ever did make it to the court of Jiaqing or Daoguang it is easy to see how it would have been immediately appreciated. Importantly, the neck, the side of the stopper and the leaf lappets at the foot of our bottle are almost identical to the treatment of the necks, stopper sides, and feet of the two Palace Museum examples suggesting that they share the same maker and also therefore possibly suggesting a more direct link with our bottles and the Imperial court. The watch faces on the pair in the Imperial collection appear to be near identical but the illustration does not allow for a definitive comparison.

273 (three views)

The mouth of our bottle is slightly concave and the underside of the stopper is slightly convex, together they fit seamlessly.

Similarly decorated pocket watches, rather than snuff bottles, are illustrated in *Scientific and Technical Instruments of the Qing Dynasty: The Complete Collection of Treasures of the Palace Museum*, pp. 254-258, nos. 227-229 and 231, and dated to the nineteenth century.

Asia in general, and China in particular, was a huge market for Swiss watch and clock manufacturers. What began as a trickle in the seventeenth century grew vastly in importance during the eighteenth and nineteenth centuries. By the nineteenth century, the Swiss makers based in Geneva set up their own commercial agreement with China, having previously only had access through the British, who attempted to limit their trading. Initially the Swiss traded in Turkey (Jean-Jacques Rousseau's father, Issac, became the official timer in charge of the clocks in the Topkapi Saray in Istanbul) and then expanded to India and China. The savvy Swiss, cleverly catered to their clients needs adapting designs to specific tastes (watches with automata depicting 'local' subjects were made specifically for the Turkish, Indian, and Chinese markets).

The eighteenth-century workshops of famous Geneva watchmakers, included Pierre Jaquet Droz (1721-1790) and his son Henri Louis Jaquet-Droz (1752-1791) and his adopted son and business successor, Jean Frederic Leschot (1746-1824) both renowned for making watches with automatons and singing birds which fascinated the Chinese.

Another Swiss watchmaker who not only named Europe's royal families among his clients, but also did business in Turkey, India, and China was Jean Francois Bautte (1772-1837). He was one of the first to make extra-flat watches; another watchmaker was Edouard Bovet (1797-1849) who was the inventor of the so-called 'Chinese' watch in 1820, a competitive timepiece with a crown and hinged bow at 12 o'clock and serpentine hands. The watch could withstand the humid conditions of Asia, where it was much in demand. (see Fondation de la Haute Horlogerie, www. HauteHorlogerie.org).

It seems that quite a lot of watches made for the Chinese market were made in pairs, including the more unusual Palace watch snuff bottles referenced above. Whilst the most likely reason is that the Swiss adapted to Chinese culture where symmetry plays a part, it might also be because the distance between the two countries made it difficult to quickly have access to replacement parts if the watch broke.

When handling a bottle like this, it is easy to see how the Swiss became synonymous with 'precision' and just why the Swiss eventually dominated the Chinese clock and watch market prior to the Opium Wars of 1839-42 and 1856-60.

The Swiss term for this type of watch was actually 'form watches', a Geneva speciality at the turn of the eighteenth-nineteenth century. They were made in a variety of shapes but with basically the same small movements. For further reading and illustrations of a wide variety of 'form watches', see Patrizzi and Sturm, *Montres de Fantasie*, Tribune Editions, Geneve, 1979.

(CBL C 472)

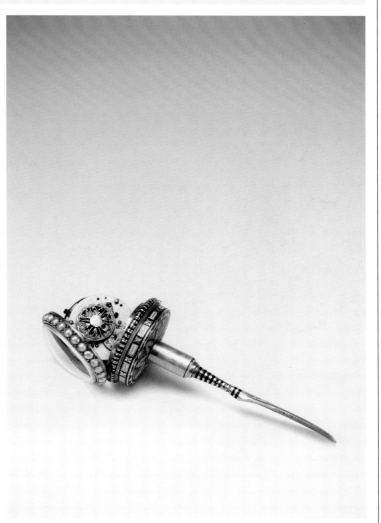

273 (three views)

274

Enamel on gold, each main face exquisitely decorated with colorful enamel vignettes on a transparent blue enamel over a hatched gold ground, *basse-taille*, one vignette depicting leafy fruiting branches of peaches, plums, cherries, grapes, and a compound berry, possibly fall raspberries, and the other side with tulips, roses, chrysanthemums, bluebells, foxglove, and hellebore, all below arch-like decoration at the shoulder formed by the curved octagonal band of half pearls, below gold dashes on a pale blue enamel band and gold leaves on a deep blue enamel which encircles the top of the shoulder, the neck with two bands of decoration, one is a series of gold vertical strokes on a white enamel ground below a band of gold running vine on a deep blue ground, the mouth slightly concave and decorated with a central eight-petal flower head in pale-blue enamel with details in white enamel and gold, the narrow sides of the bottle with vertical side panels of transparent red enamel ovals divided by white enamel horizontal dashes and bordered in vertical bands of pale blue enamel and gold, ten large C-shaped lappets above the foot of furling-leaf design with four sections each comprising pale-blue enamel, half-pearls, red enamel and repoussé gold and the base of the leaf centred by a white enamel dot, the oval gold base flat

1810-1830, Switzerland

Stopper: Enamel, gold, and half-pearls with domed crystal or glass hinged cover with a pearl-set bezel, encasing a European watch face with Roman chapters, outer minute divisions, hinged to the casing the gold lid has the stamped number 4574, opening to reveal gilt brass full plate engraved with 'A' and 'R', with cylindrical pillars, verge escapement, brass balance, continental cock or bridge, an integral gold and enamel spoon, the spoon with two oval French import stamps which each depict a stylized owl.

Height: 5.5 cm (with stopper); 4.5 cm (without stopper)
Mouth: 0.5 cm
Neck: 1.9 cm

PUBLISHED:
Chapman, 'The Chester Beatty Collection of Snuff Bottles', *Arts of Asia*, March-April, 1988, p. 57, fig. 1 and p. 61, fig. 20.

See the entry for the previous bottle, No. 273 for a discussion of the rare group of watch snuff bottles of which this is a part.

This and the previous bottle share close similarities in the mechanism of the watch itself and the only marks that differentiate the two watch stoppers, are those located on the spoon of this example. Due to the minute size of the stamps, it was impossible to photograph them, however, the mark is a '*L'hibou*' (the owl) a French import mark applied after 1893 to all watches imported in to France. It was also stamped on items that passed through public sale whose place of manufacture could not be determined as French, see Tardy's handbook, *Poincin d'or*, 12th edition, under French import marks, p. 174.

This spade-shaped bottle most closely resembles the pair of bottles in the Palace Museum illustrated in *Snuff Bottles in the Collection of the National Palace Museum*, p. 88, nos. 23 and 24, which also have fruit vignettes (though set in panels) on each side and a dark-blue ground. The fruit panels are framed by half-pearls on the 'Palace' bottles and on ours the half-pearls are used on the octagonal band that runs around the shoulder. The neck and stopper treatment is almost identical on all three bottles. The treatment of the curling lappets above the foot and the floral decoration on one side of our bottle however bears closest resemblance to those on the bottle offered at Christie's, Hong Kong, 27 November 2007, lot 1671. Our bottle may well be the most accomplished of all the examples referenced. There is more freedom in the vignettes, which can breathe as a result of not being confined within a cartouche, and the blue ground therefore envelops the entire bottle.

Unfortunately a large area of enamel has been lost on one side of our bottle. It does, however, afford us the opportunity of seeing in detail the cross-hatched gold ground (*basse-taille*) that is engraved, chased, or hammered to the surface of the gold body of the bottle prior to the addition of the translucent vitreous blue enamel and which after firing gives the delightful iridescent quality to the ground that shimmers enticingly as a result of the different thicknesses of enamel caused by the uneven surface it sits on. The transclucent blue

274 (two views)

274 (detail)

enamel also helps to highlight the opaque enamels used for the fruit and flower vignettes. *Basse-taille* ('low-cut') is an enamelling technique in which the ground surface is usually engraved or chased (ours appears as though it might be hammered) with a repeating pattern before the enamel application.

It is not entirely certain when the earliest *basse-taille* enamels entered China, but it was technique known in the West at least 400 years before the Qing Dynasty was established. During the Middle Ages it could be found on numerous liturgical vessels, having been developed, according to Needham, *Science and Civilisation in China*, p. 270, in early fourteenth-century Sienna. It spread to France, in particular Limoges, and then across Europe. The likelihood is that Western *basse-taille* enamels entered China, possibly as early as the sixteenth century, but certainly by the eighteenth century. It is almost certain, though not proven, that the earliest *basse-taille* enamels made in China, were done so under European supervision. That they developed independently seems unlikely in light of the obvious similarities of technique. We can be certain however that *basse-taille* enamel was being made in Guangzhou in the reign of the Qianlong Emperor (1735-96). According to the 'Palace presentation list, 0748', a pair of massive musical clocks, described identically to one decorated in *basse-taille* technique that resides in the Palace collection today (see *Tributes from Guangdong to the Qing Court*, p. 100, no. 84 and page 138) was jointly presented as tribute to the Qianlong Emperor from Batingsan, Viceroy of Guangdong and Guangxi, and Tuming'a, Superintendent of the Guangdong Maritime Customs on the tenth day of the eighth month of the 45th year of his reign (1781). In *Tributes from Guangdong to the Qing Court*, p. 55, it is noted that the first European clocks were brought to China by Matteo Ricci (the famous Italian Jesuit missionary who introduced the Chinese to Western mathematics) during the reign of the Ming Wanli Emperor in 1581, but that it was only in the early eighteenth century that Chinese clocksmiths began to appear in Guangzhou having learned their techniques primarily from the British. Most of the imported timepieces at that time were made in London.

That timepieces were more than a passing fashion is attested to by the numerous examples now preserved in the Palace Museum. These clocks, which were dotted around the Palace complex and number in the hundreds were all tribute from the Qianlong and Jiaqing reigns. Regarding timepieces and the Courts near obsession with them, it is worth noting comments in *Tributes from Guangdong to the Qing Court*, p. 63, 'There had always been a great demand for clocks in the Palace complex. In every hall, on every wall and on every table there was a clock. There were also pocket watches, watches for the saddle on horseback and clocks for the sedan chair. It is no exaggeration to say that the Qing emperors lived and worked under the chimes of their clocks.'

See also Cardinal, *The Watch from its origins to the XIXth century*, pp.196-199, no. 166 for an illustration of a so-called 'Chinese' watch (one made specifically for the Chinese market) with a painted enamel base set in a gold case and surrounded by half pearls that bears comparison. The enamel medallion, like ours is composed of large and small flowers in bloom, bunched tightly together forming bouquets that occupy the entire case and similarly, the flowers are painted with a meticulous realism in bright colours. Genevan enamel work on 'Chinese' watches had progressed from the late eighteenth taste for soft and light colours—pink, mauve, grey, beige and pale blue to prounounced and contrasting colours—red, violet, orange, green deep blue by the first third of the nineteenth century. The similarity in painting style and technique is unquestionable, particularly the treatment of the pink rose in the lower portion of both bouquets. The watch she illustrates has the movement signed by Bovet of Fleurier, Switzerland, which she dates to around 1820. According to the Fondation de la Haute Horlogerie at the website www.HauteHorlogerie.org, Fleurier in the Neuchatel mountains began to prosper as a watch making centre in 1820 (after a lull of half a century) as a direct result of his invention. Edouard Bovet, moved to London in 1814, then the centre of watch assembly and the watch trade. He worked at the Magniac company and was soon the head of a virtual monopoly of watch exports to Guangdong where he was sent in 1818. In 1822 he set up his own company with his brothers, Bovet became a byword for exellence at affordable prices. His endeavours inspired other companies like Vaucher Freres, Edouard Juvet, and Freres Dimier in Fleurier. Bovet was awarded a gold medal at the 1855 World's Fair in Paris for two identical watches, made to order for the Chinese Emperor.

However without a maker's stamp on our snuff bottle watch we cannot be entirely sure Bovet was the manufacturer but can be absolutely certain that the watch is Swiss with every likelihood that it comes from his workshop or another working closely in his style.

(CBL C 471)

274 (base)

274 (three views)

275

Enamel on gilt copper, the gilt copper ground engraved with nineteen registers of graduated circles which have been inlaid or applied with a pattern of circular coloured glass paste cabochon imitating spinel and emeralds, all with hexagonal facets in a floral pattern around the body, comprising two rows of six-petal flower-heads (possibly *prunus*) in red cabochons on the body of two different sizes and a third row at the shoulder of half flower heads, all surrounded by the nineteen rows of graduated green cabochons which encase the body, the gilt-copper mouth flat, the oval gilt-copper base very slightly concave

Gaungzhou, 1760-1810

Height: 5.85 cm
Mouth: 0.55 cm
Neck: 1.95 cm

The cabochons that make up the exterior decoration on this gilt-copper-bodied spade-shaped bottle are coloured glass imitating the precious stones ruby (spinel) and emeralds. As noted in the previous two entries, the eighteenth-century Guangzhou craftsmen excelled in clock manufacture, emulating and embellishing on foreign techniques and producing some of the most sumptuous clocks (and other objects) ever made using all means at their disposal to create magnificent ornate novelty tributes. Amongst the materials used for decoration on these tributes was coloured glass in imitation of precious stones. Various examples of such objects are illustrated in *Tributes from Guangdong to the Qing Court*. For an eighteenth-century automaton clock with side panels decorated in red and green coloured glass in imitation of emerald and ruby cabochons, see p. 98, no. 82; for another see, p. 100, no. 84. Similarly a copper-framed landscape jardinière in the glass collection of the Palace Museum with the figure of Liu Hai and his toad in a garden setting, uses different sheets of coloured glass to the sides in imitation of lapis lazuli, nephrite, ruby, and sapphire, ibid, p. 90, no. 62.

Our bottle can also be very favorably compared to a rare paste-embellished watch-inset *ruyi*-sceptre, which was offered at Christie's, Hong Kong, 27 November 2007, lot 1672. The entire upper surface is exquisitely inlaid with transparent coloured glass paste cabochons imitating precious stones that include ruby and diamonds. More importantly, the decoration is identical, in respect of the six-petal flower heads that cover the surface and which are centred by a cabochon of a different colour. The entire rim is banded in green glass cabochons imitating emerald. Whilst both are probably of a very similar date, it is tempting to suggest that the same artist or craftsman had a hand in both tribute gifts.

Another *ruyi*-sceptre, elaborately encrusted with primarily ruby-red glass paste insets from the Palace Museum Collection and dated to the eighteenth century is illustrated in *Qinggong Zhongbai Zhencang*, Timepieces in the Qing Palace Collection, pp. 206-207, fig. 1, also decorated with flower heads across its surface.

However, the use of precious and semi-precious stones can also be found in tributes for the court in objects like a landscape jardinière with gilt-copper and coral branches decorated with rubies, seed pearls, jadeite, and tourmaline, illustrated *Tributes from Guangdong to the Qing Court*, p. 91, no. 61. The use of precious stones in Guangzhou therefore was not unknown but they were certainly uncommon. As one would expect, when used, the precious stones were not used in profusion, the way the imitation precious-stone glass products were. Guangzhou had a long tradition of glassmaking and glass trading going back to the Han dynasty. According to *Tributes from Guangdong to the Qing Court*, p. 53, it is mentioned in early texts, which include Wan Zhen's *Exotic Items in Nanzhou* of the Three Kingdoms period (220-265) and Ge Hong's *Baopuzi, Neibian* of the Jin dynasty (265-420). Guangzhou's geographical location on the southeastern coast meant that it was always an important seaport for European and Asian trade and in ancient times Roman and Arab glass was shipped to Guangzhou. In the Qing dynasty the importation of glass grew massively.

It would not have been a difficult step for the Guangzhou craftsmen producing copper-bodied enamel snuff bottles and familiar with glass cabochon decoration to produce a bottle like this.

Only one other very similar bottle of this extremely rare design appears to be published, see Christie's, Hong Kong, 1-3 May 1994, lot 924, from the Joseph Baruch Silver Collection. The only difference being a clear glass inlay imitating diamonds at the centre of each flower head around the body.

(CBL C 496)

275 (two views)

Bartholomew, Terese Tse, *Hidden Meanings in Chinese Art*, San Francisco: Asian Art Museum of San Francisco, 2006.

Blue and White Porcelain with Underglazed Red (III), The Complete Collection of Treasures of the Palace Museum, Shanghai: Commercial Press, 2000.

Bragge, William, *Bibliotheca Nicotiana. A Catalogue of books about Tobacco in all its forms,* Birmingham: Privately printed, 1880.

Brinker, Helmut, and Albert Lutz, *Chinese Cloisonné: The Pierre Uldry Collection,* New York: Asia Society Galleries, in association with Bamboo Publishing, 1989.

Brody, Alexander, *Old Wine Into Old Bottles: A Collector's Commonplace Book,* Hong Kong: CA Design, 1993.

Bushell, Stephen W., *Oriental Ceramic Art,* New York: Crown Publishers, Inc., 1980.

Cahill, James, *Chinese Painting,* Geneva: Editions d'Art Albert Skira, 1960.

Calico, F, X.Calico and J. Trigo, *Monedas Espanolas desde Juana y Carlos a Isabel II, 1504 a 1868, 6 edicion,* Barcelona: Gabinete Numismatico Calico, 1985.

Cardinal, Catherine, *THE WATCH: from its origins to the XIXth century,* Wellfleet Press, Secaucus, New Jersey, 1985.

The Chester Beatty Library, Handbook, London Scala Publications, 2001.

China's Rare Stones, Shanghai Chinese Classics Publishing House, 1994.

Chinese Ceramics: Ching Dynasty, Taipei: Artist Publishing Co., 2002.

The Chinese Scholar's Studio, Artistic Life in the Late Ming Period, An Exhibition from the Shanghai Museum at the Asia Society Galleries, New York, 1987.

Chinese Snuff Bottles, exhibition catalogue, Newark Museum, 2 October-14 November 1982.

Chinese Snuff Bottles: Documentation of World Trade West to East, exhibition catalogue, Oakland Museum, 1977.

Chinese Snuff Bottles from the Fernhill Park Collection, catalogue of an exhibition at the Chinese Porcelain Company, New York, 9-13 October 1991.

The Collections of the National Gallery of Art, *Decorative Arts, Part II, Far Eastern Ceramics and Paintings,* Washington D.C.: The National Gallery of Art, 1998.

The Complete Collection of Treasures of the Palace Museum, Jadeware II, [*Gugong bowuyuan cang wenwu zhenping quanji, yuqi zhong*], The Commercial Press (Hong Kong) Ltd., 1995.

Cort, Louise Allison and Stuart, Jan, *Joined Colors: Decoration and Meaning in Chinese Porcelain,* Washington D.C. and Hong Kong: Arthur M. Sackler Gallery, Smithsonian Institution and Tai Yip, Co., 1993.

Donnelly, P.J., *Blanc De Chine,* New York and Washington: Frederick A. Praeger, 1969.

du Boulay, Anthony, *Christie's Pictorial History of Chinese Ceramics,* Oxford: Phaiden-Christie's, 1984.

Enamel Ware in the Ming and Ch'ing Dynasties, Taipei: National Palace Museum, 1999.

Encounters, The Meeting of Asia and Europe, 1500-1800, Victoria and Albert Museum, London: Victoria and Albert Museum Publications, 2004.

Ethnographic Objects in the Royal Danish Kunsthammer 1650-1800, Copenhagen: Nationalmuseet, 1980.

Fondation de la Haute Horlogerie, www.HauteHorlogerie.org (website).

Ford, John Gilmore, *Fine Chinese Snuff Bottles: The Edward Choate O'Dell Collection,* Baltimore: International Chinese Snuff Bottle Society, 1982.

Fuller, Richard E., *Chinese Snuff Bottles in the Seattle Art Museum,* Seattle: Seattle Art Museum, 1970.

Garrett, Valery, *Chinese Dress from the Qing Dynasty to the Present,* Tokyo, Rutland, Vermont, Singapore,: Tuttle Publishing, 2007.

Gillingham, Michael, *Chinese Painted Enamels: An exhibition held in the Department of Eastern Art, June & July 1978,* Oxford: Ashmolean Museum, 1978.

Glickman, Elsa, *Chinese Snuff Bottle Mania: Stories of Collectors, Trade, Intrigues, and Gotham's Auctions,* Hong Kong: Pressroom Printer and Designer, 2006.

Gugong bowuyuan cang 58, Scientific and Technical Instruments of the Qing Dynasty, The Complete Collection of Treasures of the Palace Museum, Hong Kong: The Commercial Press, 1998.

Gugong bowuyuan cang wenwu zhenpin daxi. (Gugong Complete Snuff Bottles, Li Jiufang, ed.), Shanghai: Shanghai kexue jishu chubanshe, 2002.

Hall, Robert, *Chinese Snuff Bottles,* London: Robert Hall, 1987.
——————, *Chinese Snuff Bottles II,* London: Robert Hall, 1989.
——————, *Chinese Snuff Bottles III,* London: Robert Hall, 1990.
——————, *Chinese Snuff Bottles IV,* London: Robert Hall, 1991.
——————, *Chinese Snuff Bottles X: The Button Collection,* London: Robert Hall, 2003.
——————, *Chinese Snuff Bottles XI: The Snowy Peaks Collection,* London: Robert Hall, 2005.
——————, *Chinese Snuff Bottles XII,* London: Robert Hall, 2007.
——————, *Chinese Snuff Bottles XIII: The Boston Snuff Party,* London: Robert Hall, 2008.
——————, *Chinese Snuff Bottles: Masterpieces from the Reitberg Museum Zurich, The Collection of Reinhard J.C. Hoeppli, the property of the Swiss Confederation, Federal Office of Culture,* Zurich: Museum Rietberg, 1993.

[Hamilton, Harriet H.], *Oriental Snuff Bottles,* Palo Alto, California: Mayfield Publishing Co., 1977.

Heavenly Creations: Chinese Snuff Bottles from the Collections of Anthony Cheung, Humphrey Hui, Po-ming Kwong, Tuyet Nguyet and Christopher Sin, University Museum and Art Gallery, The University of Hong Kong, 2005.

Ho, Chuimei and Bennet Bronson, *Splendors of China's Forbidden City: The Glorious Reign of Emperor Qianlong,* London and New York: Merrell, 2004.

Holden, Rachelle R., *Rivers and Mountains Far from the World: The Rachelle R. Holden Collection: A Personal Commentary,* New York: Self published, 1994.

Horton, Charles, *Alfred Chester Beatty: From Miner to Bibliophile*, Dublin: TownHouse, 2003.

Howard, David Sanctuary and John Ayers, *China for the West, Chinese Porcelain and Other Decorative Arts for Export Illustrated from the Mottahedeh Collection*, Vol. 2, London and New York: Sotheby Parke Bernet, 1978.

Hu, Weibiao, exec. ed., *The Imperial Palace: Chinese Landscape Storehouse*, Beijing 1996.

Hui, Humphrey K.F., Lai Suk Yee, and Peter Y.K. Lam, *Inkplay in Microcosm: Inside-Painted Chinese Snuff Bottles, The Humphrey K. F. Hui Collection,* Art Museum, The Chinese University of Hong Kong, 2002.

Hui, Humphrey K.F. and Peter Y.K. Lam, *The Imperial Connection: Court Related Snuff Bottles, The Humphrey K.F. Hui Collection*, catalogue of an exhibition at the Art Museum, The Chinese University of Hong Kong, Hong Kong: CA Design and Printing,1988.

Hui, Humphrey K.F., Po Ming Kwon, and Christopher C.H. Sin, eds., *A Congregation of Snuff Bottle Connoisseurs: An Exhibition of Chinese Snuff Bottles*, The Tsui Museum of Art, Hong Kong, 17 October-15 November1996, Hong Kong: CA Design and Printing, 1996.

Hui, Humphrey K.F., Margaret Polak, and Christopher C.H. Sin, *Hidden Treasures of the Dragon: Chinese Snuff Bottles from the Collections of Humphrey K.F. Hui, Margaret Polak and Christopher C.H. Sin*, a catalogue of the exhibition held at the Art Gallery of New South Wales, 19 December 1991-27 January 1992, Hong Kong: Kinggraphic, 1991.

Hui, Humphrey K.F. and Christopher C.H. Sin, *An Imperial Qing Tradition: An Exhibition of Chinese Snuff Bottles from the Collections of Humphrey K.F. Hui and Christopher C.H. Sin,* Hong Kong: CA Design and Printing, 1994.

Hughes, Michael C., *The Blair Bequest: Chinese Snuff Bottles from the Princeton University Art Museum*, Baltimore, Maryland: International Chinese Snuff Bottle Society, 2002.

Kangxi, Empereur de Chine, 1662-1722, La Cite interdite a Versailles, a catalogue of an exhibition held at the Musee National du Chateau de Versailles, 27 January-9 May, 2004, Paris, 2004.

Kangxi. Yongzheng. Qianlong. Qing Porcelain from the Palace Museum Collection [Gugong zhencang Kang Yong Qian ciqi tulu], Zhijincheng chubanshe, 1989.

Kerr, Rose, *Chinese Ceramics: Porcelains of the Qing Dynasty, 1644-1911,* London: Victoria and Albert Museum Publications, 1986.

Kerr, Rose and John Ayers, *Blanc De Chine Porcelain from Dehua*, Chicago: Art Media Resources, Ltd. 2002.

Kleiner, Robert, *The Bellis Collection: Card Catalogue*, Hong Kong: Pressroom Printer and Designer, 1993.

—————, *Chinese Snuff Bottles: A Miniature Art from the Collection Mary and George Bloch,* Hong Kong Museum of Art, 18 March-18 June, 1994, Hong Kong: Hong Kong Museum of Art, 1994.
—————, *Chinese Snuff Bottles in the Collection of Mary and George Bloch,* London: British Museum, 1995.
—————, *Chinese Snuff Bottles from the Burghley House Collection, Stamford, England,* Hong Kong: Pressroom Printer and Designer, 1989.
—————, *Chinese Snuff Bottles from the Collection of Denys and Eithne Cowell,* Hong Kong: Pressroom Printer and Designer, 2003.

—————, *Chinese Snuff Bottles from the Collection of John Ault,* Hong Kong: Belfont, 1990.
—————, *Chinese Snuff Bottles from the Collection of Mary and George Bloch,* Hong Kong: Herald International, 1987.
—————, *Chinese Snuff Bottles: The White Wings Collection,* Hong Kong: Pressroom Printer and Designer, 1997.
—————, *Precious Playthings: Important Chinese Snuff Bottles from the Mack Collection,* London: Robert Kleiner & Co, 2000.
—————, *Treasures from the Sanctum of Enlightened Respect: Chinese Snuff Bottles from the Collection of Denis Low,* Singapore: SNP Printing Pte. Ltd., 1999.

Lawrence, Clare, *Miniature Masterpieces from the Middle Kingdom: The Monimar Collection of Chinese Snuff Bottles,* London: Zhenliu Xuan Publishing Company, 1996.

Leidy, Denise Patry, *Mother-of-Pearl: A Tradition in Asian Lacquer,* a catalogue of the exhibition held at the Metropolitan Museum of Art, New York, 2 December 2006-1 April 2007.

Li, Raymond, *The Medicine-Snuff Bottle Connection: Chinese Miniature Containers: a Dual Role,* Hong Kong: Nine Dragons, 1979.

Little, Stephen, *Taoism and the Arts of China,* The Art Institute of Chicago, 2000.

Low, Denis S.K., *More Treasures from The Sanctum of Enlightened Respect*, Hong Kong: CA Design and Printing, 2002.
—————, *Chinese Snuff Bottles from the Sanctum of Enlightened Respect III,* Singapore: Asian Civilisations Museum, 2007.

Ma Zhengsan, *Inside-Painted Snuff Bottle Artist Ma Shaoxuan (1867-1939), A Biography and Study,* translated and annotated by Ka Bo Tsang, Baltimore, Maryland: The International Chinese Snuff Bottle Society, 1997.

Mair, Victor H. ed., *The Shorter Columbia Anthology of Traditional Chinese Literature*, New York: Columbia University Press, 2000.

Martin, Steven, *The Art of Opium Antiques,* Chiang Mai, Thailand: Silkworm Books, 2007.

Masterpieces of Snuff Bottles in the Palace Museum, (*Gugong biyanhu xuancui*) compiled by Xia Gengqi and Zhang Rong of the Palace Museum, Beijing: The Forbidden City Publishing House of the Palace Museum, 1995.

Mayuyama, Seventy Years, Vol. 1, Tokyo: Mayuyama & Co., Ltd., 1976.

McCann III, Henry N., *Herbal Training Formulas in the Taoist Tradition*, The Tao of Healing web page www.geocities.com/notsprings/2426/

Medley, Margaret, *The Chinese Potter,* Oxford: Phaidon Press Limited, 1976.

*Mei Ken Ten (An Exhibition of Noted Inkstones),*Tokyo: Mayuyama Ryusendo, 1987.

Moss, Hugh M., *The Barron Collection: Illustrated Handlist*, ICSBS Convention, Boston, 2008.
—————, *By Imperial Command: An Introduction to Ch'ing Imperial Painted Enamels,* Hong Kong: Hibaya, 1976.
—————, *Chinese Snuff Bottles of the Silica and Quartz Group*, London: Bibelot, 1971.
—————, *Snuff Bottles of China* [Illustrating a Collection formed by Count Kurt Graf Blucher von Wahlstatt], London: Bibelot, 1971.

Moss, Hugh M., Victor Graham, and Ka Bo Tsang, *The Art of the Chinese Snuff Bottle: The J & J Collection,* Vols. 1 & 2, New York: Weatherhill, 1993.
——————, *A Treasury of Chinese Snuff Bottles: The Mary and George Bloch Collection,* Vol. 1, *Jade* (1995); Vol. 2, *Quartz (1998);* Vol. 3, *Stones other than Jade and Quartz (1998);* Vol. 4, *Inside Painted* (2000); Vol. 5, *Glass* (2002); Vol. 6, *Arts of the Fire* (2008).

Moss, Hugh and Gerard Tsang, *Arts From the Scholar's Studio,* a catalogue of the exhibition held at The Oriental Ceramic Society of Hong Kong and the Fung Ping Shan Museum, University of Hong Kong, 24 October-13 December 1986, The Oriental Ceramic Society of Hong Kong, 1986.

Mowry, Robert D., *Worlds Within Worlds: The Richard Rosenblum Collection of Chinese Scholars' Rocks,* Cambridge: Harvard University Arts Museum, 1997.

Needham, Joseph, *Science and Civilization in China,* Vol. 5, Cambridge University Press, 1974.

Nicollier, Verene, *The Baur Collection, Geneva, Chinese Snuff Bottles, Flacons A Tabac Chinois,* Geneva: Collections Baur, 2007.

Okakura, Kakuzo, *The Awakening of Japan,* New York: The Century Co., 1905.

Patrizzi, Oswaldo and Fabienne Sturm, *Montres de Fantasie,* Geneva: Tribune Editions, 1979.

Other Women's Voices: Translations of women's writing before 1700 (http://home.infionline.net/~ddisse/).

Perry, Lilla S., *Chinese Snuff Bottles: The Adventures & Studies of a Collector,* Rutland, Vermont and Tokyo: Charles E. Tuttle Company, 1960.

Qinggong Zhongbai Zhencang, Timepieces in the Qing Palace Collection, Beijing: Forbidden City Press, 1995.

Qing Imperial Porcelain of the Kangxi, Yongzheng and Qianlong Reigns, Nanjing Museum and the Art Gallery, The Chinese University of Hong Kong, 1995.

Quanji 6 (Yang Boda. *Zhongguo jinyin boli falang qi quanji* [Complete compendium of Chinese artworks in metal, glass and enamel]. Vol. 6, Falangqi [Enamels]. Shijiazhuang: Hebei meishu chubanshe, 2002.

Randall, Christopher and Louise Randall, *Important Chinese Snuff Bottles: From the China Trade to the Imperial Court,* Miami: J.W.A International Inc., 1994.

Rawson, Jessica, *Chinese Jade from the Neolithic to the Qing,* London: British Museum Press, 1995.

The Refined Taste of the Emperor: Special Exhibition of Archaic and Pictorial Jades of the Ch'ing Court, Taipei: National Palace Museum, 1997.

Schloss, Ezekiel, *Ancient Chinese Ceramic Sculpture: From Han Through Tang,* Vol. 1, New York: Self published, 1977.

Scientific and Technical Instruments of the Qing Dynasty: The Complete Collection of Treasures of the Palace Museum, Vol. 58, Hong Kong: Palace Museum, 1998.

Stevens, Bob C., *The Collector's Book of Snuff Bottles,* New York and Tokyo: Weatherhill, 1976.

Snuff Bottles: Little Gems of Delight, Exhibition Catalogue, Singapore: Chinatown Snuff Bottle Society, 2004.

Snuff Bottles in the Collection of the National Palace Museum, with an introduction by Chang Lin-sheng, Taipei: National Palace Museum, 1991.

Snuff Bottles of the Ch'ing Dynasty, catalogue of an exhibition at the Hong Kong Museum of Art, 20 October-3 December 1978, text and captions by Gerard C. Tsang and Hugh M. Moss, Hong Kong Museum of Art, 1978.

Souksi, Laurence, *Merveilles de la miniature chinoise: flacon-tabatier de chine de la collection du commander,* Paris, 2000.

A Special Exhibit of Collections from Mr. Robert Chang's Studio of Lotus Fragrance, exhibiton catalogue, Special Exhibitions Galleries, Suzhou Musuem, 2009.

Tardy, *Poincon d'Or et de Platine* (French text), 12th edition, Paris: Self Published, 1988.

Tributes from Guangdong to the Qing Court, an exhibition jointly presented by the Palace Museum, Beijing and the Art Gallery, The Chinese University of Hong Kong, 28 February-12 April 1987, Art Gallery, Chinese University of Hong Kong, 1987.

Watt, James, *Chinese Jades from Han to Ch'ing,* New York: The Asia Society in association with John Weatherhill Inc., 1980.

White, Helen, *Snuff Bottles from China, The Victoria and Albert Museum Collection,* London: Bamboo Publishing, 1992.

Williams, C.A.S., *Outlines of Chinese Symbolism and Art Motives,* Rutland, Vermont and Tokyo: Charles E. Tuttle Company, 1978.

Wu Tung, *Tales from the Land of Dragons: 1000 Years of Chinese Painting,* Boston: Boston Museum of Fine Arts, 1997.

Zhang Hongxing, *The Qianlong Emperor: Treasures From the Forbidden City,* Edinburgh: National Museums of Scotland Publishing Ltd., 2002.

Zhi jin cheng, The Forbidden City, Beijing, Beijing: The Forbidden City Publishing House (Zi jin cheng chubanshe), 1993.

Zhongguo biyanhi zhenshang (Gems of Chinese Snuff Bottles), ed., Geng Baochang, and Zhao Binghua. Hong Kong: Joint Publishing and Taikong Culture Enterprise, 1992.

PERIODICALS:

Arts of Asia, a periodical published every other month in Hong Kong since 1971.

Chinese Snuff Bottle, Hugh M. Moss ed. An occasional periodical with articles and surveys of collections, Nos. 1-6 (1963-1974).

Journal, ICSBS (Journal of the International Chinese Snuff Bottle Society), a quarterly publication from Winter 1974 and presently published three times a year. Formerly known as the *Newsletter of the Chinese Snuff Bottle Society of America,* published from July 1969 to September 1974.

Orientations, a periodical published monthly in Hong Kong since 1970.

INDEX

A

Afghanistan 168
agate 86, 90, 98, 100, 102, 104, 106, 108, 110, 114, 116, 118
amber 194, 196, 200, 202, 204, 206, 260
amethyst 82, 84, 130, 146
Ancient Moon Pavilion SEE *Guyue xuan*
antigorite (serpentine) 186, 188
aquamarine (variety of beryl) 174, 176
archaism 18, 22, 26, 28, 38, 42, 46, 138, 228, 256
Arhats 222, 232
aubergine 60, 62, 308
'Autumn Hunting Trip' SEE Quili

B

ba jixiang SEE Eight Buddhist emblems
Bada Shanren (painter, 1626-1705) 260
Baishi (artist) 208
baitouweng (bird) 216
Baman Jinbao ('Eight barbarians bearing tribute') 300, 310, 314
bamboo 18, 24, 58, 62, 78, 130, 134, 138, 140, 150, 178, 218, 236, 288, 300,
    with pine 150
    with rocks 24
    SEE ALSO 'Three Friends of Winter'
bannerman 116
Baohedian Palace (Forbidden City) 38, 320
baozhu (wish-granting pearl) 156, 200, 284, 342
basket-weave decoration 46
basse-taille enameling 360, 362
bats 42, 96, 108, 114, 148, 236, 270
    bats and waves or the sea 152,
    group of five bats 120, 196, 252, 350,
    paired bats 154,
    red bats 173, 350,
    upside-down bats 196,
    with peaches 286, 288,
    with gourds 350
bees, wasps 244, 250, 259
begonia 298, 318
Beijing School 256, 266
beryl (stone) 174, 176
birds 18, 90, 114, 118, 120, 136, 186, 204, 208,
    210, 216, 234, 236, 250, 258, 336, 346, 352, 354
    SEE ALSO *baitouweng,* cranes, ducks, eagles, egrets, kingfishers,
    magpies, quail, pheasants, and phoenix
Book of Odes 32, 150, 202, 346
Bourguignon, Francois SEE Gravelot
bowenite 186
boys 30, 126, 228, 324
Bragge, William 304, 316, 320, 322
Buddha's Hand citron 34
Buddhism and Buddhist imagery 34, 48, 106, 108, 168, 228, 284, 304, 306
buffaloes 252, with a boy 244
Burma 76, 168, 172, 194
butterflies and moths 74, 78, 102, 202, 212,
    paired with gourds or melons 30, 202

C

camels 272
carp 26, 40, 70, 112, 236, 262, 266, 282, 318
Castiglione, Giuseppe (Lang Shining) 116
Cave of Watery Brightness (studio) 84, 88
chalcedony 86, 90, 102, 106, 116, 118, 120, 122, 124, 126
champlevé enamel 338, 356
Chen Rong (painter) 274
Chengdu 168
chilong SEE Dragons
chrysanthemums 24, 56, 100, 150, 250, 304
cicada 28, 66, 99
cinnabar lacquer 212, 214
Cixi (empress dowager, 1835-1909) 34
Clement XI (pope, 1700-21) 148
cloisonné 338, 340
coin bottles 162, 164
Confucianism and Confucianist imagery 104, 270
Confucius 134, 236, 280
cong 28
corundum SEE Ruby and sapphire
crabs 140
cranes 110, 116, 228, 258, 306, 346
crickets 66, 94, 106, 250
cymbidium SEE orchids
cypress 52, 234

D

Daji ('good luck') 156, 238
'Dali' stones, SEE dreamstones
Damo 182, 232
Daoguang Emperor (1820-50) and Court 94, 146, 186, 2-8, 232,
    270, 272, 282, 302, 308, 318
Daoism and Daoist imagery 16, 26, 28, 30, 36, 74, 84, 98, 108, 122,
    136, 148, 154, 190, 196, 198, 204, 206, 228, 230,
    236, 240, 244, 306, 308, 314, 316, 324, 336, 344, 356
deer 110, 296, 336
d'Entrecolles, Père Francois Xavier (Jesuit missionary, 1664-1741) 272
Ding, Prince, Zaiquan 186
dogs 70, 232, 248, 252, 272
Dou Yujin (scholar, 907-960) 272
doucai ('joined colours') enamel 286, 294, 300, 314
Dragon's Gate (Longmen) Falls 40, 236, 262, 352
dragonflies 168, 250
dragons 18, 22, 26, 38, 40, 42, 44, 46, 70, 78, 86,
    106, 108, 112, 152, 156 168, 188, 200, 208,
    210, 228, 274, 276, 282, 284, 308, 318, 342, 352,
    chilong dragons 18, 26, 28, 38, 78, 104, 152, 174, 242, 340
    kui dragons 22, 78, 228, 242,
    five-clawed dragons 108, 242, 274, 276, 282, 284, 308, 342,
    four-clawed dragons 342,
    three-clawed dragons 242
Dream of the Red Chamber 302
dreamstones 16, 20
Duan stone 20, 78, 18
ducks 26, 46, 118, 186, 250, 298, 346,
    paired with lotus 250

E

eagle	114, 118
egrets	214, 250
paired with lotus and reeds	250
'Eight Buddhist Emblems' (*ba jixiang*)	36, 168, 304, 306, 308, 316
'Eight Treasures' of Daoism	28, 148
'Eight Trigrams'	13
elephants	66, 160, 300, 314, 320,
with vases	320
European enameling	360
European porcelain production	306

F

farmer	128, 270
figural porcelain bottles	322, 324, 326, 328
fish	18, 26, 40, 70, 100, 112, 124, 154, 168, 182, 214, 230, 236, 240,
	256, 258, 262, 2666, 270, 276, 300, 304, 306, 310, 318, 336, 352
with lotus	240
SEE ALSO carp and goldfish	
'Five Blessings'	90, 114, 120, 128, 196, 350
flowers	24, 36, 50, 60, 62, 100, 126, 134, 168, 170,
	216, 235, 250, 252, 256, 260, 286, 290, 292, 296, 398,
	306, 318, 324, 328, 344, 346, 350, 352, 354, 362
ALSO SEE entries for individual types of flowers	
foreigners as subjects	50, 160, 162, 164, 300, 314, 354
'Four Gentlemen Among Flowers' (bamboo, chrysanthemum,	
orchid and plum)	134, 2
'Four Noble Professions' SEE *Yi Qiao Geng Du*	
Frederick Augustus I of Saxony	332
fruit-shaped bottles	32, 66 74, 220
Fujian province	122, 127
Fuxing (Daoist immortal)	306
Fuzhou (city)	36, 168, 212, 214

G

goats	104, 144, 232, 252, 280
goldfish	26, 40, 100
gourds and gourd-shaped bottles	28, 32, 46, 13, 31, 46, 60, 64,
	72, 74, 84, 94, 124, 138, 142, 153, 156, 186,
	202, 204, 220, 228, 230, 232, 238, 250, 278, 296,
	306, 308, 325, 330, 338, 340, 350
with bats 350, with butterflies	202
grass	142, 256
Guangxi province	168
Guangzhou	166, 216, 228, 240, 342, 344, 346, 348, 350, 352, 354, 362, 364
Guanyin (goddess)	154
Guizhou	168
Guyue xuan (Ancient Moon Pavilion)	248, 250, 252

H

hair crystal	132, 140
Hall of Constancy (studio)	186
Hayman, Francis (painter, 1708-76)	354
He Xiangu (Daoist immortal)	154, 196, 234, 284, 306
Hehe Erxian (immortals of Harmony and Unity)	30, 114, 120, 324
heliodor (variety of beryl)	174
hibiscus	168, 194, 286, 306
Hindustan	194
Hong Lou Meng SEE *Dream of the Red Chamber*	
hornbill	86, 208, 240
horses	104, 108, 262
Muwang's horses	262, 274
horse with a monkey and wasp	232
Hua Yan (painter)	230, 252
Huang Chengyan	116, 198, 204, 232
huashi ('slippery stone')	272, 280, 282, 304
Huizong (emperor, 1101-25)	298
Huzhou	84, 88, 154

I

Imperial enamels, Guangzhou	342, 344, 346, 354
Imperial glass workshop	228, 238, 242
Imperial jade workshop	22, 24, 28, 64
Imperial Master, so called	212, 218, 222, 224
Imperial Palace workshop	156, 170, 194, 212, 218
Imperial porcelain kilns, Jingdezhen	274, 276, 282, 284, 286, 288, 290,
	292, 294, 296, 298, 300, 302, 304, 306, 310, 312, 314, 316, 330
India	52, 172, 194, 222, 354, 358
ivory	218, 220, 222, 224

J

jadeite	74, 76, 78, 92
Japan	210, 212, 214, 220, 222, 224, 318, 336
Japanese bottles	210, 222, 224
jasper	86, 92, 94, 96, 106, 186
Jesuits	116, 240, 272, 362
Jiaqing Emperor	134
Jiaqing period	214
Jingdezhen	94, 106, 146, 22, 242, 270, 272, 274, 276, 278, 280,
	282, 284, 286, 288, 290, 294, 296, 298, 300, 302, 304, 306,
	308, 310, 312, 314, 318, 320, 322, 324, 326, 330, 336, 342
Jinyu Ting (Pavilion of Today's Rain) SEE Li Junting	
Jiu Hui Duei ('assembly of old things')	260, 264
Jiujiang	168

K

Kangxi emperor	148, 210, 274, 282, 292, 324, 340, 344, 350
Kashmir	172
katydids	318
kingfishers	168, 214
Kuhn, S. H. (Peking dealer)	144

L

lacquer   210, 212, 214
Lan Caihe (Daoist immortal)   196, 234, 306, 344
lapis lazuli   168, 170
laque burguate   210
Li Junting, School of   230, 232, 234, 236, 252
Li Tieguai (Daoist immortal)   28, 74, 84, 124, 230, 306
Li Taibai (poet, 701-762)   142
limestone   180, 182, 184
Lin Cai Nan (artist)   138
lingzhi   30, 124, 126, 144, 208, 236, 256, 288, 294, 296, 346, 352
lions   50, 240, 248, 252,
      group of nine lions   314
Liu Bang   290
Liu Hai (god of wealth and prosperity)   36, 144, 324, 364
Liu Yuanying SEE Liu Hai
Liushujing (willow spirit)   198
lotuses and lotus gathering   36, 68, 74, 218, 220, 250, 282, 310
      paired with egrets   250
Lotus Fragrance, Studio of SEE Ouxiang zhai
Lu Dongbin (Daoist immortal)   196, 198, 306
Lu Zigang (carver)   54
Luo Hongxian (poet and scholar)   66
Luxing (Daoist immortal)   110, 306

M

Ma Shaouxuan (painter, 1867-1939)   256, 260, 264
macaroni agate   86
magnolia flowers   292
magpies   68, 90, 136, 258, 316
Magu (goddess of longevity)   196, 242, 296
mallow flowers   146, 286, 290
'Master of the Rocks School'   18, 28, 30
meiping (bottle shape)   22, 58, 146, 150, 242, 278, 298
melons   32, 212, 240,
      paired with butterflies   202
Meng Haoran (poet)   116, 198, 204
Meng Zishou   266
Mi Fei SEE Mi Fu
Mi Fu (scholar, 1050-1107)   196, 234, 312
millet   120, 140, 298
mokume (technique for creating metal bottles)   336
monkey(s)   94, 106, 244, 336
mother-of-pearl   210, 216, 246
moths SEE Butterflies and moths
Mughal style SEE Hindustan style
Muwang (emperor, 1001-946 BCE)   262, 274

N

Ni Zan (painter)   332
Niulang   316

O

octagonal bottles   136, 292
Official School   94, 104, 106, 108, 110, 112, 114
opium   322
orchids   134, 280, 326, 328
      SEE ALSO 'Four Gentlemen among Flowers'
Ouyang Xiu (writer, 1007-1072)   264
Ouxiang zhai (Studio of Lotus Fragrance)   258

P

peaches   42, 286, 288, 290, 294, 296,
      peach of immortality   306
Pekinese dogs SEE dogs
peony   50, 170, 194, 250, 286, 288, 332, 344, 346, 352,
      with phoenix   352
pheasants   260
phoenix   26, 118, 122, 138, 158, 188, 346 with peony 50, 271, 352
pine   44, 52, 58, 70, 78, 108, 110, 122, 126,
      128, 130, 144, 146, 150, 258, 294, 336
pink enamels   332
plums and plum trees   30, 58, 78, 90, 94, 96, 108, 116, 134, 136, 216, 344, 346
      SEE ALSO 'Three Friends of Winter'
pomegranates   52, 68, 120, 212
poppies   290
praying mantis   66
puddingstone   72, 184

Q

Qianlong emperor and Court   22, 24, 26, 32, 42, 72, 78, 100, 106,
      1116, 144, 146, 150, 152, 186, 194, 210, 212, 230,
      238, 242, 244, 248, 250, 252, 270, 286, 288, 290, 292, 294,
      298, 302, 304, 306, 310, 318, 340, 348, 350, 352, 354, 362
qilin (mythical beast)   42, 202, 300
qin (musical instrument)   44, 210, 234, 294, 300
qing (musical instrument) SEE Stone Chime
Qixi festival   316
quail   186, 220, 234, 298, 354
Quili ('Autumn Hunting Trip')   272

R

Ran Dao Ren (artist)   206
realgar   98, 238, 240
Romance of the Three Kingdoms (*Sanguo yanyi*)   116, 198, 232, 310
Rong Qiqi   236
Rustic Crystal Master (school)   18, 84, 88, 128, 144, 146, 154, 162
ruyi scepter   98, 228, 234, 240, 294, 300, 306, 344, 356, 364
      with a vase and apples   234
Ryukyu Islands   210

S

Sanshiluxu Zhai (Studio of 36 Documents) 258
sapphire 172
Seal School (Yangzhou) 230, 232, 234
'Seven Worthies of the Bamboo Grove' 236
shakudo (alloy) 336
Shangsu 196
sheep 144, 252, 280
Shen Zhou SEE Shitian
Shishou Shanren SEE Ran Dao Ren
Shitian (artist, 1472-1509) 256
Shou He (carver) 84, 88
shou (character) 44, 196, 212, 286, 338, 344, 352
Shoulao (god of longevity) 44, 128, 176, 306
Sima Xiangru (poet, 179-117 BCE) 210
'slippery stone' SEE *huashi*
snail 36
'soft-paste' SEE *huashi*
Spanish dollars 162, 164
stone chimes (*qing*) 148, 158
Su Dongpo (poet, 1036-1101) 310, 312
Su Shi SEE Su Dongpo
Suzhou 16, 20, 30, 38, 50, 52, 54, 56, 104, 112, 116, 122, 124, 126, 174, 180, 186, 196, 212, 230, 244
swastika 48, 144, 228
sweet olive flowers 286, 292
Switzerland 356, 360, 362

T

Taihedian (Hall of Supreme Harmony, Forbidden City) 38, 320
Taihu rocks 122, 180, 234, 240, 294
Tang dynasty 38, 42, 116, 142, 170, 180, 184, 198, 204, 210, 222, 244, 258, 260, 264, 272, 280, 292, 294, 328
Tang Yanquin (poet) 116
Tang Ying 292, 298, 330, 332
Tao Qian SEE Tao Yuanming
Tao Yuanming (scholar and poet, 365-427) 56, 100, 150
Taoism and Taoist imagery SEE Daoism and Daoist imagery
taotie masks 28
Thailand 172
Thirty Six Documents, Studio of SEE Sanshiluxu Zhai
'Three Friends of Winter' (bamboo, pine, and plum) 58, 62, 78, 150
'Three Leisures' 182
'Three Star Gods' 306
toad (three-legged) 36, 144, 324
Turkistan 22, 174, 194, 264, 272

V

Vietnam 172

W

wadang (roof tiles) 50, 90
Wang Su (painter, 1794-1879) 230
Wang Xiang (184-268) 276
watches, European 292, 356, 358, 360, 362
White Snake Story 310
willow 54, 198, 222, 252, 256, 258, 262, 274, 294, 336
Wu School 256
wucai ('five colours') enamel 294
Wuxing 84, 88, 154

X

Xiang Yu 290
Xingyouheng Tang SEE Hall of Constancy
Xinjiang province 92, 116, 168, 174, 186, 194
Xiwangmu (Queen Mother of the West) 122, 124, 324
Xue Tao (poet) 310

Y

Yan Yutian (painter) 256, 260
Yangzhou 174, 212, 230, 232, 234, 248, 250, 252, 340, 342
Ye Zhongsan (painter) 256, 258, 262, 266
'Yellow Millet Dream' 198
yellow steamed-chestnut jade 32
Yin-yang symbol 16, 42, 102, 136, 194, 202, 236
Yitang 16,18
Yongzheng Emperor (1723-35) and period 30, 48, 100, 146, 152, 240, 242, 270, 272, 286, 292, 300, 324, 326, 330, 332, 342, 344, 346, 348, 350, 352
Yu Ji 290
Yu Qiao Geng Du ('Four Noble Professions') 270, 300, 336
Yuanmingyuan (summer palace) 134 248, 344

Z

Zaiquan SEE Ding, Prince
Zhangbu (city, Fujian province) 144, 154
Zhangzhou (city, Fujian province) 144, 154
Zhinu 316
Zhiting, School of 122, 124, 126, 244
Zhongli Quan (Daoist immortal) 84, 198, 306
Zhou Leyuan 244, 256, 258, 260, 262, 266
Zhou Mengfu (painter, 1254-1322) 262
Zhou Shaoyuan 260